The Executive Role Constellation

The Executive Role Constellation

An Analysis of Personality and Role Relations in Management

RICHARD C. HODGSON

Assistant Professor of Business Administration
School of Business Administration
University of Western Ontario

DANIEL J. LEVINSON

Assistant Professor of Psychology
Department of Psychiatry
School of Medicine
Harvard University

ABRAHAM ZALEZNIK

Professor of Organizational Behavior
Graduate School of Business Administration
Harvard University

HARVARD UNIVERSITY · DIVISION OF RESEARCH
GRADUATE SCHOOL OF BUSINESS ADMINISTRATION
Boston 1965

Library of Congress Catalog Card No. 65-23443

PRINTED IN THE UNITED STATES OF AMERICA

Foreword

THIS STUDY represents an unusual research collaboration in that it brings together two independent research programs interested in the formulation of a dynamic social-psychology of organizations. One program is located at the Massachusetts Mental Health Center in Boston where Professor Daniel J. Levinson directs the sociopsychological research activity. The second, under the direction of Professor Abraham Zaleznik of the Harvard Business School, consists of a series of research projects on problems of individual adaptation to work and organizations. Both programs have published earlier studies within their respective research efforts. (See Daniel J. Levinson and Eugene B. Gallagher, *Patienthood in the Mental Hospital,* Houghton Mifflin, 1964; David Moment and Abraham Zaleznik, *Role Development and Interpersonal Competence,* Division of Research, Harvard Business School, 1963.) Professor Richard C. Hodgson, formerly of this faculty and now at the School of Business Administration of the University of Western Ontario, joined the work here and in a real sense made it possible for the two activities to come together in the study of executive administration in a mental hospital.

The study of executive behavior in the mental hospital is important on two counts. First, careful research observation and analysis in this setting may result in closer attention to problems of administering health agencies—an area of great significance in our society where increasing funds are being allocated for the prevention of illness and the care of the sick. The authors of this study, however, did not undertake the project with the intention of improving the work of the hospital in which this study took place or for that matter the work of administering health agencies. Their aims were in one sense much more modest yet in another much more ambitious. They were modest in their belief that human problems in organizations represent deeply rooted aspects of man's condition and deserve careful investigation in any setting. They were ambitious in their premise that human control of organizations and events is possible through the increased understanding that follows painstaking study and research.

The second way in which this study may be important grows out of these aims of the research. Superficially, the mental hospital, the business corporation, the government agency, the school, and other diverse kinds of formal organizations have little in common, but because they all seek to achieve their purposes through human action, they have much in common. While the contents of purposes and activities vary from one organization to the next and while the personalities vary widely, nevertheless the scientific study of men and work makes it possible to search for the elements that can relate experience in varying types of organizations. This study therefore contributes to a comparative analysis of organizations of interest to practitioners and social scientists alike.

The authors speak for themselves on what kind of comparative analysis the study exemplifies and toward what kind of theory it provides a building block. I can only add that the view of organizations is from the "inside" where human feelings and the development of individuals are of central concern. To this end, the authors bring a special interest in the applications of psychoanalytic psychology to the study of man at work in organizations. The authors intend to pursue the work exemplified by this book in many other ways. We can look forward to additional publications that will continue building the structure which in the authors' view will result in a dynamic social-psychology relating man, his work, and organizations.

Finally, may I express deep appreciation to the sources of financial support that made this study possible. Professors Zaleznik and Hodgson received financial support through a grant of the Ford Foundation for research in the area of organizational behavior, and from an allocation of funds given by The Associates of the Harvard Business School. The Foundations Fund for Research in Psychiatry provided the major support that enabled Professor Levinson to collaborate in this project. We gratefully acknowledge this generous support of research at Harvard.

BERTRAND FOX
Director of Research

Soldiers Field
Boston, Massachusetts
June 1965

Preface

THE STUDY of management is a growing concern in our increasingly organizational society. It assumes an important place in numerous disciplines and educational settings: industrial psychology, sociology, and psychiatry; graduate schools of business administration, public administration, hospital administration; and an expanding number of private firms offering professional consultation and service concerning management problems of all kinds. The published literature in this field has a strongly practical or applied character. In it one can find multitudinous, often conflicting, diagnoses of the ills that beset management and prescriptions for their cure. Many are merely essays purporting to define the successful manager, their effective management team, the productive organization. Efforts at empirical research are less common. They are usually made by persons under contract with the host organization, with the purpose of bringing about some form of improvement: in hiring or promotion practices, in interpersonal relations, in modes of communication and decision making, and the like. The published reports on such research ordinarily advocate certain techniques for improvement, such as testing, in-service training, or T-groups, and give some evidence (usually rather sparse) regarding the improvements achieved.

The present study is a departure from the above tradition. It is an examination and analysis of executives at work. We began with neither the formal contract nor the private intention to make improvements, to change executive functioning in the direction of certain normative standards. Rather, our primary aim was to delineate in detail the workings of the top executive echelon in one organization, and to develop a comprehensive theoretical perspective for the analysis of executive groups generally. It is hoped that research that provides a fuller understanding of organizations as they are will in time lead to more effective, and more judicious, efforts at change.

This study focuses on the three psychiatrist-executives who constituted the top echelon of a highly innovative mental hospital. In recent years mental hospitals have become available for social science research, and there is a rapidly growing body of research dealing with hospital structure, modes of patient care, occupational roles, changing functions, and the like. However, in the mental hospital as in other organizations very little research has been done on management structure and roles. Indeed, the term "executive" has rarely been applied to the psychiatrists who serve this function; nor do they ordinarily identify themselves in this way. We assume that the present study will have relevance not only for other mental hospitals but for organizations of widely differing character.

We bring to this research diverse interests and backgrounds. Two of us (Richard C. Hodgson and Abraham Zaleznik) have worked primarily in a school of business administration, and have been strongly influenced by concepts and methods of psychology, sociology, and psychoanalysis. The third (Daniel J. Levinson), originally trained in psychology, has also drawn upon sociology, psychiatry, and psychoanalysis, and for a number of years has been involved in research on the mental hospital. Our shared goal—and it is the major concern of this book—is to develop a dynamic social psychology, one that will have major relevance in the study of organizations and of occupational careers. The primary components of our theoretical approach in the present study may be summarized briefly as follows.

We conceive of the individual executive as an occupant of a particular *position* within an *organizational structure*. By virtue of holding this position, he is confronted with myriad opportunities and demands—externally given goals, facilities, obligations, inducements, cross-pressures. From various sources he receives messages, often mutually contradictory, concerning the expectations that others have of him, personally and with regard to more explicit organizational functions. Taken together, these explicit and implicit messages provide a contextual definition of his role. However, each man has to form his own *personal role-definition,* which he does on the basis both of external realities and of his inner, relatively enduring characteristics: professional outlook, life goals, abilities, values, character traits, personality dynamics.

We thus regard the executive's work as an evolving process of role-definition, reflecting fundamental aspects of his personality but also shaped by his situation in the organization and by societal influences. Of particular importance in our analysis is the concept of *role-tasks*—problematic issues with which every executive must deal in seeking to make productive use of himself and his organizational position. In our view, what is involved here is not simply "learning a set of behaviors" but, rather, engaging in *role-task work,* an inner process that engages the deepest aspects of the self. Similarly, the executive's role performance involves not merely impersonal decisions and behaviors but the use of the self with all of its wishes, conflicts, anxieties, defenses, fantasies, aspirations. In short, both the delineation of individual role performance and the analysis of its causal matrix require the conjoint consideration of the social environment of the individual personality.

The major analytic unit of this study is the top executive group. Within the over-all management structure we found a subsystem of three executives which exerted the most potent influence on the conduct and growth of the organization. This is not to say that power was totally concentrated in their hands or that others had no voice in organizational affairs. We are saying simply that, out of a larger management group, these three men evolved a functional subgroup of strategic importance. The emergence of this subgroup depended in part upon the fact that these men occupied high positions in the organization structure. However, high formal position is not enough: this group-formation is, as we shall show, a sociopsychological phenomenon having complex roots in individual personalities and in social structure.

We use the term *executive role constellation* to denote the kind of group-formation observed here. By "role constellation" we mean to imply an emerging and evolving system rather than a static, formally defined group or a simple aggregate. A role constellation comes into being under certain social conditions through the active efforts of the persons involved to develop a viable, personally meaningful enterprise. It requires a "division of emotional labor," as it were, along with the more explicit divisions of function with regard to specific administrative tasks.

In a relatively durable role constellation the psychosocial functions of the executive group are divided among its members in a way that suits their personalities as well as the needs of the organization. There is *specialization* of function by each member. There is *differentiation* of function; individuals differ in the nature of their specializations. And there is *complementarity* of function: the specializations of the various members complement and balance one another to form a relatively integrated whole.

The executive triad in our study formed a role constellation of a particular kind. We cannot say how commonly this constellation may be found in management groups generally; that is a problem for further research. Our chief concern is to elucidate the structure and dynamics of this one, to present a mode of analysis that can be applied elsewhere, and to offer some hypotheses concerning other possible constellations as well as nonconstellar ("aggregate") executive groups.

Our theoretical viewpoint may be hard to classify in terms of existing disciplines and theoretical schools. We deal with the three executives (a) as individuals; (b) as interdependent members of a crucially important managerial group; and (c) as wielders of authority within the over-all organization. Accordingly, we seek to distinguish, and at the same time to interrelate, three modes of analysis: individual personality and role-definition; small group (conceived of as role constellation); and organizational structure. We do not regard any one of these modes of analysis as the most crucial or as yielding causal factors more "basic" than the others. The essential problem, at this stage in the development of social psychology, is to work toward a theoretical framework capable of encompassing and interrelating these several modes of analysis. In time, the causal contributions of different factors (stemming from the individual personality, the small group, the organization, and the surrounding environment) to any given condition can be determined.

Starting with this theoretical perspective, we have found it possible and useful to draw upon various sources: psychoanalytic and related theories of personality; role theory; family theory derived from cross-cultural analysis; experimental and clinical small-group research; "symbolic interaction" sociology, and organization theory. To say that we have drawn upon these diverse sources is not to claim that we have integrated them into a single unified theory. Nor do we offer the present work as a "model" to be maintained intact in further studies. Our hopes are more modest. We believe that this work indicates a fruitful *direction* of theoretical and empirical endeavor, one that cuts across, and brings together, formerly disparate lines of investigation. It presents a view of the organization not as an impersonal apparatus but as a human enterprise, permeated by the full range of psychological qualities its members bring to their working lives. And it presents a view of the individual executive as an "incumbent of a position," his role and career influenced by social forces not of his making, and at the same time as a complex personality making responsible choices and, for better or worse, guiding his own destiny. In short, as noted above, our major aim is to contribute to the development of a dynamic social psychology of organizations and of individual careers.

The mental hospital and the executives who form the subject of this research must remain unnamed. It is not possible for us adequately to acknowledge our indebtedness to them. The "research contract" was negotiated directly with the three executives. We agreed to function solely as observers and analysts; we had neither the obligation nor the right to serve as agents of change—to take responsibility or even to offer advice with regard to hospital affairs. In return for this non-authoritative status, we had permission to observe the executives in *all* aspects of their work (with a few exceptions such as in their therapeutic work with patients) .

Our research arrangements and procedures are described in the body of the book. It must suffice here to express our appreciation and admiration to these men for the openness and candor with which they continued to honor our agreement. It was often not easy for them to be under observation, and for us to be observers, in situations of considerable stress and turmoil. At the same time, we should perhaps point out for those executives and those researchers who may consider embarking on a similar adventure, there were also rewards for all the parties involved. The presence of a trusted observer, who offered a sympathetic and interested (if not informative) response at difficult times, frequently helped to relieve the loneliness and strain of the executive. Similarly, each of the researchers derived considerable gain both from what he learned about the subjects of the research and, equally, from what he learned about himself as a vicarious participant in the events being studied. Like the therapist and the novelist, the fieldwork investigator has a remarkable opportunity for personal growth by learning selectively to see himself in others, and others in himself.

Once it was clear that the main subjects of our research were the three executives, other staff members were intrigued with the study and willing participants in it. Our debt to them will be apparent throughout the book. The requirement of anonymity again prevents us from acknowledging the contributions of particular individuals who facilitated our work in special ways.

Successive revisions of the manuscript benefited greatly from the criticism and suggestions of several readers. Fortunately, *their* names can be stated publicly: Professors Fritz J. Roethlisberger, Neil Smelser, and Lewis B. Ward. To Dr. Myron R. Sharaf we are grateful for making available his observations and interpretive insights concerning the process of leadership succession (see Chapter 8).

Also, the assistance of Elizabeth Karpati, Marie McCarthy, Gertrude Nierman, Clara Black, Jacquelyn Hodgson, Ruth Ann Hockney, and Nina Dolben was invaluable in moving the data and interpretations of this study through the several phases from initial data gathering, through analysis and revision, to the completed product.

We are grateful to Professor Bertrand Fox, Director of the Division of Research of the Harvard Business School and Miss Ruth Norton, Editor and Executive Secretary of the Division, who provided support, encouragement, and help in seeing this book into print.

We are pleased, finally, to acknowledge our own full responsibility for this book.

RICHARD C. HODGSON
DANIEL J. LEVINSON
ABRAHAM ZALEZNIK

London, Ontario
Boston, Massachusetts
June 1965

Contents

Through Group Action; The Future as Worth Working Toward; Teaching versus Other Commitments . . . Interpersonal Transactions Around Work: Performance and Response: *Teaching Rounds and the Communication of Professional Role Models; Interpersonal Style as Communicated in Teaching Rounds; Professional Opinions and Role Performance as a Teacher of Therapists; The Melding of Position, Performance, and Personality; The View of Life Underlying a Patterned Role Performance; The Superintendent's "Philosophy" and His Style of Interaction; Affective Specialization of Response to the Superintendent's Role Performance; Reinforcement of an Affectively Specialized Self-Concept . . .* The Resulting Balance

The Purposive Context of Administration: *A Long Day's Journey into Life; "Open Door" Interactions with Residents; Preferred Mode of Interaction: Therapeutic and Didactic; Facilitating the Work of Others versus Directing Others . . .* Interpersonal Transactions Around Work: Performance and Response: *The Underlying View of Life; Dr. Cadman's "Philosophy" and His Style of Interaction; Charisma; Modal Response of Cadman's Role Performance; Role Management: The Conduct of Simplicity, Stubbornness, and Anger; Offstage and Onstage Performance . . .* The Resulting Balance: *Costs and Rewards of a Specialized Role Performance; Latent Roles and Latent Issues; A Sense of Identity: Oneness in the Person-Position Encounter; Career Development Beyond the Early Adult Years*

The Purposive Context of Administration: *Work as a Way of Life; Mobilizing the Workers of the Future . . .*

PART I.   INTRODUCTION
Establishing the Framework of the Present Study

To HIGHLIGHT the meaning of the present work, we will in Part I delineate the organizational, contractual, and theoretical context from which our study arose. The systematic study of behavior in organizations is a relatively recent enterprise among social scientists and students of administration. Research of this nature reflects growing interest, perhaps concern, about the structural characteristics and dynamic forces that are emerging in our increasingly organizational society. Research into behavior in organizations also reflects the properties of the particular organizations that welcome or permit such scrutiny. The relevance of both these sets of influences is examined in Chapter 1.

Chapter 2 presents the social psychological framework of our present study. Chapter 3 presents findings from other studies that we found useful in sharpening our analysis of executive roles and executive role relations. In succeeding parts of this book, we will present what we consider to be the first attempt to use the theories of Chapters 2 and 3 in the systematic, clinical analysis of an executive group in action.

CHAPTER 1
The Nature and Aims of the Study

WHAT THIS STUDY IS ABOUT

WE PRESENT here a clinical observational study of an executive group in action. The study attempts to describe, analyze, and interpret the actual behavior of three executives as they went about the personal, interpersonal, and group business of running the organization for which they were responsible. The study assesses the dynamic interpersonal significance of each executive's behavior for the others with whom that executive interacted. It traces the impact of executive action and interaction upon group structure and group relations in the organization.

More specifically, this study reports on the role specialization and differentiation that existed within the top executive group in which our research was conducted. It examines the functional complementarity that existed between these top executive roles. It analyzes the explicit and implicit coalitions that existed between the executive role specialists. It interprets the resulting executive system as an *executive role constellation*. In order to accomplish these objectives, the study describes the role performances of the three executive subjects. It analyzes the personal role-demands and interprets the interpersonal dynamics that brought the executive role constellation into being. This same set of forces maintained the constellation for a period of several years, modified it, and prompted its eventual dissolution.

This constellation had a detectable impact upon its members, and upon their subordinates. The secondary objective of this study therefore was to investigate the impact of the executive role constellation upon the administrative transactions that flowed up and down the organization's chain of command. This impact was seen to be reflected not only in subordinates' administrative behavior, but also in their feelings toward their superordinates and in their own personal and professional development.

WHY SUCH RESEARCH IS CONDUCTED

HUMAN BEHAVIOR in organizations is a topic of growing interest to many behavioral scientists and managers. Ours is an increasingly organizational society. More people live and work in large, interdependent social systems than ever before in the history of mankind. The work of maintaining and improving these systems, which is the work of the modern world, is no longer accomplished by solitary individuals or isolated groups. It is accomplished by complex organizations, through the specialized and differentiated efforts of people in those organizations.

Much of today's work has already developed to the point at which extreme degrees of technical specialization are needed merely to *keep up with* the latest advances in many fields. Even more specialization is needed actually to accomplish such advances. It is only within the multisegmented structure of a formal, purposive organization that a range of these specializations can be carried forward, in a coordinated fashion, toward the accomplishment of a coherent set of purposes. Responding to these circumstances, executives find themselves in charge of organizations whose bureaucratic form is characterized by planned division of labor and integrated specializations of function. This permits sub-units to exercise their highly differentiated skills in the achievement of a range of tasks that no individual or group could duplicate alone. Given the planning and integrative functions of top management, an organization can produce more results and generate more rewards for its members than most of them could have hoped to produce for themselves, by themselves.

However, one result of these trends is that executives are often faced with the task of managing corporate systems that extend well beyond the limits of the executives' own expertise. An executive must take the initiative in formulating organizational goals that he will have to depend on others to attain. How does he respond to the ambivalent administrative situation in which he directs the behavior of others, while depending on them to produce the results on which *he* will eventually be judged?

The executive must develop alternative courses of action for his organization. These probably include several with which he is personally unfamiliar. The possibility of adopting an unfamiliar course of action may be quite unnerving to him. Yet external conditions may point to the necessity of moving in that direction. How does the executive respond? Does he make the necessary decisions and follow them up with enthusiasm? Or does he spend a disproportionate amount of his time anxiously scrutinizing the information provided to him by his subordinate specialists, distrustful of them and of himself?

Does he view the structure of his organization, the caliber of his people, and the condition of his markets as constraints or as challenges? Does he reactively follow the developments in his sector of the economy, or does he proactively go about making a few developments of his own?

There will always be some people in an organization who disagree with an executive's decisions and actions. How does the executive respond to them? Does he quietly ignore them as he goes about his business? Does he strive persistently to convince them of his rightness? Does he attempt deliberately to eliminate them from the organization? When such disagreements arise around him, he may feel relatively at ease with them, considering them to be a natural part of working with different people in a common undertaking. Or he may experience a deep sense of injury over what he construes as deliberate obstruction directed malevolently against him as a person. His life perhaps becomes one of increasing productiveness. Or the pressures of being an executive may push him into a state of increasing self-absorption, in which his brooding over symbolic wounds causes the reality components of his position to become increasingly difficult for him to manage.

The problems of command, both civilian and military, have stimulated the interest of many observers of the modern world. Decisions of centrally located and authoritative individuals have potential ranges of consequence that are sometimes difficult to anticipate, estimate, or comprehend.[1] The possible recipients of such consequences understandably turn their attentions to the people who hold the positions of authority and central decision-making initiative in the major organizations of the nation and the world. From this has arisen the growing awareness—one might say, apprehension—that psychological and social forces are important in determining what members of an organization do; and through that behavior, what the organization does.

The behavior of executive members of the organization plays a crucially determining function in this system of interdependencies. Organizations are no longer considered to be operationally autonomous entities, functioning with inscrutable rationality through the exclusion of all the human foibles and group prejudices of its members and clients. It is the behavior of fallible executives that provides the vehicle for sequences of action whose outcomes can and do mold the structure of modern society. The attempt to raise a price, or lower it; the intention of testing a weapon, or stopping the

---

[1] See C. W. Mills, *The Power Elite*, 1959. (Note: full bibliographical information on these references is to be found at the end of the book.)

test; the desire to introduce a tariff, or to abolish it; the declaration of a political idea, and the attempt to block that declaration; all are sequences of critical events initially put into action in organizations by executive behavior. Such behavior reflects executives' interests, values, motivations, and character traits. It reflects their upbringing, their aspirations, and their anxieties. It expresses the sort of person they wish to become, and the sort of person they wish others to become. Yet we have few well-established findings about the relations that are involved in these dynamics.

WHERE THE STUDY WAS CONDUCTED

OUR STUDY was conducted at what we have chosen to call the Memorial Psychiatric Institute, a privately owned psychiatric hospital in the eastern United States. The M.P.I. had bed space for 300 in-patients. It was, however, actively pursuing the practice of keeping its patients as closely integrated with the community as the patients' capacities would allow. Therefore, the number of beds and the number of in-patients did not reflect the emphasis that the management of the hospital placed on its operations. Nor did the number of in-patients reflect the scope of the Institute's total operations. For every patient living on a full-time basis in the hospital, there were approximately three living on a full-time or part-time basis in the community, while continuing their treatment at the Institute.

The services of the hospital were divided into two main categories. There was the "house," in which adult in-patients were treated, and there were the clinics that handled a predominantly out-patient population. The house was divided into five service units, each with its own relatively autonomous staff. Patients in the house services could be administratively assigned to several treatment programs besides being full-time in-patients. There was a day care program for those who could live at home at night, but who needed care and treatment during the day. There was a night care program for those who could hold down a job, but who needed professional supervision at night. There was always a number of beds vacant as patients tried out their newly achieved levels of personal strength in home visits, of specified duration, with their families. A patient on home visit always knew his or her bed was available. If the visit did not work out, he or she could always return to the care and protection of the Institute, before making another attempt to re-establish functioning social relations.

The clinics dealt with people who had never been admitted to the hospital, as well as with those who had been discharged from it. One of the clinics was devoted to the treatment of children. Another concentrated on diagnostic and therapeutic services to people whose disabilities had not reached the stage or were not of the type that required hospitalization. A third clinic specialized in psychiatric work with elderly persons, mostly on an out-patient basis.

Even for full-time in-patients in the hospital the treatment regime was, in relation to prevailing levels of psychiatric care in other institutions, quite advanced. This was an "open" hospital. The wards were not locked. The rooms on each service that used to be seclusion rooms, where violent patients had been forcibly sequestered, had had the locks removed from the doors, and were now referred to as "quiet rooms." There was no admission ward or violent ward where the "lunatic persons, furiously mad," of previous decades used to be concentrated. Patients were admitted to the regular wards of the house service, and they continued their residence and treatment in the ward to which they were admitted until such time as they were discharged or transferred elsewhere.

The hospital was experimenting with a variety of admission procedures, particularly with a voluntary form of admission. If an individual felt he needed psychiatric care, and an examining psychiatrist concurred, that individual could sign himself into the hospital under a voluntary admission. If his treatment did not go well with him, the individual could give notice and sign himself out, unless extraordinary measures were taken to stop him. This form of admission was an important innovation in psychiatric administration. The top management of the Institute was convinced of the necessity of such innovations. They were attempting this particular experiment on somewhat more than a provisional basis, despite the reluctance of other hospitals to venture into operations outside the boundaries of established legal precedent.

Contrary to the situation in many mental institutions, this hospital was well staffed. It had an excellent reputation in its field, based on past pioneering work that had proved its professional and therapeutic worth, and had become part of the accepted body of American psychiatry. At the time of the research, its success with patients was generally considered to be good. In-patients could usually count the duration of their stay in the hospital more easily in weeks, rather than in the years of hopelessness that used to be the prognosis for mental patients. The hospital had several affiliations with nearby colleges and medical schools. This brought undergraduate and postgraduate students into the Institute, and into contact with patients. It also permitted a number of its staff to hold joint hospital and university posts.

In general, the internal atmosphere of the Institute was one of excitement, dedication, and ferment. The organization received many more applications for training and staff positions than it was able to accept. Therefore, those who were working and training in the hospital were quite highly selected. Residency training in psychiatry was offered, as well as professional training in related fields such as clinical psychology, psychiatric social work, psychiatric nursing, and occupational therapy. Much of the work of the organization was carried on by these trainees, particularly by the doctors taking their residencies in psychiatry. These doctors were the ones who handled the bulk of the diagnostic and therapeutic work in the house and the clinics. In addition, many of them participated in a variety of research projects that were being carried on in the hospital.

The hospital's top management group was its medical executive committee. This committee was made up of the superintendent, the assistant superintendent, the director of the hospital's in-patient clinical services, the heads of the clinics, and the administrator. The hospital had a table of organization and several levels of formal authority were represented in the committee. This implied a decision-making hierarchy among the executives, but these prerogatives were exercised only rarely. These men were all professionally qualified psychiatrists. Their planning of the hospital's service and training operations, and their evaluation of people and results, took the form of relatively equalitarian discussions among professional colleagues.

The Institute was governed by a board of trustees. This board was composed of representatives of the community. It met quarterly with the superintendent to discuss past events and future plans for the hospital. Relations with the community were an important matter to the superintendent, and for the hospital. Its patients were not segregated from the surrounding community. Constant attention had to be paid to matters pertaining to the comings and goings of patients. Also, the hospital was seeking to expand physically. Certain connections had to be maintained in order to assure the advancement of civic and legal proceedings that would make available the space needed to expand. Funds for the expansion had to be obtained. The trustees were able to be of some help in this, but it was the superintendent who assumed the major initiative in these duties. The conception of a mental hospital as a small society,[2] functioning in relative independence

---

[2] See W. Caudill, *The Psychiatric Hospital as a Small Society*, 1958.

from its environment, might perhaps have been applicable at the ward level of this hospital. Certainly it was not applicable at the top executive level. Relations with the wider community had to be actively elaborated. Without these external relations, the "small society" within the organization would soon have withered from lack of resources and from the lack of a challenging future.

The three senior executives of the hospital—the superintendent, the assistant superintendent, and the clinical director —worked closely together in managing the internal operations of the organization and keeping it related to the outside world. As indicated, the superintendent did the bulk of this outside work: "Living on T.W.A.," he jokingly called it. This was not a burden for him. He enjoyed the work and actively developed it well beyond the minimal limits required of anyone holding the superintendency of the hospital. The assistant superintendent and the clinical director were more than content with this arrangement. Although they were also involved in the activities of groups and associations outside the hospital, they were more interested in directing their professional and administrative attentions to what was going on inside. The assistant superintendent was more than busy in the administration of the nonmedical operations of the hospital, particularly in the planning and administration of the growing number of research projects being carried on in the hospital. The clinical director was the most active of the three in his practice as a therapist, and in the teaching of therapists both in the hospital and in outside professional groups. With the additional work of administering the clinical services of the house, and supervising the work of many of the resident psychiatrists, the clinical director was fully occupied, often for as much as twelve hours a day.

These three men formed the *central executive triad* of this study. Their working relations were specialized in the task functions they performed, and in the emotional quality they

expressed in their administrative interactions. Each man had
his own specializations. Each man's specializations were differentiated from those of the others. This differentiation was
of a kind that one man was good at, and did, what the other
two were less good at, or preferred not to do. That is, the task
activities and the affective communications of these men were
largely complementary. This matrix of interpersonal relations, with its specialization, differentiation, and complementarity of roles, comprised a system we have called the *executive role constellation*.

THE INSTITUTE AS A RESEARCH LOCALE

THE FACT THAT our research was conducted in a hospital had
a bearing on the results we were able to obtain. The first influence of the research locale arose from the nature of the
goals of the organization. The hospital was in operation (1) to
train professional workers in the field of mental illness and
health, (2) to develop greater knowledge in that field through
research, and (3) to apply it in helping sick people to become
well. These goals were an organizational expression of perhaps the noblest of man's ideologies: dedication to the advancement of knowledge and commitment to helping others.
On the first point—the advancement of knowledge—the presence of researchers was not at all strange to the members of
the organization. There was a variety of persons carrying on
several forms of research in the organization. Research objectives were not foreign to the staff. We were interested in doing research and the top management group was widely considered an interesting focus of study. This was sufficient for
most of the staff members with whom the researchers came in
contact.

On the second point—helping sick people become well—
repeated incidents demonstrated the latent functioning of
humanitarian feelings and altruistic motives among staff
members. Humanitarian feelings and altruistic motives are,

of course, no substitute for professional knowledge and skill in psychiatry in helping patients to become well. But they help. They help in the therapeutic process. They help even more in the administration of clinical services. The researchers noticed that if a crisis arose, if a patient needed help, he usually got that help. This occurred regardless of personal inconvenience to staff members, disruption of administrative schedules, and violation of budgetary limitations. "You can always get more money," the clinical director told one of the house administrators, "but you can't get a life once it's gone."

Surrounding that bedrock helping relationship, however, was such a ferment of misunderstanding that the existence of the helping relationship was often covered up. It became almost customary for members of this and other hospitals, when they found out that two of the researchers were from business schools, to take them aside and inform them that hospitals were "absolutely the most poorly administered organizations in existence." It was, these informants felt, "about time they got someone in here from the Business School to increase efficiency." But the researchers were more impressed by the way the essential work of the hospital got done, despite the disagreements and disorganization that many of the staff were so vocal about. It seemed that, if the hospital was "poorly administered"—whatever that meant—it was because it could afford to be. Given the basic ideological commitment of the organization, through its staff members, there was little danger of its operations breaking down in moments of crisis. It was in moments of crisis that the organization pulled together, not apart. Pulling apart might occur after a crisis, as in finding out whose fault the crisis had been. The same sort of divisiveness also contributed to future crises. But "when the chips were down," the staff usually worked together to do what was necessary.

The senior executives of the hospital were fully aware of

this. They could "let things go" to a great extent, knowing that "in the pinches" the staff would pull themselves together with a minimum of guidance from the top. If this had not been the case, the executives would probably have felt the need to keep a tighter "lid" on the organization than was the case here. However, they were quite relaxed in the face of considerable "bitching and griping" among subordinates. Such openness was of great benefit to the gathering of data.

At the top executive level, openness was further reinforced by the independent professional standing of the men who were the senior administrators of the hospital. These men were doctors, psychiatrists, and in some cases psychoanalysts. They were fully qualified to carry on private practices of their own. This they all did to varying extents on a part-time basis. The alternative was always open to them to leave the organization, to "hang up a shingle," and to make a very good living by practicing on a full-time basis on their own.

In other words, the executives held positions in the hospital because they wanted to, not because they had to. They worked in these positions in order to help accomplish some of the objectives they wanted to see realized in their field. These objectives were of a kind that could be obtained better in an organizational setting than through private practice or independent clinical research. Should the Institute cease to strive toward those objectives, the executives were free to leave the organization. They were much freer to do so than had they been individuals with no independent professional standing, with skills of little use outside the particular organization that employed them. This fact of independence, and of voluntary affiliation with the organization, was very much related to the openness of the executives with the researchers. Once the discretion of the research team had been established, the executives provided a wide range of thoughts, opinions, and feelings about themselves and others in the organization.

Provided the researchers were accurate in their analysis of the management situation, the executives were surprisingly unhesitant about "letting go" with information.

For the researchers, this provided the opportunity to get to the quick of an administrative, interpersonal situation in two years instead of two decades. It provided the challenge to make the most of the extremely rich data that were being presented. This task took the researchers much further afield, in a theoretical sense, than had been initially anticipated.

Establishing and Conducting the Research

Our research began with a study of the total Memorial Psychiatric Institute organization. This study, based on observations and interviews, covered segments of the nonmedical administrative groups, the operation of the hospital's psychiatric training program, and the structure and dynamics of the top medical executive group. It ranged from attendance at meetings of the medical executive committee and the board of trustees, through the observation of activities in the business office, to an inspection of the operations of the hospital's boiler rooms. Interviews were conducted with the personnel involved, to ascertain the relationship, or lack of relationship, among these various subunits of the total organization. This work covered a period of four months.

This preliminary field work was written up during the following three months in a report. The purpose of the report was initially to present the analysis of an organization, interpreted in social system terms, for use in Harvard Business School class discussions of organizational behavior. In this report, there was a brief section on the "latent role structure" of the top management group. This section contained short sketches of the personalities of the three senior medical executives, the interaction of the three personalities with one another, and the impact of those personalities and interpersonal

relations on the functioning of the organization at subordinate levels.

The executives were quite taken by this section of the report. The remainder of the report seemed quite plodding and
pedestrian to them, but for a variety of reasons, the substance
of our remarks on the latent role structure existing among
them stimulated their interest. First, it seemed that they were
somewhat surprised that relations they already felt to exist
implicitly were picked up by psychiatrically untrained outsiders in such a brief period of contact. Second, our remarks
accorded with their own apperception of the interpersonal situation existing among them. They felt themselves to be a
competent executive team. They considered the structural
and dynamic properties of their triad to be closely in line
with what, in their opinion, were the social psychological *requirements* of an effective executive team. The substance of
our analysis of their team appeared to be taking a few tentative steps in the direction of their own conclusions, particularly in highlighting the symbolic meaning of interpersonal
relations.

On this basis, we were invited to continue our research, to
"find out what you are talking about," as one of the members
of the top executive triad phrased it. Another executive recommended that we "soak in the organization," to develop our
preliminary ideas and render them less speculative. As it
turned out, the nature of the interpersonal situation within
the triad underwent change during the second phase of our
field work, as did our preliminary ideas about that situation.
However, the initial arrangement underlying the second
phase of field work, specifically focused on the top management group, proved strong enough to withstand the inroads
of these changes, and the present book is the result. The executives' dedication to the development of knowledge and skill
in areas related to psychiatry, their unquestionable professional competence, their confidence in their ability to admin-

ister a high caliber organization, all contributed to the stability of the research relationship that brought about this analysis of their executive group.

Consequently, our research began again in the M.P.I. We re-entered the organization at the top management level. A month was spent getting the "feel" of the executive milieu by being present at most of the hospital activities in which the executives participated, taking notes, and then asking questions of those whose behavior seemed to possess a significance unknown to the observers.

Next, we spent between one and two weeks "shadowing" each executive as he went about his business in the organization. This observation was conducted on as full-time a basis as possible, given the limitation of the privacy demanded by some of the doctor-patient contacts occurring within the work day, and by the privacy requested now and then by hospital personnel wishing to consult with the executives. Notes were taken throughout the day, with questions asked or conversations initiated whenever the opportunity arose.

Each period of time spent with a single executive tended to be a rather intense personal as well as data-gathering experience, as the data to be presented may indicate. The concerted and continuous attempt to understand the world from another's point of view, to understand and document his experiential frame of reference in relation to people and events in the hospital, was a tiring and often discomforting job. Approximately one week was required to "decompress" after such a field work experience, the time being spent re-establishing one's own sense of identity and catching up on one's field notes. Thus, this phase of the field work took approximately two months in all.

After that, a month was spent at the other end of the medical chain of command, learning about ward operations from the point of view of the nonmedical staff, the resident psychiatrists, and the chief residents. We did not have the time, nor was it our objective, to study the wards from the patients' points of view, as others have already done.[3, 4, 5] Our data on ward operations were gathered by attendance at ward staff meetings, and by interviews and conversations with the personnel involved.

Next, we spent a month tracing the connections between people, situations, and events on the ward management level and those on the top management level. This we did by interviewing a few nonmedical staff personnel and some resident psychiatrists training in the hospital, and by talking with all the chief residents who supervised the services, the service consultants who advised the chiefs, and the assistant clinical director, who reported directly to a member of the top executive triad, the clinical director.

The final data-gathering phase lasted six months. It consisted of observing a series of regularly held administrative meetings attended by different groups of the medical-psychiatric staff. These different groups comprised interlocking sets of psychiatric personnel, such that the entire medical chain of command, from superintendent to resident, could be followed by attending the meetings. In this way, the structure of relationships and the conduct of administration could be observed, somewhat simultaneously, at several levels and in several different locations throughout the Institute. This provided the vantage point from which the development of critical incidents and their subsequent ramifications were observed throughout the organization. During the same period, interviews and conversations continued to be held with the staff personnel involved in important issues in the meetings, to make sure that individual points of view were more fully understood than was possible within the limits of group meetings.

3 *Ibid.*
4 E. Goffman, *Asylums,* 1961.
5 A. H. Stanton and M. S. Schwartz, *The Mental Hospital,* 1954.

Throughout the eleven months of field work, all observations and interviews and most group meetings were recorded on the spot by rough, hand-written notes. These notes were transcribed in the evening of the day they were taken, or on the following day. Often, as much time was spent transcribing selected critical incidents as had been spent in the entire observation or interview in question. We tried initially to categorize our data as we obtained them, by transcribing them onto classified, cross-referenced cards. This seemed to disrupt more than facilitate the development of our understanding, so this system was soon abandoned in favor of a largely chronological report of events and conversations, with points of emphasis and interpretation inserted in parentheses in the body of the report.

Some of the meetings we attended were tape recorded. Few such tapes were taken. Without them, we still had more data than could be managed easily. With them, we were faced with an unmanageable quantity of raw information. We faced the same problem with a tape that we did with the original group meeting. This, combined with participants' continuing nervousness in the presence of a tape recorder, caused us to use the machine sparingly. We used it to check our observations among us three researchers, to get further documentation on the process of a particular interpersonal exchange, to capture without errors of recall and distortion an individual's verbal mode of presenting himself in a meeting. Once these tests of accuracy and interpretation had been conducted, the tapes were abandoned in favor of the more flexible and selective method of note-taking.

In observing our executive subjects in action, we paid particular attention to the *content* of their interactions with people. It was necessary to know with whom the executives interacted and how frequently. We got to know this by "soaking" in the organization. However, to have made a systematic who-to-whom frequency count would have precluded gathering the data we did. Had our study progressed further, a quantitative analysis of interactions might have been a useful next step. It was no substitute, however, for listening to the substance of what people were telling us about themselves and the organization.

By deliberate decision, we gave free reign to an unstructured, clinical wonder over what we observed taking place as the executives went about their work in the hospital. In some ways it would have been easier to establish an orderly pattern for gathering coded data right from the start. Looking back, we believe it was fortunate that we held our anxieties in abeyance, and remained open to unfolding events. Many of the data that proved to be analytically most useful were gathered unexpectedly, almost despite our attempts at systematizing the data collection. Unconscious forces would suddenly break into open expression. An episode critical to the administration of the organization, and to the development of its members, would be precipitated unexpectedly. The breaking forth of unconscious forces, and their expression in critical episodes, occurred according to their own rhythm and not according to a time sampling schedule. They were open only to an observer on the spot. Once a critical episode had been precipitated, the researchers were kept busy following its ramifications and studying the gradual working through of its implications by the organization members most involved.

Having more than one researcher was as necessary at this stage of the research as it was in the later, more analytic stages. If a particular act or event caused a particular response in and among the researchers, then it was thought likely to have caused similar responses among the executives or subordinates involved. On this basis, certain members were sought out for further questioning and discussion. The participation of more than one researcher served as a controlling and validating device. It limited the personal idiosyncracies of gathering clinical data. At the same time, it freed the researchers to become as personal as capacity would allow in gathering data. The control of another researcher's opinion, and occasional consensual validation, relieved us of many solitary preoccupations about one's own attitudinal biases and motivational distortions.

As field notes were transcribed, they were typed in triplicate and distributed among the researchers. When full-time field work was terminated at the end of eleven months, the researchers spent two months reviewing the data, discussing its meaning, and establishing an over-all conceptual framework for organizing and analyzing the data. The following year was spent discussing, analyzing, writing up a partial presentation of data-in-relation-to-theory, and going back to the field to check specific undocumented ideas that had emerged during discussion.

A final draft of the present book was written completely away from the Memorial Psychiatric Institute. The writing of this manuscript also took close to a year. Thus, approximately two years elapsed between the end of full-time field work and the completion of the final document. The executive group that was our focus of analysis had changed much in that period. Ours was not a study of change *per se*. Our main objective was to describe the structure and dynamics of executive relations as they existed during the period of our field work. Nonetheless, change did add a significant, if secondary, dimension to our analysis. In adding this dimension, we were aided greatly by a fellow social scientist who made available to us data he had gathered in the M.P.I. prior to our study. Also, we did stay informed of developments in the M.P.I. during the major period of writing this book. This information was significantly related, at several points, to our own understanding of the dynamics of the Institute's top executive group. We considered the implications of personal development, change in interpersonal relations, and the evolution of group structures to be important enough to add to our more static analysis of the executive role constellation we had observed in operation.

The next-to-final draft of this book was submitted to the three executives. Of course, change had rendered our analysis inaccurate on several important points. However, as a representation of the interpersonal situation existing among them at the time of the study, the executives found the report to be "startlingly accurate." Several less complimentary opinions were also voiced, and several points for revision and correctable errors were indicated. These were helpful in bringing about a few relatively specific changes to the present document. Not all inaccuracies were removed. What one executive considered inaccurate, one or two others considered to be completely accurate. These "inaccuracies" we tended to leave in the manuscript.

Finally, it should be pointed out that the decision to disguise the name and locale of the organization, and the names of the subjects of our study, was *our* decision. It was not required of us by our subjects. Hopefully, this disguise will help a bit to transfer interest from a particularistic focus upon intriguing individuals, and toward a more universalistic focus on the scientific understanding of interpersonal relations in management groups.

SOME REMARKS ABOUT THE RESEARCH "CONTRACT"

WE WERE INVITED into the organization by the top executives to study the top executives, in order to understand the situation existing among them, and between them and the organization, but not to change that situation. This agreement, or contract, between the researchers and the researched provided an unusual opportunity for field work of a type rarely permissible in organizations. A group such as ours is more usually invited into an organization by middle or upper middle management to study lower status levels. The top and bottom levels of the hierarchy are only vaguely interested in the research. Sometimes they are actively hostile, due to an actual or imputed intention of the upper middle managers to use the research to "prove something" to skeptical superordinates, or against resistant subordinates. Being invited into the organization by the top executive group, our research was sanctioned by the ultimate source of power in the organization.

Not only did we have the organizational sanction of the top executive group, we had the active personal interest and involvement of the executives in the study, since they were themselves the focus of our research. This research relationship avoided defensiveness, or lack of honesty, in representing the study. The executives contracting the research usually feel that a problem exists, but consider it to exist everywhere but in and among themselves. The researchers are invited to study an "interesting situation" among people "down there," where the superordinates feel the problem to exist, at a level in the organization safely removed from themselves. If a contract is formed on this basis between researchers and executives, the researchers then "go to work on" the lower status target group. The research is hampered by the resistance of the subjects. It is hampered by the fact that, despite their academic and professional neutrality, the researchers have become an agent of organizational warfare between different levels or groupings in the organization.

The fact that we were invited by top executives to study the top executive group was sufficient to gain us acceptance throughout the organization. As soon as the professional discretion of the researchers was established, and in many cases even before that, members at all levels of the organization were willing to help describe how it was in the organization, and what their relations were with the top executive group. As far as most of the organization was concerned, the top group needed study, and they were pleased to see it being studied. They were eager to assist. The researchers accepted their help and used the data they provided, but rejected the assumption that was now reversed; namely, that the "problem" existed among the superordinates but not among the subordinates.

Our study was devoted to describing a portion of the organization—its top management group—as it actually functioned. We were not oriented to *changing* what we observed, but rather to analyzing fully the substance of our observations. We held out no promise for improvement and took no responsibility for change. This, of course, was a basic feature of the executives' invitation to us. We were invited into their group to find out how things were in at least one top management group. This was for the betterment of our professional skills and knowledge, not for theirs.

The subordinates were disappointed that this was not a change study. The descriptive orientation of the study was viewed as something of a failure by those who had hoped for an action orientation. Our increasingly theoretical interests did not fit some persons' stereotype of Harvard Business School research. Nor did it correspond to their wish to "do something" to executives who had been "doing things" to them for so long. However, the project was intriguing, the researchers were trustworthy, and that was sufficient for most informants and discussants.

The remarkable openness of the executives and their subordinates to this study can be gauged by even the most casual perusal of the data in this book. This openness was in part a feature of the organization. It was in part a product of the intelligence, sensitivity, and professional training of all the staff. Two factors allowed us to make use of their openness. First was the contractual integrity of the study, referred to above. Second was our attempt to describe the organization from the point of view and experiential framework of many individuals in it, rather than from any absolute point of reference established by ourselves or by executive policy. In smoothly functioning administrative situations, the descriptions we gained from different individuals had much overlap and commonality. In malfunctioning situations, these descriptions were disorganized and disjunctive. By gathering our data according to the internal frame of reference of participants, our description of the organization as a whole suffered from the confusions of our informants. Yet our understanding of their behavior benefited immensely from the wealth of personal material people actively volunteered when they found out that we were not there to evaluate them but to find out how it was with them. Multidimensional descriptions of this nature allow the investigator to delineate an organizational situation that incorporates individuals' experiences and points of view, while at the same time gaining some descriptive inclusiveness and accuracy that is greater than the sum of the constituent parts. Such an approach to data gathering can produce a greater depth of analysis than that based on individual informants' somewhat solipsistic frames of reference, or on the investigator's independent and equally incomplete opinion about a situation.

The relation between the contract of this study and its descriptive approach is worth noting. We were invited by the top group to study the top group. Yet we approached all members of the organization from their own experiential framework. Thus, we avoided the doubly two-faced situation of being invited in by a superordinate group to study subordinates, then interviewing those subordinates ostensibly from their point of view, in order to report something back to top management, usually for the purpose of changing the subordinates' situation.

The congruity of the entire project was enhanced by avoiding this double double-bind. Our interviews were mostly conversations. When we were asked questions, we answered them. People wanted to hear us talk as well as have us listen. They wanted to get a feel for our opinions, our view of the world in general, and their organization in particular. They gave us a lot and wanted a little in return. Maintaining an unremittingly listening stance, as in the nondirective interview, made our subjects and their subordinates suspicious and resentful. They demanded to be let in on at least a bit of our response to what they were giving us. The congruity of our research stance in the organization was such that we were able to give some of our thoughts and feelings, upon request, without acquiescing to requests for "gossip" and "dirt," and without alienating our sources of data.

CHAPTER 2
Personality and Social Role

INTRODUCTION

As CHAPTER 1 indicated, the object of this study is to analyze and interpret observed executive behavior. In order to do this, we need a theoretical framework that highlights the meaning of observed behavior, both for the individual actor and for the members of his organizational audience. Chapter 2 attempts to establish such a framework. It presents an eclectic conceptual scheme that we consider basic to the understanding of all behavior in organizations. Chapter 3 will then deal more specifically with our particular topic of analysis: namely, the behavior of *executives,* the nature of executive roles, and the role relations that tend to get established in operating executive groups.

Chapter 2 consists of three sections. The first, "Personality Development and Socialization," outlines current theory that we consider useful in explicating the nature of personality and its development in *all* stages of life, from infancy through adulthood. The theory of post-adolescent personality has proved difficult to come to grips with, given the limits of currently established personality theory. One of the difficulties is a derivative of the nature-nurture controversy that has existed for some time in the psychology of social behavior and the sociology of personal development.

Current theories of personality development have dealt intriguingly with those stages of the individual's growth in which his stance in relation to his social environment is one of incorporating features of that environment into himself. That is, he internalizes salient properties of the culture immediately surrounding him, hence adding a component or function to the existing structure of his personality. As an input mechanism, the developing personality is no longer a complete scientific mystery. But, when the individual reaches stages in which his stance toward his environment is no longer primarily incorporative, but emittive, then theories of personality development and socialization tend to view him as a finished product. The remainder of his life is viewed implicitly as a repetition, a somewhat anticlimactic series of manifestations of the sameness of his personality structure, gradually unwinding into outright senility.

Personality theorists have, in this way, we submit, become partly captive to the youth culture of the North American continent. The adult personality as an output mechanism, if we can think of it briefly as such, is still unmapped territory in the total continent of human development. Yet our observations of our executive subjects, all adults, indicated that the continuing development of their personalities was a lively issue with them, engrossing to them and to those around them. Were we to close out this aspect of observations because of a lack of clearly developed theory around which to organize the data? Our search for theory, particularly to help understand the development of personality through the *expression* of existing adult personality, as opposed to pre-adult personality development through the *incorporation* of social forces, led us conceptually further afield than we had anticipated. Much of the resultant integration of theories, and theory building, was used as a general orientation to a large body of data, out of which arose the more specific theoretical interpretations of situations and events in the hospital. The first section of Chapter 2 begins to outline the theoretical background of our orientation to the executive subjects of this study.

The second section, "Personal Style and Performance," represents a shift from ideas about the developing personality to ideas about the contemporary behavior of the individual. We were seeking a theoretical framework that would help us to describe, in an organized fashion, the here-and-now behavior we were observing, not merely as a series of impersonal acts or interactions, but rather as a means of transaction between individuals, by which and through which each person conveyed wishes, demands, hopes, needs, fears, conflicts, and values. Personality theories *per se* were useful in interpreting observed behavior, but they provided little help in organizing the description of the behavior that was being interpreted. We found the ideas of interpersonal relations theorists, forced by their interests to approach personality more from the point of view of observable behavior, to be useful in this context.

The third section, "Self-Representation and Symbolization in Social Life," continues the line of development of our thinking, moving from the developing personality, through the behavior that was the expression and the vehicle of that development, to the social meanings that the individual's behavior established in the minds of the others in the organizational context surrounding him. This aspect of our investigation drew heavily on "symbolic interactionist" thinking. In relating this school of thought to developmental, dynamic, and interactionist approaches to personality, we felt we were able to use the best of symbolic interactionism without falling heir to the depersonalized and inadequately descriptive liabilities of this approach to interpersonal relations.

From this outline, it can be seen that we view personality as a constantly developing structure of forces, or predispositions to behave in certain "characteristic" ways. This structure exists within the individual, expressing ontogenetic tendencies of the organism, and reflecting the expectations of salient members of the individual's social environment. In the organizational setting, the patterned behavior that results is termed the individual's *performance,* the pattern itself constituting the individual's role in the organization.[1] Our use of the concept of role, therefore, differs from those that consider role to be the sum total of all expectations as to how the individual *should* behave in the organization. Neither do we consider role to be synonymous with the concept of *position.* For us, role has a behavioral point of reference, expressing the individual's personality as much as, sometimes more than, the expectations of others in the organization. Certainly this view of "role" helped us to make more sense of our observations than any of the alternative meanings assigned.

PERSONALITY DEVELOPMENT AND SOCIALIZATION

THE EMPIRICAL FOCUS of this study was on the here-and-now behavior of three top executives, and on the responses of their subordinates. Our attempt was to establish the uniformities in the interplay of psychosocial forces taking place in the management hierarchy of the Institute. Our method was ahistorical, but our theory could not be so. Although our empirical focus was on contemporary behavior, a developmental theory was necessary for its analysis. Although we were not studying the personality development of our subjects, our concept of personality development played an important part in analyzing their observed, present behavior. This was due to the unavoidable fact that the observed interactive behavior of "today" reflected many "yesterdays" of the interactors' social experiences. It was responded to by each in terms of his personality, and his past personal history, as well as in relation to the present realities of operating the Institute. Historically given issues, derived from various earlier periods, operated in the present. In many instances, the executives were quite explicit about this, and subsequently their behavior validated many of their own interpretations about themselves. The

[1] For a fuller presentation of these ideas, see D. J. Levinson, "Role, Personality, and Social Structure in the Organizational Setting," 1959.

present situation was given meanings by each person, and activated motives, feelings, conflicts, and defenses within him that had origins in his recent and distant past, as well as in the existing organizational situation. To deal with such phenomena, it was necessary to build a conceptual scheme that highlighted the connections between the several points in time, stages of development, and administrative issues to which each executive's actions were addressed.

Personality Development

A number of theories have been developed to explicate various dimensions of psychological functioning. Few of these have attempted to delineate the development of the total personality in all the stages of the life cycle from infancy to old age. The most comprehensive developmental scheme is that of psychoanalytic theory.[2, 3] The widely attributed "overemphasis" of psychoanalytic theories upon childhood and adolescence proved no drawback in our analysis of adult behavior. The more cognitive insights of role theory were helpful in organizing and analyzing the data of this study. However, the interpretations of these data derived largely from psychoanalytic ideas about the psychology of interpersonal issues and developmental themes.

We shall begin by examining the crises and issues of personal development, as portrayed in Erikson's scheme.[4] In this scheme, there are eight stages of life: infancy, early childhood, the play age, school age, adolescence, young adulthood, adulthood, and mature age. The exact differentiation between juxtaposed stages is not clear or important. Erikson himself underlines the continuous, flowing quality of the developmental process. Each stage is characterized by a particularly prob-

2 S. Freud, "Three Essays on Sexuality," *Standard Edition of the Complete Psychological Works of Sigmund Freud,* 1959.
3 E. H. Erikson, "Identity and the Life Cycle," 1959.
4 E. H. Erikson, "The Problem of Ego Identity," 1959, pp. 101–164.

lematic interpersonal issue. This issue precipitates an intrapsychic crisis, the resolution of which affects the course of an individual's subsequent life. Our study focuses on adult behavior. However, the life issues posed during the stages from young adulthood to mature age can best be understood in relation to the crises that have gone before.

As an *infant,* the individual learns from his early experiences with objects in the social world around him, mostly from his mother, whether that world provides satisfactions on a fairly regular basis, and can be *trusted,* or whether the satisfactions are too few and too capriciously administered for any response other than a basic sense of *mistrust* toward everything seen and unseen "out there" in the world. In *early childhood,* when the individual comes to sense the degrees of freedom that exist between his control of his own behavior and other people's control over it, he begins to exercise this awareness. These are the "terrible two's," when the child's favorite word often is, "No"; no, he will not behave the way his mother wants him to; no, he will not do as she asks. Having found that the causal chain between what adults tell him to do and what he actually does is linked only through his own consent, he withdraws that consent experimentally, to test the relationship. If successful, the child achieves in this stage of life a sense of *autonomy.* If this process has either been squashed or overindulged, the child feels *shame* for experiencing what he does, and for doing what these inner experiences prompt him to do. He feels *doubt* about his ability to keep these urges and acts under control.

Soon the developing individual reaches a stage at which he begins to focus his libidinal energies on objects in his environment. He has reached the *play age.* His play is directed toward increased mastery of himself, his physical environment, and his interpersonal relations. If the individual has already achieved a sense of autonomy, if he lives in a family that has helped him with that achievement, he is better able to work through certain frustrations of the underlying instinctual phallic and oedipal issues that he is experiencing. If successful, he moves forward in the ego aspects of his development. He achieves *initiative.* The individual who already experiences considerable *shame* is likely to experience considerable threat in response to phallic and oedipal play. He tends to develop a sense of *guilt* about his inner energies, and about his "playful" expression of these energies.

When the growing individual reaches *school age,* he is in the latency period of his psychosexual development. Sexual urges are reduced to a minimum in the same stage at which the developmental processes are removed from the make-believe of play at home, and attached to the reality of school work. The previously established *initiative* becomes transformed into *industry.* The individual finds himself in an environment where the task alternatives are more numerous, where his initiative can achieve a wider range of effects, where in fact he has the opportunity, encouragement, and reward for being industrious. On the other hand, the school age faces the hesitant, *guilt-ridden* individual with the situation in which a greater number of different ways of failing are open to him than was the case before. As he proceeds to fail these new challenges, there are persons outside his family to tell him his failures are his own fault, and to help lead him to the conclusion of his own *inferiority.*

The individual grows in these countervailing modalities up to the time he reaches *adolescence,* at which stage he enters into abundantly psychosexual issues. These present new problems for ego development. Working between a certain range of biological intensities, on the one side, and a certain set of internalized values, on the other, the individual works to achieve a stable conception of himself in relation to his society and his own body. He attempts to establish an *identity.* In this he incorporates the forces of his *id,* and the properties of the social *entity* he is to others, into something that is partly separate from both and uniquely his own. Identity is an achievement of the ego and an essential component in further healthy development of that ego. Without it, the individual must cope with *identity diffusion*. He must live with the absence of a stable point of reference in the shifting fields of biological, psychological, and sociological force that move his life.

Moving beyond adolescence, and into the range of observation of this study, the *young adult* faces the necessity of deciding as to the closeness or distance he will maintain in his transactions with the people living and working around him. This is an issue that is the first major choice of young adults once they become members of purposive organizations. Their decision has implications for them at whatever level in the organization they happen to attain. Presumably, the decision for *intimacy* or *isolation* arises largely from the individual's established sense of identity. The solitary individual elects isolation, while the friendly one chooses intimacy. The "loner" who chooses to work intimately with those around him will only be able to do so for a limited period. The highly sociable person who chooses to work alone will find the romance of isolation to be shortlived. Individuals who get themselves into serious conflicts along these lines must be considered to be burdened with considerable identity diffusion, which they are attempting to overcome or to avoid through inappropriate intimacy or isolation. Those who do not get themselves bogged down in such conflicts move ahead productively in life.

In Erikson's terms, the individual who works successfully through this issue as a young adult has a greater chance of settling down to work, and to a life of *generativity*, than does the individual who is constantly seeking to get closer to people or further away from them, or both. Given the agonies of such sociometric vacillation, the latter type of individual is destined to spend much of his *adulthood* bound up in stultifying *self-absorption,* thereby reducing the likelihood of his being able to lead a productive or satisfying life.

Extending this process for several decades to the stage that Erikson euphemistically calls *mature age,* the irresolute and unproductive individual is seen as having a basic mistrust for the world. He is shamed by his inner life, doubtful of his capacity to cope, and guilty over his failure to develop competence. He evaluates himself as inferior. He has no sense of personal identity, or suffers from a negative or inhuman one. He is unresolved as to the intimacy or isolation of his contacts with others. Painfully self-absorbed, he spends the last years of his life, when the attempt at generativity has been given up, living with an underlying and all-pervasive sense of *disgust* and *despair.* He is disgusted with himself for having wasted his life in pathetic self-absorption and degrading inferiority. He is full of despair for the world that caused him to be that way.

On the other hand, the individual who has spent his adulthood productively, whether in intimate contact with others or in relative isolation, has a greater likelihood of going to his grave with an overriding sense of *integrity.* He is secure in the knowledge of having done justice to himself and his powers. He is quietly convinced that he has contributed more than he took out of the world. He feels that the world was worthy of his contribution, and better off for it.

The issues to be resolved at each stage of development have been presented here, as they are in Erikson's model, in terms of their extreme modes of resolution. In the developmental reality of life, these extremes cannot be separated from each other any more than one stage in development can be separated from the next. Working through these issues is a matter of establishing a balance between the extremes. For optimal development, the balance needs to be in favor of the more positive response to the challenges and constraints of a given stage in life. Presumably, the more positive the balance, the more the individual grows in wisdom and stature, and in productive relations with others, as he moves through life. Nonetheless, in the adult many of these issues are unresolved, or only partially resolved.

There is no implication, in other words, that an individual must be all trust, autonomy, initiative, industry, *et cetera,* if he is to arrive at the end of a productive life with a basic sense of integrity. Erikson's paradigm has room for the development of individuals who have been tempered in the furnaces of adversity, who carry the burden of considerable mistrust, shame, doubt, guilt, and inferiority, who are virtually overwhelmed by a diffusion of identity, and yet who somehow struggle through to lives of generativity and integrity. Perhaps these are the people whom James referred to as the twice-born.[5] If Erikson's model does in fact elucidate the nature of developmental reality, these are people who, at a particular stage of development, and with a deliberate act of will, take the potentially stultifying experiences of their earlier development and convert them into some modicum of trust, autonomy, initiative, industry, and identity. In effect, such individuals give birth to themselves again by making their past experiences work for them developmentally, by building on them instead of being immured by them. Erikson's study of Luther provides a case analysis of one such individual.[6]

Of course, Erikson's model of individual development has nothing specific to say about the organizational setting in which most adults spend most of their work lives. Neither does the model tell us anything about the influences that the culture of an organization, through its social system, has upon the personal development of its individual adult members.

[5] W. James, "The Divided Self, and the Process of its Unification," *The Varieties of Religious Experience, Lecture 8,* 1961.

[6] E. H. Erikson, *Young Man Luther: A Study in Psychoanalysis and History,* 1962.

The significance for the developing personality of particular social objects and the specific content of relations with these objects do not receive explicit attention in Erikson's model of development. For that, we will turn to Parson's model of the socialization process.[7]

The Socialization Process

An individual is born into a social system that possesses a culture. The socialization of that individual is a three-fold process. It involves the inculcation of the culture upon the individual by the social system. The transmission of culture through socialization is never complete. The individual learns only a selected number of elements in the culture of his society. He introjects, or commits himself to even fewer elements of that culture. In so doing, he brings to bear the influence of his own personality upon the survival and growth of the culture. Also, the social system itself does not act upon the individual in his socialization. It is individual members of the system who act upon him. Their influence upon him reflects the uniformity of relationships that comprise the social system. Their influence also reflects their own idiosyncratic response to culture, based on the dynamics of their personalities. In this way, the individual is trained in the common bonds of society. But the pattern of his being taught and the lessons he learns are unique to him.

This view of socialization incorporates conformity and individuality. It is a view that is probably common among social scientists interested in both the human and the societal aspects of the process. However, it is not an easy view to capture and hold in a theoretical analysis. This is a socio-psychological process, but extensive analyses of it tend to split at the hyphen. Despite a realization of the interdependent nature of the "socio" and the "psycho," the tendency often is to slip

[7] T. Parsons, "Social Structure and the Development of Personality," 1958. Also in Smelser and Smelser (eds.), *Personality and Social Systems,* 1963.

into unexamined assumptions about the individual being molded by society, or society being the collective expression of individual psychodynamics.

Parsons' view of socialization and personality development is interesting in this regard. In an examination of social structure and personality development,[8] Parsons places great emphasis on the *interpenetration* of organismic individuality and societal commonality.

> . . . the personality becomes an independent system through its relation to its own organism and through the uniqueness of its own life experience; it is not a mere epiphenomenon of the structure of the society. There is . . . not merely interdependence between the two, but what I shall call interpenetration.[9]

Yet Parsons' primary understanding of personality is that "the main content of personality is derived from social systems and culture through socialization." [10] This view of personality becomes clearer in relation to Parsons' statement that "the major structure of the ego is a precipitate of the object relations which the individual has experienced in the course of his life history." [11]

In other words, Parsons gives more emphasis to the individual as the product of society than to the society as the product of individuals. Parsons' theory of socialization comprises an important part of the theoretical orientation of this study. We do not, however, share his apparently greater emphasis on socialization over development. In our view, "the essential concept of *role*" does not arise solely "from the sociological side. . . ." [12] We consider the concept of role to encompass

[8] *Ibid.*
[9] *Ibid.,* in Smelser and Smelser (eds.) , 1963, p. 35.
[10] *Ibid.*
[11] *Ibid.,* p. 34.
[12] *Ibid.,* p. 35.

the functioning of personality dynamics as well as the inter-meshing of social forces.[13] It is this definition of role that has guided the present study.

In the next section of this chapter, the issue of balance between individual and collective forces will be developed more fully. Having called attention to some of the latent issues, we will use Parsons' theory to explicate the nature of the socialization process, and to lift up a few of its organizational implications.

As has been seen, the links between the individual and the social system are not highlighted in Erikson's model of personality development. Parsons, on the other hand, gives a position of central importance to these links. As we have indicated, Parsons stresses the interpenetration of the social system and the personality, emphasizing particularly the influence of the social system upon the development of personality through socialization.[14] In Parsons' scheme, an individual's development as a personality is accomplished through the agency of the *specific social objects* whom the individual introjects. Of particular importance in this process are the values represented by these social objects. The values are an existing and institutionalized part of the society around him. The individual internalizes these values as he introjects the social objects that possess them. It is this double-faceted mechanism that provides the vehicle for personal development and social change. Parsons states the developmental phases of this model most succinctly: "Psychologically, the essential point is that the process of ego development takes place through the learning of social roles in collectivity structures." [15]

---

13 D. J. Levinson, *op. cit.*, 1959.

14 The term "interpenetration" implies that the personality has equal influence upon the social system. However, this aspect of Parsons' model is largely implicit. It is secondary in consideration to the imparting of a personality to the behavioral organism by surrounding objects in the social system.

15 T. Parsons, in Smelser and Smelser (eds.), *op. cit.*, p. 42.

The process whereby this learning is thought to take place is as follows. The individual is born into a family, and receives care and attention mostly from his mother. The infant rapidly establishes recognition of, and a primitive identification with, this nurturing object. He soon learns something of the schedule of reinforcement that controls the gratification of his needs. He learns that if he behaves in a certain way, gratification will be ceased or drastically reduced. He learns that if he behaves in other ways, gratification will be increased or prolonged.

Before long, the infant learns the nature of a few of the basic values that govern his mother's behavior. Through her behavior, they come to influence his own. He internalizes these values, and strives to act on them even in his mother's absence. He is considered at this point to have established the beginnings of a full identity with her. Simultaneously, the infant begins to realize the existence of an integral and independent individual "out there." In developing this realization, the infant comes to realize something of what is going on inside himself. As the "thou" of his mother grows in his awareness, the realization of an "I" accompanies it. Together these provide a "we" that differentiates out from the "they" made up of the rest of the family.

As the infant grows up and becomes a child, the realization is forced on him by his parents and siblings that the "we" of mother-and-I shall not prevail in the world. He learns he cannot continue his total immersion in the "I-thou" relation with his mother. This is brought about from the apperception that the mother willfully persists in disappearing for intervals with that object that is his father. She insists on feeding and playing with the other children around the house. She gives them baths and puts them to bed, whether King Tot likes it or not, and regardless of how much he may protest. He is encouraged to capitulate, tries it experimentally, and finds there are rewards to be achieved elsewhere in the family that feel better than the frustration he has been having recently with his mother.

The ill-defined category of "they" now becomes more sharply defined as "father" and "brother" and "sister." These new figures become differentiated objects in the child's social world. Along with these differentiations come a host of clarifications. In particular, the child learns about "father" and about "mother." He learns about "brother" and about "sister." At a more general level, he begins to learn about "parents" and "children," about "grownups" and "kids," about "men" and "women." He learns about "my family," and nonfamily becomes the new residual "they" category at his next level of development. It is from this extrafamilial "they" category from which further and more universal distinctions will be drawn when the child goes to school.

This evolving process of discrimination and differentiation is known as *binary fission*. It is through binary fission that the individual (1) becomes cognizant of ever-widening circles of societal reality, (2) introjects certain of the salient social objects thus revealed, and (3) internalizes the value orientations of these figures. He fuses these new values into his existing system of values, thereby making himself part of the larger society, and society a larger part of himself.

At whatever stage of development, there is always a residual "they" that the individual ventures in his further socialization. Progress is made when the individual chooses between the objects thus made available to him, introjects the chosen object, and internalizes the values that the object represents.

This scheme of development-through-socialization has great relevance for the analysis of behavior in organizations. The individual who enters an organization does so at a particular point in its system, where his integration usually depends on his existing or soon-to-be-developed expertise in a subcategory of the organization's operations. There he must develop some "we" sense in relation to his immediate co-workers, and the rest of the organization becomes something of a "they."

In the initial phases of an individual's membership in an organization, particularly at the lower ranks, this specialization is a necessary condition for effective performance of assigned tasks, and for the possibility of future development. If, however, the individual remains at his initial level of specialization, with the "we's" and the "they's" he developed at the beginning of his organizational career, he becomes of no added use to the organization or to himself, and begins a lifetime of sameness at that level. Otherwise, he has two major pathways along which he can differentiate and introject figures that are superordinate to his present level of development. He can differentiate upward in the professional system built around his field of specialization, or he can differentiate upward in the organizational system of which he is a member. The first path of development is universalistic in the sense that growth is motivated and directed by identification with distant exemplars; that is, with the distinguished contributors to one's field. The second path of development is more particularistic, in the sense that growth is motivated and directed by identification with concrete exemplars, such as one's boss or some other superordinate figure in the organizational system surrounding one's work.

Theories of management achieve high consensus around the point that successful managers are those who can look beyond their own interests. Such hypothetical individuals can abandon narrow departmental points of view. They can grasp the nature of their profession or their organization as a whole. They see the articulations between the levels of specificity or inclusiveness. They think in terms of maintaining and improving relations between those levels. From the administrative point of view, the major difficulty in the introduction of technical and professional specialties into the modern organization arises from the problems of articulating these specialities within the organizational systems into which they have been introduced.[16]

Development and Socialization:
Two Views of Man in Society

There are, however, certain difficulties with Parsons' view of personality and its development through socialization. These have a bearing on the approach taken to the data of this study. For instance, the statement was made that successful managers can be conceived of as individuals who are capable of looking beyond their own interests, apperceiving the objectives of the larger situation, internalizing the value-orientations of the larger situation, and acting on these internalized values. Yet research has shown that successful managers are those who never stop looking out for their own interests.[17] More exactly, successful managers are those who know their personal objectives and those of the larger situation. They can look out for both, either simultaneously or alternately. They never lose sight of either, or get them confused.

This is a difficult act of balance. What is important is that it requires balance. It involves a continuing dialectic between coexistent and interdependent opposites. It does *not* involve the continual ascendancy of socialization. The perpetual internalizing of "larger," more inclusive, "higher," and more abstract values is not synonymous with effective adult behavior. The perpetual modification of the more personal components of one's values, as implied in the pure socialization model, is little short of pathological. The functioning of binary fission in adults—that is, beyond the stage of adoles-

16 See "Changes in the Business Environment," Harvard Business School, 1963.

17 W. R. Dill, T. L. Hilton, and W. R. Reitman, "How Aspiring Managers Promote Their Own Careers," 1960.

cent identity formation—is difficult to reconcile with healthy development. Continued fission, object-choice, and introjection at the adult stage of life would have to be drastically different from the multiplicative process of development and socialization in infancy, childhood, and adolescence. If it were not, continued adult development according to the principles of binary fission would indeed be like riding off in all directions. Presumably, such development would be the product of a weak identity, or would soon demolish what identity had been achieved.

As the findings of Dill, Hilton, and Reitman suggest, the adult who is most successful at getting things done in organizations is probably the one who can maintain his personal values and objectives while being able to appreciate the value-orientations and goals of the surrounding situation. He is the one who can take action on both dimensions without capitulating to either.

The personality is an active selector and regulator of transactions between itself and its apperceived environment. It is not quite the *tabula rasa* that seems implied in Parsons' scheme. Parsons' view of personality derives from that of Freud, but it is somehow transmuted in the process of becoming Parsons'. Parsons states the commonality of his and Freud's view of personality as follows:

> . . . the major structure of the ego is a precipitate of the object-relations which the individual has experienced in the course of his life history. This means that internalization of the socio-cultural environment provides the basis, not merely of one specialized component of the human personality, but of what, in the human sense, is its central core.[18]

We focus on the word "precipitate" as applied to the nature of personality. In our view, such a term overly emphasizes the static quality of personality, the personality as a receptive

[18] T. Parsons, in Smelser and Smelser (eds.), *op. cit.*, p. 34.

rather than a selective system, the blank slate waiting to have the content of culture transcribed upon it by the educating hand of the social system. It overly emphasizes the socializing of the superego components of the individual, without maintaining their process in balanced conceptual relation to the constitutional bases and the instinctual vicissitudes of development.

Adult socialization cannot be considered a mere extension of earlier socialization. Perhaps "adult socialization" is a contradiction in terms, considering that at some point in life further socialization must become a relatively dead issue. R. W. White has reached conclusions about personal development as an adult that are contrary in nature to the basic conception of personality as a precipitate, and personality development as a proliferation of sociometric alternatives.

. . . A person is a nexus of competing and conflicting influences to which he must *respond selectively,* creating for himself a workable synthesis. He is inevitably the scene of frustration and conflict, and he can avoid hopeless confusion only by becoming an active transformer of his experience. Clearly the concepts we need in order to understand natural growth must be such as to encompass the highly selective nature of the response to shaping influences.

. . . No one doubts the general principle that there is a constant interaction between the person and his environment. This implies both that the environment acts on the person and that the person *acts on the environment.* Scientific workers, however, have been loathe to examine the second part of the transaction, preferring to regard the person as the thing to be explained and the environment as the thing that explained him. Thus a social role tends to be perceived only as something that moulds the person; little thought has been bestowed on the way social roles become transformed through the innovations of those who play them. Similarly, parental attitudes have been described chiefly as producing certain effects on the child's personality; little attention has been paid to the effects of the child's response on parental attitudes. The fact is that people very definitely affect their environments, even in childhood, and that what happens next in their development is often determined by these effects. Clearly the concepts we need in order to understand natural growth must include the action of the person on his surroundings.[19]

It is clear that White's emphasis is placed equally on what society does to the individual and on what the individual does to society. However, in response to an overemphasis of the first vector of this two-way relationship, White has stressed the countervailing vector more strongly. Our approach to the data of this study will be as balanced in this regard as we can make it, but if one emphasis does outweigh the other, we will err in White's direction. In studying our data, we were more impressed by the situations in which given actors placed themselves, or which they created for themselves, more than we were by their having to cope with purely independent and external social system realities pressing against them. In all person-position relations there was perhaps more freeeedom to act, more "wiggling room," than many individuals throughout the medical hierarchy of the Institute could manage effectively. How those individuals rose to the challenge of that freedom, how they "wiggled," was largely a matter determined by their own personalities. Also, the consequences were often of their own initiation. They got, in this sense, what they deserved.

A second of White's emphases that stands in some contradistinction to those of Parsons concerns the narrowing and deepening of human relations among mature adults, something other than their expansion and proliferation through binary fission.

Sometimes there is very little demand for quick change in the adult's life. What is needed is a capacity for steady

19 R. W. White, *Lives in Progress,* 1952, pp. 329–330.

growth within a relatively constant framework of activities and relationships. . . . Some features of life call for the broadening of experience; others require its deepening.[20]

. . . Under reasonably favorable circumstances the natural growth of personality moves in the direction of human relationships that are less anxious, less defensive, less burdened by inappropriate past reactions, more friendly, more spontaneous, more warm, and more respectful. . . . development proceeds partly by selection and concentration. Friendships are pursued when there are congenial similarities of interest and outlook, but people with whom interaction proves difficult are dropped out of the orbit.[21]

The process of deepening occurs through satisfying transactions with objects of interest. . . . Just as growth in personal relationships makes one increasingly responsive to the characteristics of individual people, so growth of interests makes one increasingly alert to the properties of individual objects. Interests grow deeper through the cumulative effects of learning.[22]

The basic issue here is, of course, simply another form of the nature-nurture argument that has been carried on in psychology and sociology for so long, and evidently still persists. Parsons recognizes this, and states it as follows:

There are two main approaches to the nature of personality development. One may be illustrated by analogy with the plant. The main characteristics of the mature organism—for example, the number and quality of wheat grains produced, or the brilliance and shape of the flowers—are predetermined in the genetic constitution of the species. There will, however, be differences in outcome as a function of the favorableness or unfavorableness of the environment. This process of interaction with the environment, however, does not determine the main pattern, but only the degree of excellence with which it "comes out."

The other view sees the genetic constitution as a nonspe-

[20] *Ibid.,* pp. 330–331.   [21] *Ibid.,* p. 343.   [22] *Ibid.,* pp. 350–351.

cific base from which the pattern of the adult personality
will be evolved, and, as the main pattern-setting components,
the values of the culture and *meanings* of the social objects
experienced in the course of personality development.[23]

Developmental models, such as Erikson's, place a somewhat
greater emphasis on the "flowerlike" growth of man in society, despite the distinctly weedy nature of some of the individual results in certain patches of society. Socialization models such as Parsons' place a somewhat greater emphasis on the
"mold" of society, and its shaping of the individuals that get
poured into it. In our view, it is not necessary to choose between extreme resolutions of this issue of development versus
socialization. We agree with White in his statement that
"Clearly the concepts we need in order to understand natural
growth must be equal to both aspects of development." [24]
However, we share White's and Parsons' dilemma in maintaining a very difficult act of balance. Although natural
growth implies both development *and* socialization, we, like
White, will approach it perhaps more often through development than through socialization.

PERSONAL STYLE AND PERFORMANCE

WE SHIFT HERE from development to the description of contemporary behavior in psychologically meaningful terms. The
behavior we observed was predominantly interpersonal behavior. Our data were the most interesting when, in the process of interpersonal and administrative transactions, one executive's creating a situation became the stimulus for another
executive's coping with that situation. In order to interpret
such data, we had to make this distinction between *coping*
and *creating.* Coping is used in the sense that the individual
is faced with an external social world whose forces impinge
upon him in a manner completely independent of his own ac-

[23] Smelser and Smelser, *op. cit.,* pp. 35–36.
[24] R. W. White, *op. cit.,* p. 331.

tions. He copes with that set of forces as best he can in order to maintain some adjustive balance with it. Coping thus connotes something of the "social mold" approach to behavior in socially organized settings. Creating is used in the sense that the individual manifestly or latently succeeds in building social situations around himself, or of placing himself in ongoing situations that satisfy a particular structure of needs that exists within his personality. In this way he goes through life choosing and building social situations that, in turn, foster the expression of his inner demands, which can be either constructive or destructive in consequences, or perhaps both. Creating thus connotes more of the "unfolding flower" approach to individual behavior in social settings.

Sullivan [25] and Leary [26] are two who have contributed to the theoretical and methodological opening up of this most difficult area of research. Frequently the question is raised as to what interpersonal relations have to do with organizations. Leary, for one, has a clear delineation of the organizational importance of such relations.

Unverbalized interpersonal assumptions tend to pervade every social organization. The unwitting evaluation of differing roles of orderly, nurse, psychotherapist, psychiatrist, and administrator in relationship to each other is an inevitable phenomenon in any psychiatric hospital. The way in which eddies from these power whirlpools reach and relate to the patient is probably more important in terms of the remission rate than the number of electric shock machines or the skill of the psychotherapists. Factory, department store, office, university—all have these complex networks of routine, unverbalized evaluation through which power, prestige, contempt, punishment, acceptance, etc., are expressed. Systematic understanding of these social hierarchies and their effects on the clients, patients, employees, customers, and students is a problem for the sociologist or the industrial

25 H. S. Sullivan, *The Interpersonal Theory of Psychiatry*, 1953.
26 T. Leary, *Interpersonal Diagnosis of Personality*, 1957.

psychologist. Investigations in these areas will very likely reveal that individuals tend to select jobs and occupational roles in accordance with their interpersonal techniques for anxiety reduction. We consider these phenomena here because they demonstrate the implicit and automatic nature of interpersonal reactivity.[27]

The difficulties of researching the flow of here-and-now interactive behavior, with its initial unverbalized assumptions and its subsequent latent consequences, have so far proved almost insurmountable for the sociologist, the industrial psychologist, and everybody else. First of all, the researcher is often denied access to many crucial interpersonal transactions, because of the customary privacy with which many of these dealings are conducted. The researcher is thus left with the almost impossible task of making sense of a developmental sequence or an organizational pattern from which the most significant materials have been censored. The second problem is that when such transactional dynamics have been observed, the researcher moves interpretively away from the purely interactional material toward the psychodynamics of the individual, or toward the social structure of the collectivity.[28] For these reasons, theories of the interpersonal have not attained much autonomy yet. Leary's has been the most extensive to date.

One assumption about interpersonal behavior that is often made is that a person's exchanges with other people are somehow fleeting and unstable, changing as the interactors change, and passing out of existence as soon as interaction ceases. Therefore such behavior is not amenable to scientific study. However, Leary's approach to the interpersonal diagnosis of personality demonstrates that perhaps the most stable property of an individual is the manner in which he goes about

[27] *Ibid.*, pp. 93–94.
[28] See A. Zaleznik, "Interpersonal Relations," in March (ed.), *Handbook of Organizations.*

the business of interacting with other people. It is from these properties or styles of interaction that other people form their impression of that person. It is from the tendency of certain interactive forms or materials to be repeated that the psychologist forms his opinion of the personality structure that must underlie such behavior, and the sociologist forms his opinion about the social structure of which that behavior must be the dynamic impression. This repetitive element in an individual's interpersonal relations is what Leary calls the *interpersonal reflex*. Leary explains in the following way how he came to think of such complex social behavior as reflexive.

In studying the interpersonal purposes which underlie human behavior, the following hypothesis has been developed. It seems that in a large percentage of interactions the basic motives are expressed in a reflex manner. They are so automatic that they are often unwitting and often at variance with the subject's own perception of them. This facet of behavior is therefore a difficult one to isolate and measure. It is often unverbalized and so subtle and reflex as to escape articulate description. Sometimes these interpersonal communications can be implicit in the content of the discussion. . . . Behind the superficial content of most social exchanges it is possible to determine the naked motive communications: I am wise; I am strong; I am friendly; I am contemptuous; as well as the concomitant messages: you are less wise, less strong, likeable, contemptible. Jung has described the "persona" as a mask-like front behind which more basic motives exist. The purposive behavior we are dealing with in this chapter is similar, but in emphasis something more than a social facade. It is closer, perhaps, to the "character armour" concept from the early writings of Wilhelm Reich, in that it assumes a major role in the personality organization. Its relationship to the "conversation of gestures" developed by Mead is, as we shall see, quite close.[29]

[29] Leary, *op. cit.*, pp. 91–92.

Leary's definition of an interpersonal reflex is as follows:

. . . The individual units of this behavior [interpersonal actions] we call interpersonal mechanisms or interpersonal reflexes. They are defined as the observable, expressive units of face-to-face social behavior.

These reflexes are automatic and usually involuntary responses to interpersonal situations. They are often independent of the content of communication. They are the individual's spontaneous methods of reacting to others.[30]

Leary provides many interesting examples of how persistent and reflexive styles of interpersonal behavior characterized people's relations with historical figures in their lives, and their relations with others during here-and-now behavioral situations. These examples demonstrate that character structures underlie interpersonally reflexive role performances. Such performances are an expression of the underlying character structure and the responses elicited from others tend to reinforce that structure. It can be seen that basic to this approach to interpersonal relations is the thinking and work of Freud,[31] Abraham,[32] and Reich.[33] Leary's work is also a somewhat more operational extension of Sullivan's basic interpersonal orientation to psychiatric phenomena. The value added by Leary is in the intensive, microscopic analyses of the minute behavioral and dynamic properties of interaction that express the characters of the interactors and determine the outcome of their interactions.

The consequences of reflexively interactive behavior are not difficult to anticipate. The individual tends to get what he is "asking for." Or, in Leary's terms, the "general probability principle" is that:

[30] *Ibid.*, p. 96.

[31] S. Freud, "Character and Anal Erotism," *op. cit.*, 1959. S. Freud, "Some Character Types Met with in Psychoanalytic Work," *op. cit.*, 1959. S. Freud, "Libidinal Types," *op. cit.*, 1959.

[32] K. Abraham, *Selected Papers on Psychoanalysis,* 1927.

[33] W. Reich, *Character Analysis,* 1949.

> Interpersonal reflexes tend (with a probability significantly greater than chance) to initiate or incite reciprocal interpersonal responses from the "other" person in the interaction that lead to a repetition of the original reflex.[34]

Certainly the data of this study demonstrated clearly the functioning of interpersonal reflexes in the interactive processes that make up the flow of administration. An executive cannot transact the business of his position completely by himself, in an interpersonal vacuum. At some point he must come into contact with other members of his organization; his superordinates, his peers, and his subordinates. When he does so, and regardless of the organization or content of his transactions, he infuses his own personal style of interaction into the process. The tendency for others is then to respond to him in terms of the reciprocal forms of behavior that are symbolically called for.

We can now appreciate how firmly rooted is Leary's thinking in the interpersonal theory of Harry Stack Sullivan. We have just delineated the nature of an *interpersonal situation,* which in many approaches to organizational behavior passes unobserved and unemphasized, but which for Sullivan was an important concept: "The concept of interpersonal situation, necessary for the occurrence of activity in the satisfaction of need is of fundamental importance in psychiatric theory." [35] It is also of fundamental importance in any theory that seeks to interpret the dynamics of behavior in organizations. For Sullivan, "personality is the relatively enduring pattern of recurrent interpersonal situations which characterize a human life." [36] This view of personality takes the interactive expressions of personality and considers them as the personality itself. This view holds that there is nothing incidental about the "little incidents" that an individual gets involved

[34] Leary, *op. cit.*, p. 123.   [36] *Ibid.*, pp. 110–111.
[35] Sullivan, *op. cit.*, p. 111.

in as he moves through life. Quite the opposite. Sullivan considered these incidents to be the sum and substance of personality, their commonality to be the expression of that personality, and their evolution to be the manifestation of the growth and change of that personality. It is through the analysis of the interpersonal situations in which the individual lives his life that Leary, in developing Sullivan's basic conception of the individual, has sought to establish his interpersonal diagnoses of personality.

In doing this, Leary posited eight basic modes of "adjustment" by which the individual seeks to organize his interpersonal environment, and thereby to express and reinforce his personality. These modes of adjustment, and the correlative personality types are as follows:

1. Adjustment Through Rebellion: The Distrustful Personality.
2. Adjustment Through Self-Effacement: The Masochistic Personality.
3. Adjustment Through Docility: The Dependent Personality.
4. Adjustment Through Cooperation: The Overconventional Personality.
5. Adjustment Through Responsibility: The Hypernormal Personality.
6. Adjustment Through Power: The Autocratic Personality.
7. Adjustment Through Competition: The Narcissistic Personality.
8. Adjustment Through Aggression: The Sadistic Personality.

The adjustment patterns reflect the influence of Sullivan. The personality types, varying considerably in the depth of the denoted characteristic, reflect some of Freud's thinking. The specific points of connectedness, and the nature of the relationship between an adjustment pattern and a personality type, are unexplained and problematic in Leary's scheme.

However, his delineation of the adjustment modalities of personality types is most evocative. The characterizations that he draws highlight many of the persistent personal characteristics one meets with every day, not only in others, but in oneself. In fact, reading these characteristics is reminiscent of the experiences of reading lists of symptoms related to medical or psychiatric diseases: one soon feels oneself to be suffering from almost every disease and disorder in the book. Excerpts from Leary's delineations of three types are given below. They evoke the potential usefulness of his theoretical scheme for the analysis and interpretation of behavior in social settings.

Self-Effacement:

The message which they communicate to others in their face-to-face relations is "I am a weak, inferior person." Through their automatic reflex operations they train others to look down upon them with varying intensities of derogation and superiority.

Self-effacement pulls depreciation and patronizing superiority from others. . . . That is to say, if a person acts in a glum, guilty, withdrawn and weak manner, he will tend to train others to look down on him and to view him with varying amounts of contempt. . . .

The docile person tends also to avoid equal relationships and to see strong, guiding partners. . . .[37]

Docility:

The interpersonal message it conveys to others is "I am a meek, admiring person in need of your help and advice.". . .

Docility pulls strong, helpful leadership from others. Dependence provokes nurturance. . . .

Circular chains of interaction, of course, develop. The respected, responsible, nurturant person in turn presses the dependent person to increased dependence. Where these

[37] Leary, *op. cit.*, pp. 282–285.

symbiotic tendencies are uncomplicated by underlying conflicts on the part of either partner, a most comfortable durable relationship develops. . . .[38]

Competition:

. . . He acts in a strong, arrogant manner. He communicates the message that he feels superior to the "other one."
He appears independent and confident.

In its adaptive intensity this interpersonal reflex is a most
impressive social maneuver. In its maladaptive extreme it
becomes a smug, cold, selfish, exploitive social role. . . .

The adaptive person who uses this security operation in a
sensitive manner wins the admiration and flattering envy of
others. They look up to him and pay him the tribute of a
grudging, envious approval.[39]

These excerpts illustrate the weakness as well as the
strength of potential applications of this system of classification to concrete interactions. For instance, how is one to differentiate between self-effacement and docility, when in the
delineation of the self-effacing masochistic type we find that
"The *docile* person tends also to avoid equal relationships?"
We have added the emphasis, to indicate that, in this and
other paired comparisons, the internal boundaries of this
typological scheme are permeable in the extreme. Also,
Leary's use of the term "adjustment" is a little puzzling. It
connotes the bringing-into-line of one's personality in relation to external forces; but in Leary's scheme it denotes the
establishment of a social environment that reflects the forces
and addresses the needs of one's inner life. In the latter sense,
it is for the individual not so much a matter of adjustment
(coping) as it is of seduction and demand (creating). It is the
other people who do the adjusting, insofar as Leary's scheme
is concerned.

---

[38] *Ibid.*, pp. 292–294.   [39] *Ibid.*, pp. 332–334.

SELF-REPRESENTATION AND SYMBOLIZATION
IN SOCIAL LIFE

OBVIOUSLY, neither coping with other people's interpersonal reflexes nor reflexively creating one's own desired interpersonal milieu are totally one-way propositions. Every individual who is in a relatively stable matrix of interpersonal relations elicits reciprocal behavior from others. At the same time, that individual responds reciprocally to the elicitations of others. This is particularly the case in organizational settings, where members are faced with the necessity of getting along with each other for considerable periods of time, perhaps decades. In such situations, the individual is not free to set up diadic relations according solely to the dictates of his own needs and predispositions. He is not permitted to receive satisfaction from others and give nothing in return. The necessity of going beyond the limits of one's personal need structure for the satisfaction of other people's needs poses problems in all diadic relations.

In organizational settings, where individuals with highly flexible role repertoires constantly interact with each other over long periods of time, interpersonal reciprocities must be established if conditions of group stability are to be achieved or maintained. An important dynamic of administration consists of the establishment of these reciprocities, the achievement of personally satisfying or endurable sets of interpersonal rewards and costs, and the interpersonal working out of patterns of coping and creating. Of course, there are imbalances related to the nature of the demands being made, the dramaturgic persuasiveness of given individuals, and the relative power positions of the interactors within the hierarchy of the organization. Nonetheless, some balance must exist to keep the interpersonal matrix of the organization in operation. Within that matrix, the internal dynamic for change arises from the coexistent imbalances of interpersonal reciprocity.[40] Our analysis of the executive role constellation will demonstrate the interrelatedness of these factors in the emergence and evolution of that constellation.

The psychosocial approach to organizations holds that one function of an organization is to provide a stage upon which individual members act out their roles. In doing so, they assume the "personae" that are assigned to them by others, and the ones that spring from the inner dialogue of their own personality. Each actor has more than one "persona," and chooses which one to put on according to the nature of the psychosocial situation; that is, according to the make-up of his audience, what he is feeling within himself, and the plot that he is seeking to communicate. The plot, of course, is the story of the organization: its glorious past, its challenging present, and its promising future. In a successful dramatization of his managerial "persona," the executive member of an organization establishes his influence over other fellow players, and over the audience that is made up of people outside the executive group, both within the organization and in its environment. This influence then increases the likelihood that the plot of the organization will be successfully carried out and the future of the organization assured.

The writings of Erving Goffman present the clearest explication of this approach to the social behavior of individuals in organizational settings. In his book, *The Presentation of Self in Everyday Life,* Goffman illustrates some of the techniques used in communicating certain images of one's self or one's collectivity to the audience of the social surroundings. Goffman emphasizes the *dramaturgical* elements of social behavior, the manner in which interpersonal and group plays are carried out in an organizational setting, and the functional consequences thereof for the organization.

---

40 See Peter Blau's analysis of the dynamics of interpersonal reciprocity in *The Dynamics of Bureaucracy,* Part II, 1955.

It seems to me that the dramaturgical approach may constitute a fifth perspective to the study of organizations, to be added to the technical, political, structural, and cultural perspectives. The dramaturgical perspective, like each of the other four, can be employed as the end-point of analysis, as a final way of ordering facts. This would lead us to describe the techniques of impression management employed in a given establishment, the principal problems of impression management in the establishment, and the identity and interrelationships of the several performance teams which operate in the establishment.[41]

In Goffman's listing of perspectives, there is no mention of a personological, characterological, or motivational approach to organizational analysis. Nonetheless, his general orientation to data was found very useful in organizing much of the executive behavior observed in our study, particularly communication between the executives themselves, and between the executives and the audience of their subordinates within the organization. This orientation to data has been used throughout our analysis, as the reader will soon see. The concept of *region management* was found to be particularly useful in establishing a meaningful description of the lives of our executive subjects within their organization. "We often find a division into back region, where the performance of a routine is prepared, and front region, where the performance is presented," states Goffman.[42] This was certainly true in the staging of the top executive performances observed during the field work period of this study. As such, the distinction between "off-stage" and "on-stage" regions and performances proved to be useful throughout our analysis.

In Goffman's general notion of the staging of one's self or one's team, the crucial nature of the audience's response is always implied, but not explicitly highlighted. Our observa-

41 E. Goffman, *The Presentation of Self in Everyday Life,* 1959, p. 240.
42 *Ibid.,* p. 238.

tions indicated, however, that audience response was reflected back upon an actor in ways that affected him personally, and affected what he was and was not able to do administratively. The effect of the audience upon the actor was, in other words, of too great importance, personally and organizationally, to receive only implicit attention. Similarly, the forces governing an audience's responses—often these forces were completely beyond the control of the actor—became recognized as important determinants of the episodes that made up the life of the organization and the crises that were turning points in the lives of the participants.

In dealing with matters of audience response, we developed the concepts of *reification* and *reflection,* the specific model for which will be presented later in this book. Every member of an actor's audience takes the behavioral data manifested by the actor, evaluates that data, establishes patterns analytically, and interprets these patterns according to his own state of knowledge of the actor and the situation, his own feelings about himself and the actor, and his own strivings in relation to the actor. From all this, each member of the audience constructs his own notion of who the actor is, what he is like, what he is trying to do, how good he is at it, *et cetera.* This construct is a *reification,* in the sense that it is usually acted on *as though it were the real thing,* rather than a representation of it; that is, as though the audience's conceptions of the actor were what that actor actually was. The audience never gets to know the actor completely, but this does not stop them from acting toward him as though they were totally informed as to the subjective reality of what is for them an object.

The actor has no direct control over these processes whereby he is reified in the minds of his audience, yet he is constantly faced with the necessity of coping with *reflections* that are directed toward or against him in the course of interaction with people who think and act as though they know what he is "really like," what it is that he is "really after," and what it was that he "really said" on a certain occasion. These reifications may be accurate, but they also possess elements of inaccuracy varying from the minimal to the almost total misapperception of the actor and his activities. In the partial solipsism of the interpersonal world of administration, the executive must face both the accuracies and inaccuracies of the reifications reflected back upon him by those around him. Not only must he cope with them in the personal sense, he must also continually strive to create interpersonal relations that are "straight" with his intentions, that get the administration of the enterprise back within the limits he prescribed for it. All this is part of an executive's role, the nature of which we will now consider.

CHAPTER 3

Individual Roles and Role Relations in Executive Groups

A DISTINGUISHING CHARACTERISTIC of executives is their involvement in the processes of generating and using power in organizational settings. The executives in an organization comprise its "polity," [1] and their affiliation with this subsystem in the organization differentiates them from the other organization members whose major affiliations are either technical or administrative. The power that executives generate and use is the basis of whatever capacity they possess to influence the behavior of others in their organization. With this power, executives can direct the course of their organization toward its objectives. Without this power, executives are unable to guide their organization. They cannot fulfill the responsibilities of their positions, and thereby become executives by title only.

In order to generate and use the necessary power, executives become involved in a network of interpersonal transactions in striving to realize organizational objectives. This interpersonal involvement comes about in two ways, one involving the generation of power, the other relating to its use.

First, in the process of *generating* the requisite power, the executive commits himself to a series of reciprocal transactions related to organizational objectives. These transactions also involve symbolic interchanges between personalities. From them emerge interpersonal affinities and repulsions

[1] T. Parsons, "Suggestions for a Sociological Approach to the Theory of Organizations—II," 1956.

whose relation to the organization's goals are indirect, difficult to determine, but real.

In developing a series of reciprocating relationships, the executive must give to others as much as, and often more than, he gets back from them in the cooperation necessary for the proper discharge of his responsibilities. This does not mean that the executive is influenced equally by every person around him. He may give to one set of individuals in order to get back from them the sanctions required to direct and control the behavior of another set of individuals. He may, for instance, devote his attentions to his superordinates, in order to be able to influence his subordinates. Or he may establish reciprocities with his subordinates, in order to be able to influence his superordinates. There are indications that these two orientations—aspiration upward or orientation downward—represent a basic differentiation between executives as to their response to authority in organization.[2]

Once executives have generated a certain amount of influence, they seek to *collect* on the interpersonal debts they have accumulated from those around them. They seek to use the power they have generated.[3]

Executives must use their power in order to establish certain sought-after relations between their organization and its environment. Within the limits of the formal charter of the organization, each executive establishes his own area and mode of power utilization, through which he influences the

[2] P. M. Blau and W. R. Scott, *Formal Organizations,* 1962, pp. 159–164. Future research may indicate more clearly that men with responsible positions in the authority structures of organizations attempt either to reinforce that structure, or to modify it. We are speaking, once more, of the over-all characteristics of a man's actions, rather than single acts. Executives may be found to specialize in their primary orientations in these matters. Presumably, the most effective administrative stance involves elements of both orientations to authority, plus the personal freedom to move back and forth between them, as required by the realities of the organizational situation.

[3] See G. C. Homans, *Social Behavior,* 1961, especially Chapters 14 and 15, for a particularly pointed analysis of these processes.

course of events in the organization and hence the organization's future structure. From these relations between the informal and the formal arise the profitability, growth, prestige, percent of the market, efficiency, or whatever organizational objectives are being striven for.

An executive cannot avoid constant involvement in a reciprocating network of interpersonal transactions. The encounters in which these are enacted comprise an important element of everyday administration in any organization. To say that executives *cannot* avoid involvement in interpersonal transactions is not to say that they necessarily find such entanglements unpleasant. Successful executives seem to enjoy "doing business" with others. They actively seek out interpersonal transactions, sometimes even before there are concrete organizational objectives to which the resultant commitments may be related. There are, of course, moments of disgust and depression in which the proactive pattern of interpersonal behavior breaks down. However, anyone who is consistently disinclined toward the seeking out of interpersonal involvements probably makes a dissatisfied and ineffective executive.

In other words, both organizational *and* personal factors are involved in an executive's generation and use of power. To do his job, the executive must engage in the "power politics" of interpersonal relations. In doing so, he activates certain behaviors whose symbolic meaning may have little to do with the here-and-now objectives of the organization. He adopts a certain role performance or set of performances. He brings to bear a certain interpersonal style. Both the performance and the style are to a great extent rooted in the executive's personality. They are given specific content through his earlier developmental childhood experiences with the role relations that existed within his family of origin. They are also influenced by his adolescent experiences in the community, the school, and the peer groups in which he grew up. It is the repertoire of roles developed in these earlier settings which he activates and modifies in carrying out the responsibilities of his executive position. The richness of this repertoire, and the skillfulness with which the executive selects particular roles to meet specific administrative and interpersonal requirements, contributes greatly to his organizational effectiveness.

The executive's involvement in the generation and use of power poses certain primitive, familistic issues not only for him, but also for the others with whom he deals. Themes relating to powerfulness and powerlessness, affection and aggression, guidance and control, authority and dependence, closeness and distance, giving and getting, competition and cooperation, necessarily intrude to some extent into the administrative interactions of the executive. He can turn the powerful psychodynamic forces involved toward the service of the organization, or toward its destruction. His control is by no means complete, but he has no other place to begin the performance of his executive responsibilities than in his face-to-face interactions with those around him.

ROLE SPECIALIZATION AND DIFFERENTIATION IN ORGANIZED GROUPS

THE SCIENTIFIC GUIDANCE we obtained in our study of an executive group came, not from the study of other executive groups, but from groups heretofore more open and interesting to social scientists. This transfer of knowledge to the locale of the executive group may help in the development of understanding that might usefully supplement the ideas of the general management expert, the statistical decision maker, and the economist.

Roles in Small Problem-Solving Groups

The top management organization of the M.P.I. presented three very clear and very different executive roles. From the comparison of these roles emerged the realization that we were observing, *in vivo,* certain executive role specializations and differentiations similar to those reported in the literature on problem-solving groups in experimental situations. The work of Bales [4] and Slater,[5] plus the extension and development of that work by Moment and Zaleznik,[6] was especially pertinent.

In their studies of small groups, Bales and his colleagues discovered cyclical patterns of group process occurring as their experimental groups alternated between working on externally imposed problems and on internally emergent tensions. These cycles were termed, respectively, the *instrumental-adaptive* and the *expressive-integrative* phases of group process. It was found that groups could persevere in any one phase for only a limited amount of time before stresses built up that forced them into the other phase of group process. For instance, a group could work on an assigned task for a period of time. Then some incident would initiate a period of laughter, relaxation, and cohesion-building chatter. Similarly, a group would joke around in casual intimacy for only a limited amount of time before certain of its members began prompting and effecting a return to the task at hand. Bales summarized these findings in the following manner.

> . . . the instrumental-adaptive activity of the preceding participant tends to build up tensions in the present participant to some point where he enters the process and changes to activity of an expressive-integrative relevance, which tends to "bleed off" the tension to some point at which he changes the focus himself and continues again with instrumental-adaptive activity. *The problem of equilibrium is essentially the problem of establishing arrangements (or an*

4 R. F. Bales, "The Equilibrium Problem in Small Groups," 1955, pp. 424–456.

5 P. E. Slater, "Role Differentiation in Small Groups," 1955, pp. 498–515.

6 D. Moment and A. Zaleznik, *Role Development and Interpersonal Competence,* 1963.

"orbit of activity") *whereby the system goes through a repeti-*
tive cycle, within which all of the disturbances created in one
phase are reduced in some other. The dilemma of all action
systems is that no one disturbance can be reduced without
creating another.[7]

There are both personal and organizational implications to
these findings. Bales' major emphasis in the above statement
is organizational—the alternating sequence of phases required for group equilibrium—and we will examine, a little
later on, the importance of such phases of relationship in a
group of executives in the nonexperimental situation of a
"real," ongoing organization.

At the same time these phenomena can also be examined
from the perspective of the *individuals* involved. This perspective is exemplified in Slater's work. The alternation of
instrumental-adaptive and expressive-integrative phases in
the experimental groups was brought about by individual
group members who tended to specialize in one type of activity or the other. Not all members were seen to specialize, but
those who did evidently clustered into a bi-modal distribution
of *"task" specialists* and *"social" specialists.* Task specialists
were those who preferred a group role that was predominantly
instrumental and adaptive, while social specialists preferred
predominantly expressive and integrative roles. Slater summarized his findings on role specialization in problem-solving
groups as follows.

We have found that the most fundamental type of role
differentiation in small experimental groups is the divorcing
of task functions from social-emotional functions. Presumably, the ideal leader of a small group would be sufficiently
skillful and flexible to alternate these types of behavior in
such a way as to handle both problems, and maximize his
status on all possible dimensions. He would be able to make

7 R. F. Bales, *op. cit.,* p. 453.

both an active, striving response to the task and a sympathetic response to the individual needs of group members. He would be a high participator, well-liked, rated high on task ability and eventually chosen leader.

Such individuals are rare. . . . There are at least two kinds of reason for the rarity of such men. First, there are sociological factors, revolving around the noncompatibility of the task and social-emotional roles. Adaptation to pressures from outside the group, such as are created by a task which must be performed, involves, by definition, change. The individual who presses toward solution of a task inadvertently forces those around him to make continual minor adjustments in their behavior, and to continually re-examine their ideas and values, in the light of these external demands. The individual who concerns himself with internal social-emotional problems, on the other hand, is supportive in his responses to the ideas and behavior of those around him, and continually reaffirms their dominant values. The orientation of the task specialist is thus more technological, that of the social-emotional specialist more traditionalistic. It is presumably the latter type of behavior which seems more appealing to members called upon to indicate whom they personally like best.

This is not to say that the task specialist will actually be disliked, but rather that his task emphasis will tend to arouse some negative feelings—feelings which may not be expressed, and which will never outweigh his value to the group in the minds of its members. Such feelings merely neutralize any strong positive feelings other members may hold toward him. . . .

The second set of reasons for role specialization and differentiation may be called psychological. These have to do with the individual's predisposition to assume a particular role. Men who are best-liked, e.g., may "have to be liked" and may achieve prominence in this role because of the ingratiating skills they have acquired during their lives in bringing this desired situation about. Avoidance of conflict and controversy may be a felt necessity for this type of person—hence, his behavior will show nothing that could be a source of disharmony. He will avoid even the thought that he might like some of his fellow members better than others. His rate of interaction will be average—not too high, not too low. He will in fact retire into the safety of the "average Joe." He may even avoid the performance of task functions altogether, because of the personal threats which task activity might hold for him. Instead, he will express the group's feelings and questions, and place its stamp of approval upon what has already come to pass.

The task specialist, on the other hand, may assume this role only because of an unwillingness or inability to respond to the needs of others. A compulsive concentration on an abstract problem will serve as an intellectual shield against the ambiguity of human feelings. Needs to express hostility may be channeled into aggressive and dogmatic problem-solving attempts.[8]

There is an obvious interrelationship between role specialists, with their psychodynamic characteristics, and the sequencing of group processes, that forms the basis of the group's equilibrium. This sequence is not a mystic phenomenon, whose origins lie in an inscrutable group mind that sees all and knows mysteriously just how much of which process is needed, when it should begin, and when it should be superseded by the reciprocal process. The sequencing is brought about by the individual members of the group, responding both to what is going on in the group and to their own feelings about it. Bales noted this in the above quotation. Too much work "tends to build up tensions in the . . . participant to some points where *he* [emphasis added] enters the process and changes to activity of an expressive-integrative relevance." But what is tension-reducing for that group member is tension-producing for others with different personalities and role specializations. Soon, therefore, the participant either switches the process or others will take over and switch

8 P. E. Slater, *op. cit.*, pp. 511–513.

it for themselves. Expression of interpersonal closeness and support is superseded by the distance-producing process of getting on with the job, where the impersonal, task-oriented members feel more comfortable, and the personal, emotion-oriented members less so.

This interrelation between individual psychodynamics and group dynamics was very much in evidence in the top management group of this study. Similar differentiations and specializations of role were also evident. Group meetings and other forms of executive interactions in the hospital went through phases that were functionally similar to those outlined by Bales. All three members of the central executive triad were, to some extent, involved in both the instrumental-adaptive and the expressive-integrative aspects of administration. However, they differed in the nature and degree of their involvement in these aspects. That is to say, each man tended to *specialize* in his organizational role—to emphasize certain functions and to minimize or neglect others that were in turn given emphasis by his co-executives. The forms of their role specialization comprised the *structure* of the executive role constellation. The manifold devices by which these specializations were sustained and modified reflected its *dynamics*.

Cross-Cultural Studies of Familial Roles

It has been shown by Bales, Slater, *et al.,* that each of the two types of role specialization they describe—specializing around the tasks of the group or around the expression of emotion within it—involves distinctive patterns of style and emotional emphasis. The symbolic and emotional connotations of specialized role performances receive further clarification from anthropological work on familial roles. A point worth emphasizing here is that the sharp dichotomy between task and expressive role specializations—all task and no emotion, or all emotion and no task—is difficult to observe in real life. Quite frequently, the expression of emotion becomes the task of the group, if it is to return productively to its work. Further, the task specialist's role is not purely impersonal. It often conveys forceful expressive qualities without once deviating from total involvement in the group's task. Homans' work [9] provides further insight into the complex nature of these qualities and into their functions for the group.

Specialized executive roles are clothed in a host of personalistic and familistic connotations that are intricately bound up with the organizational context in which they occur. It is from these connotations that a role derives its meaning, both for the person who adopts the role and for those with whom he interacts. The connotations are latent in the role relations that develop; the interpersonal issues that role specialization elicits in the minds of both the actor and his audience are only tangentially associated with the manifest organizational purposes of the administrative encounter. The operational significance of such "unbusinesslike" phenomena is often overlooked. Nonetheless, we suggest that the workings of administration cannot be fully understood without an examination of these latent role issues.

Executives adopt specialized organizational roles for important personal reasons, as well as for administrative reasons. It is not surprising, therefore, that they tend to elicit reciprocally personal responses in others. The patterns of performance and response tend to crystallize around a limited number of modalities that appear repeatedly in a wide variety of social organizations, in widely dispersed geographical and cultural settings.

Homans summarizes, in the following quotation, a body of anthropological data concerning patterned relations between superiors and subordinates. The persistent constellations of relationship and sentiment are very relevant to our study.

9 G. C. Homans, *op. cit.*, 1961.

In patrilineal societies, for instance, a father inherits from *his* father the right to exercise authority over his family and sometimes over his brothers' families too. In words of the social anthropologists, he possesses jural authority: he acquires and wields his authority according to the recognized norms of the society in question. In these societies, a son's sentiment toward his father is apt to be very far from what we call liking. He may respect or even admire the old man, but liking in the form of easy friendliness is not the sentiment he displays, and he is even apt to keep clear of his father except when they have a job to do together. The attitude of respect gets more firmly established the more regularly he works with his father and under his father's orders, for instance, in tilling the land, and the more fully the father's means of controlling him are limited to punishment and threat. Poor fellow, we must not blame the father too much for using negative sanctions: they may be almost the only ones at his disposal. In this respect, a father is usually at a disadvantage compared with a mother, who especially in a child's early years has many and valuable rewards of a positive sort that she can give him; and accordingly a boy's sentiment toward his mother is apt to be warmer and less ambivalent than his sentiment toward his father.[10]

Two consistent patterns of role relations between older and younger members of a system are thus: (1) interpersonal distance, ambivalent feelings of fear and respect, in an instrumental-adaptive context; and (2) interpersonal closeness, warmth and affection, in an expressive-integrative context. These are relations that are archetypically experienced in, respectively, the father-son and mother-son relationships. There is another consistent pattern of role relations—that of uncle and nephew—that is distinguishable from the above two. The uncle-nephew relationship combines certain elements of the above two patterns in an atmosphere of equalitarianism, or relaxed authority, that is differentiable from the above.

[10] *Ibid.*, pp. 301–302.

The mother's brother is a classic figure of anthropology. . . . A boy's mother's brother is on particularly friendly and intimate terms with him in a patrilineal system, where jural authority is located in the father. His mother's brother works and plays with him often, teaches and helps him in many of the difficulties of life, and, above all, holds his hand in all crises from birth to death and is rewarded by the boy's father for the trouble taken.[11]

These role patterns cannot be considered as outcomes either of the sex roles of the individuals involved or of the diffusion of influence from one culture to another. Rather, they are the products of certain consistent human responses to repetitive structural and dynamic properties that are present in any organized social system, be it a family, a tribe, a platoon, a business organization, a monastery, or a mental hospital. We would suggest also that these widespread properties of social systems reflect in part the inner structure and dynamics of personality. Such personality factors transcend particular ethnic groupings. They are expressed through interpersonal relations in any social context, and are attached to enduring roles, such as exist in the family. Thus Homans demonstrates that in matrilineal societies, where jural authority is located in the mother, or the mother's brother, the superordinate-subordinate relations between father and son, and between uncle and nephew, are the reverse of the ones described above.

In certain matrilineal societies, on the other hand, where jural authority over the boy is vested in his mother's brother and not in his father, the boy tends to take the characteristic attitude of respect toward this authority figure, and then he is free to be much more of a friend and companion to his father than he could have been in a patrilineal society.[12]

11 G. C. Homans, *The Human Group*, 1950, p. 252.
12 G. C. Homans, *Social Behavior*, 1961, p. 302.

Given the ubiquity of these systems, we were not surprised to find relationships within the top management group of the hospital, and between these authorities and their subordinates, that approximated the patterns of relationship outlined above. What is perhaps more surprising is that such findings have not been reported in other studies of administration and organizational behavior. We believe that symbolically meaningful executive role relations are present in all organizational systems. In any case, our aim here is to describe such relations and to demonstrate their importance for an organization and for its members.

THE ORGANIZATIONAL AND PERSONAL SIGNIFICANCE OF ROLE SPECIALIZATION

IN ORDER TO COPE with potentially disruptive forces, every senior executive group must have an operational system of role relations that goes deeper and ranges wider than the commonly observed division of concrete work tasks between individual executives. The system of roles must have some specificity and some stability so that the participants therein, and their subordinates, know "who's who" in the organization. This system must adequately encompass the instrumental-adaptive functions indicated by the organization's goals, as well as the required expressive-integrative functions posed by the necessity of maintaining a viable level of cohesion within the organization. In addition, the system of specialized and differentiated roles must represent a *modus vivendi* that provides a rewarding and satisfying way of life to each executive. This is necessary if the executive is to bring to his work a high degree of motivation, energy, and attention. To achieve an arrangement that combines organizational productivity and personal satisfaction requires considerable psychosocial work by executives.

The existing literature on organizations contains few findings that bear directly upon the above approach. Those who have the ideas and the techniques for developing research into these hypothesized relations have not entered into the arena of "live" executive groups to do their research; and those who have entered into that arena have not done the research. However, some weight is lent to our thinking about executive groups by the statements of those who have studied other types of purposive groups.[13] For instance, Bales presents certain ideas about the "coalition" between top ranking role specialists in the groups he studied, and the relationships between the nature of this "coalition" and the effectiveness of its control over the functioning of the total group.

There is some reason to believe that one possible arrangement by which the status struggle between the top instrumental-adaptive leader and the best liked man can be prevented or stabilized is the formation of a kind of "coalition" between them, such that the two tacitly agree, as it were, not to undercut each other, which is to say, not to be "seduced" into attempting to form a coalition with lower status members in order to displace each other. If such a coalition can be formed, it becomes quite difficult for lower status members to revolt, unseat the top men, or develop the norms of the group in any different direction.[14]

There are rewards and costs for the executive when he ventures into role specialization. Correlatively, there are other rewards and costs associated with the conscious or unconscious decision *not* to specialize in any interpersonal sense, but in-

[13] Research into "blue-collar" groups is conspicuously unhelpful in this regard, largely because the workers' personal involvement in the purposive context of the larger organization is usually of a neutral and often negativistic nature. This finding, though representative of personal circumstances that are widespread in organizational settings, pertains to a specific set of conditions in the man-in-organization encounter. The tendency has been to extrapolate this finding into a general postulate about the antithetical relations between all men and all organizations. The findings of this study stand in some contradistinction to this nonspecific man vs. organization postulate.

[14] R. F. Bales, *op. cit.*, 1955, p. 455.

stead to develop a "good all 'round" set of role performances. Bales outlines some of the rewards and costs that cluster around the different modalities of role specialization.

> . . . The more "directive" and "constricting" the quality of activity, the more likely it is to arouse negative reactions. If a man begins to specialize noticeably in this direction, the negative reactions tend to be centered on him. The displacement of hostilities on a scapegoat . . . is one mechanism, apparently, by which the ambivalent attitudes toward the instrumental-adaptive specialist—the "top man"—can be diverted and drained off. The centering of positive affect on a secondary man is another mechanism by which the solidarity of the group—its integration as a collectivity of persons—can be re-established. Such a man can be warm, receptive, responsive, and rewarding, can "conciliate" and "bind up the wounds," without diverting the movement of the system too far from the kind of movement in the instrumental-adaptive direction which is also felt to be necessary. He can do this because he does not assume the "responsibility" for the movement of the system in these directions, but leaves this to the technical or executive specialist.[15]

This particular statement is perhaps more explicit about the costs associated with being the "top man"—and with being the "scapegoat"—than it is about being the best liked man. We will see, however, that there are very real and very painful costs associated with *all* specializations, as well as rewards to be gathered therefrom. From the point of view of the collectivity, these costs must be assumed by its ranking members if the "movement of the system" is to be insured. A system whose ranking members cannot or will not assume the costs of requisite role specialization is one that has stopped moving and has started to decay. Bales speculates in the following way about the polity whose members are not satisfied

15 *Ibid.*, pp. 453–454.

with, or cannot personally sustain, the requisite system of specialized, differentiated, and complementary executive roles.

But suppose the best liked man is not willing to do this; i.e., stay within the limits of his role specialization, and assume the costs as well as the rewards of that specialization? Suppose that the perception of the likes of others "goes to his head" and encourages him to begin to "take over" from the technical or executive specialists? He is in a position to command considerable support, and the "top man" is in a vulnerable position because of the latent or overt hostility centered on him. Or suppose, on the other hand, that the top man is emotionally unable to stand the hostility, or is unable to tolerate the fact that not he, but another, is best liked? The top man is under strains, we might suppose, to try to "undercut" his nearest rival. Here are the seeds of a fundamental status struggle, exceedingly damaging, in potentiality, both for the instrumental-adaptive achievement of the group, and for its affective integration.[16]

The fundamental issue in all executive roles has now been joined. Every executive has certain predispositions and antipathies that dictate what interpersonal transactions and administrative role specializations he can undertake successfully over the long term. As a member of an executive team, he must work interdependently with a number of other individuals who likewise have predispositions and antipathies that dictate what *they* can successfully undertake along the same lines. As an executive, the individual must delineate the organizational demands of the larger system for which he is responsible. He must also institute action that will meet those demands, so that the "movement of the system" can be guaranteed and his executive responsibilities fulfilled. His task is, therefore, to diagnose the structure of forces that exists at the personal, the interpersonal, and the organizational levels of reality that surround him and bring them into some mean-

16 *Ibid.,* p. 454.

ingful relationship with each other. He must "do business," in more than just the technical sense, with these contingent sets of forces. If his negotiations with himself and others along these lines are successful, the result is presumably both satisfying for himself and productive for the organization, though never without concomitant costs and hazards.

In conclusion, we quote one further statement by Bales. It applies as well to the top management group of this study as to the experimental groups used in Bales' research.

> . . . However, the stable structure is never, in our data, a "simply organized" one. It is rather one in which differentiated roles have appeared, in which one specialist "undoes" the disturbance to equilibrium created by another, and in turn is dependent upon another to remove the strains he himself creates—the total constellation of specialists being one which allows or aids the system to establish a full orbit in its dimensions of necessary movement.[17]

In the following chapters, we shall report on one constellation of executive role specialists. The nature of the individual executives' specializations will be described in Part II, following immediately. The emergence of an organized role constellation will be presented in Part III. In Part IV, we shall examine the dynamics of this system, the "doings" and "undoings" of the executives' transactions with each other. In Part V, the scope of analysis is broadened, as we examine the constellation's orbit of influence upon administrative behavior in one segment of the hospital.

17 *Ibid.,* pp. 454–455.

PART II. EACH EXECUTIVE AT WORK
Role Analyses of Organizational Behavior

WE BEGIN our analysis of the executive role constellation by describing the constituent role performances of the executives. These descriptions present the superintendent, the assistant superintendent, and the clinical director as each was observed going about his work in the hospital. In Part II, our attention is on individual roles. Parts III and IV will deal with the historical and dynamic relations among these roles. However, in this part our focus is on each executive as the principal actor of his career, at the center of his positional stage in the larger setting of the Institute.

There are four chapters in Part II. Each of the first three focuses on one of our executive subjects. These chapters describe individual role performances as they became manifest in the interpersonal transactions of hospital administration. In these descriptions, we highlight the properties of individual role performances that most influenced the emergent constellation of roles.

These three chapters are built around a standard format. First, each chapter has a major subtitle. These subtitles portray the purposive vector of the executives' professional and organizational lives. They convey our best estimate of the essential purposive intent underlying the executives' administration of their organization. In the executives' administrative actions there was a significant infusion of personal materials. The executives were not "all business." However, their personalizing of their jobs was not based on pure whimsy. It was done in the service of stimulating others to get done what the executives wanted to see done in the organization, for the patients, and for the future of their profession. With certain "personal touches," each executive had his own way of prompting, cajoling, threatening, and charming those around him into actively contributing to the accomplishment of the objectives he held for the Institute. The emotional qualities of the executives' role performances are one of the major analytic objectives pursued in the body of the chapters. However, to establish firmly the goal-directedness of this behavior, each chapter's subtitle outlines the purposive orientation of the executive's affiliation with the Memorial Psychiatric Institute.

At the time of this study, the executives' striving after these purposes governed almost every facet of their lives. It influenced the time they got up in the morning and when they went to bed. It regulated their activities during the week and over the weekend as well. It selected *what* they did, and *whom* they did it with. It was the pace of this purposive, goal-directed behavior—arising from personal forces but rooted in the organizational setting—that seemed uppermost in establishing the pattern and setting the tempo of the executives' lives. These dynamic situations are described in the chapter sections entitled, "The Purposive Context of Administration."

The chapter sections entitled, "Interpersonal Transactions Around Work: Performance and Response," contain descriptions of how each executive got linked up with others in the Institute organization, in working toward the personal and organizational objectives of the administrative setting. These objectives were constantly being attained, but were also continually receding into the future in the face of current advances. They were, in other words, "open-ended." This caused the engagement between the executives and their organization to be a continuing process. Each executive was constantly interacting with others, demonstrating and reinforcing his interpersonal-administrative style, elaborating and deepening his executive role performance. He communicated to others a never-ending stream of behavioral messages about himself, his conception of others, and the organization in which they were commonly associated. These messages were received by the executives' organizational audience. They were evaluated in terms of the feelings, wishes, opinions, and purposes of each member of that audience. These were reflected back upon each executive in the course of his interactions with others in the M.P.I. They often had an observable effect upon the executive, both in the personal sense of how others saw him, and in the organizational sense of how well his programs for actions were being acted upon by his subordinates.

Such reflections were sometimes very pleasing, and sometimes very painful. They established a system of coexisting rewards and costs in the psychosocial situation surrounding each executive in the Institute. The positive or negative balance of this system contributed to the executives' continued growth in their positions, or to the onset of personal and professional stultification. It contributed to their departure from the organization, or to their continued membership in it. In the chapter sections entitled, "The Resulting Balance," we attempt to delineate the nature of the balance between psychosocial rewards and costs as these existed for the executives at the time of the study. We attempt to establish how this balance contributed to the executives' generativity and self-absorption, and to the mixure of integrity, disgust, and despair that characterized the evolving feeling tone of their lives.

The final chapter of Part II develops this theme of balancing individual needs and organizational requirements, personal goals and group demands, with potential consequences for the continued growth of the individual and the betterment of the organization. Both these facets of the man-

in-organization situation—balance and growth—are represented in our concept of role-task, which we develop in Chapter 7. It is in this chapter that we try to pull together some
of the uniformities existing among all three of our executive
subjects in response to their encounter with the organization
and with each other.

CHAPTER 4

The Superintendent: Building the Future of His Organization and His Profession

THE PRIMARY INTEREST of the researchers was in the *interpersonal processes* by which work was accomplished in the hospital. The interest of the executives being observed was different. Their attentions were focused primarily on *accomplishing the work* they wanted to see done, and secondarily on the interpersonal transactions involved. They experienced the latter affectively, but in their executive capacities, they did not often make them the central topic of problem-solving scrutiny. As professional psychiatrists in the context of psychotherapy, they did turn their attention fully to this "secondary" area. However, as practicing executives, their organizational objectives were at the center of their attentions.

In order to establish firmly this hierarchy, and to portray its meaningfulness in the executives' work lives, this chapter and the following two will describe: (1) each executive's work context; (2) the interpersonal transactions he engaged in around this work, the role performance he adopted, and other people's response thereto; and (3) the resulting balance of rewards and costs for the executives, and the direction in which each planned further to develop his career. These categories are only approximate, but they capture the flow of the executives' professional, organizational, and personal careers within the boundaries of the hospital. The data in these three chapters have been organized to portray that flow.

THE PURPOSIVE CONTEXT OF ADMINISTRATION

THE ACTIVITIES of all the top executives, including the superintendent, were so many and so varied that some simplifying
device was needed to convey the major repetitive elements in
those activities. We have used the convenient fiction of the
"typical day" for this purpose. No such thing as a "typical
day" was ever observed. Emergencies, unpredicted events, and
unscheduled interactions were always occurring. However,
these did occur within a structure of regularity that we have
attempted to portray.

The activities of the day had, for the superintendent as for
the other executives, both the immediate objective of maintaining hospital operations and the longer term vectors that
characterized the individual's professional interests and his
personal idiosyncracies. Our analysis will move from the activities of the day, through the professional interests expressed therein, toward the personality and longer-term objectives that were being expressed as the superintendent went
about the business of managing the Memorial Psychiatric Institute.

A Typical Day of Work for the Superintendent in the Hospital

Each of the three executives had his own way of organizing
his work day. The superintendent, Dr. Frank Suprin, was usually at his desk by 7 A.M. and worked by himself until the daily
activities of the hospital began. He was often able to work for
more than an hour uninterrupted except by his secretary, who
brought him his morning mail and a cup of coffee she had
made for him. He called this period of the day his "quiet
hour," during which time he would catch up on his correspondence, read professional journals or manuscripts that he
had been asked to comment on, and write or dictate the many
speeches that he gave to a wide variety of organizations. He

had a scheme worked out that helped him with this last-mentioned task. Sometimes he dictated his speeches, but when he felt like it, he wrote them out longhand. "I play little tricks on myself," he explained, "to keep myself working."

Usually, the first interaction of the day that related to the administration of the hospital occurred shortly after 9 A.M. At that time, the clinical director (or in his absence, the assistant clinical director) would report to the superintendent on admissions and on the events that had taken place in the hospital overnight. The two men would sit by the superintendent's desk as they reviewed whatever events had appeared on the report sheets. The superintendent would chat quietly about his impressions of the patients or the staff who may have been mentioned in the reports, or whom the reports had brought to his mind. In a relaxed atmosphere, the two men would exchange whatever information each had, and their opinions about these people. The superintendent often asked questions concerning the matters the clinical director was bringing to his attention, and sometimes the superintendent requested further information. The clinical director was often not able to answer immediately the questions that were asked, or to provide the information requested. He told the superintendent he would let him know.

The superintendent then frequently informed the clinical director about events and decisions that had taken place outside the hospital that he, the superintendent, had participated in, or of which he had been informed by colleagues. The clinical director would occasionally reply in kind. After a brief discussion, he would rise and leave the office, repeating that he would find out about what the superintendent wanted to know.

Following this daily event, the variety of the superintendent's activities was great. He was sometimes able to work relatively undisturbed in his office for considerable portions of the day. It was not unusual to walk by his office and see him seated alone at his desk, reading, writing, or dictating. It was important to him that he should be able to do so. He devoted some effort to insure that he was not unnecessarily disturbed by staff members bringing problems to him that he thought should more properly have been taken to the clinical director, the assistant clinical director, or the assistant superintendent.

At other times, however, the superintendent was engaged in a wide variety of meetings and conferences: executive committee meetings, meetings of the board of trustees, research meetings, conferences with the resident psychiatrists and the other staff of the hospital, case supervision of some residents, and the teaching of medical students. He was often visited in his office by people of diverse interests from outside the hospital. He also saw a limited number of patients. He estimated that the time he left his desk in the evening was, on the average, around 6 P.M., except when he had something "on" for the evening, such as a professional meeting or a departure for an out-of-town engagement.

The superintendent's view of his day's work conveys the relative emphases that he placed on the several aspects of his role in the hospital. During his "quiet hour" one morning in August he replied to the observer's query about a typical day.

"I usually have two analytic patients a day, and there are sometimes about two others whom I do not treat analytically, who come in sometime during the week. (He described the persons he was currently treating.) I do this to keep my hand in. You have to keep your hand in, especially in this clinical business. You'll find that all the top people here are taking patients. Dick Sherman [the former superintendent] used to do it, and I used to do it no matter what job I had. I'd take a certain number of patients every day. . . .

"I use this hour as my quiet hour, before people start running into my office. I use it as my writing hour."

Observer: "What do you write?"

Suprin: "These." He pointed to a pile of papers on his desk.

"These are my speeches that I'm working on, and papers, and things like that." He went on to describe his method of writing; alternating periods of handwriting and dictating to a machine.

". . . There is something in this district almost every evening of the week. I try to limit myself to one night a week now. You know I'm a member of several committees at the medical school. For instance, I'm a member of the curriculum committee which takes up a lot of my time, and I place a great deal of importance on it. I'm the only psychiatrist on the committee, and when I'm not there, psychiatry goes unrepresented. It's not like the other committees where, if I'm not there, there's always Paul [Dr. Cadman, the clinical director] to stick up for me. For instance, last year I was out in the midwest for something or other, and there was a meeting of the curriculum committee. So I flew back for that evening, and flew back out west the next morning.

"I'm also on the appointments committee, the fellowship committee, and—oh, yes—the library committee, and this is important too these days, since we are trying to build up a library."

Observer: "How much supervision of the residents' case work do you do?"

Suprin: "Yes, I do some supervision of the residents. Eight of them, I think. People like me and Cadman, we don't have to supervise the residents. We used to, but our staff is adequate for that now, and if we didn't want to, we would not have to. But we do it for fun. We'd lose touch with the place if we didn't. I enjoy it too. I get to know some of the residents a lot better than I would otherwise, and I sort of get a feel for what's going on around the place, much better than I would if I didn't [supervise]. So," he smiled, "I put my name down on the list, and was scheduled for regular sessions with eight of the first-year residents. Of course, there is the added complication for these people that I am the boss, but I straightened that out with them in the first session, telling them that I certainly was the boss outside of the hour, but in it there was just supervision, and there would be no repercussions outside this office of anything they told me in supervision.

"Then, usually, we have medical students around the place.

Of course, there are none now, but when school is in session, I spend some three or four hours a week with them here. [Mondays, Wednesdays, and Fridays, in small groups in his office.] I like to teach these guys. They are really a lot of fun.

"Of course, every morning about this time [circa 9 A.M.] Paul comes in and gives me a report on the clinical picture around the hospital. There he goes now." Dr. Cadman walked by the open doorway to Suprin's office, on the way down the corridor to his own office. He carried in his hand what may have been the overnight reports of the residents on duty during that time. "I sometimes make a few suggestions or requests, but it's only very rarely that I tell someone to do something. I'd say it was only about once a week that I really make a point of telling somebody to do something that I want to see done. These are a hot bunch of clinical boys, you know. You don't have to bother them much, when I'm gone, Cadman and Asche [the assistant superintendent] take over for me just like that. With Ackroyd [the assistant clinical director] and Cadman running the show, there are only about one or two clinical things a month that come up to me that I have to deal with, and these usually have something to do with the court cases. It's a funny thing. I don't know why they should want to bring the court cases to me instead of to Paul. I suppose it is because they are legal cases, or something like that. But I'm not actively involved by any means in the [clinical] administration of the hospital. Cadman and Ackroyd are the best in the business.

"Occasionally I get a request for an admission from a friend or from some political bigwig. I handle these, of course, but any of the others that happen to come my way go straight down to Crosier [the psychiatrist who was the hospital's admissions officer]. He takes care of all that. It's an old hospital, and well organized."

Observer: "How much paper work do you have to do?"

Suprin: "Today, I've got about two times more than I usually have. I was away last week, and I'm still catching up. You get the silliest stuff in the mail. There is always some group that wants you to come and talk to them about some of the darndest subjects. And there is salesmen's stuff. That all goes in there." He pointed to the waste basket and smiled. "I've got what you would call high sales resistance. Well, it's all a bunch of fiddly little details. It's like my writing. I play little tricks with myself to keep myself working. I guess I usually spend about thirty minutes—maybe a bit longer—every day on this sort of stuff. It all depends on how much I've been away."

Engagements Outside the Hospital

The superintendent's commitments to professional associations, governmental bodies, and public interest groups caused him to spend a great deal of time away from the Institute, traveling throughout the nation and beyond. Having been asked what some of these commitments were, Dr. Suprin read aloud the tentative list of engagements he had planned during the forthcoming fall term. The following table presents these engagements in a slightly disguised form.

DR. SUPRIN'S TENTATIVE SCHEDULE OF OUTSIDE ENGAGEMENTS, SEPTEMBER–DECEMBER

Approximate date	Approximate locality	General nature of scheduled activity
Sept. 1	New Hampshire	Health survey, advisory capacity.
Sept. 7	Connecticut	Consultation with a general hospital concerning its psychiatric services.
Sept. 12	Washington, D.C.	Meeting of Committee A, Federal Agency X. Meeting of American Psychiatric Association, Committee A.
Sept. 13	Washington, D.C.	Meeting of A.P.A., Committee B.
Sept. 20	Pennsylvania	Speech at a hospital in Philadelphia.
Sept. 25	Massachusetts	Attend meetings of an association of hospital administrators. Deliver two speeches.
Sept. 30	Illinois	Meetings of the American Medical Association committee on psychiatric services.
Oct. 5	Illinois	Administration of certificate examinations in psychiatry and neurology.
Oct. 10	Maryland	Speech at a Baltimore hospital.
Oct. 15	Iowa	Speech at meetings of a mental health association.

Approximate date	Approximate locality	General nature of scheduled activity
Oct. 26	Pennsylvania	Seminar on research in psychiatry, sponsored by a Philadelphia medical school with which Dr. Suprin was affiliated. Suprin planned to attend the first day's meetings and then fly to Washington.
Oct. 26–27	Washington, D.C.	National health survey.
Nov. 6–7	Location to be announced.	Governors' conference.
Nov., date to be announced.	Location to be announced.	G.A.P. meetings.
Nov. 15	California	Speech to an association for mental health.
Nov. 21	Pennsylvania	Speech to a suburban group of lawyers, "How to Get Along with Your Wife." *
Nov. 29	North Carolina	Speech to a regional board of education.
Nov. 29	Washington, D.C.	Dr. Suprin planned to fly from Durham to Washington to attend a conference on psychiatric training programs, where he would be until Dec. 2.
Dec. 4	Washington, D.C.	Meeting of federal advisory committee.
Dec. 7–8	Pennsylvania	Conference on psychiatric research, to be held at the M.P.I.
Dec. 9	New York	Administration of certificate examinations in psychiatry and neurology.

* Dr. Suprin grimaced. "This," he said, "indicates that everyone suffers from lapses of memory. I have hundreds of these requests a year, which I turn down. I have no idea why I accepted this one. Often it makes a big difference how people approach you. This one must have been well put or I would not have accepted it."

"From that date," Dr. Suprin concluded, flipping shut his calendar, "I am free of appointments until January. Of course," he added, "some could be added in the meantime." He smiled. "This list doesn't include any of the medical school faculty committee meetings I attend whatsoever, or the ones I hold regularly with Dr. Holland [the superintendent of another hospital]."

Professional Development and the Round of Events

After Dr. Suprin gave the observer his list of engagements through December, he developed his thinking on the functions served by his entry into such a round of professional events.

Observer: "Is my image of the doctor with his patient, or the researcher working alone in his laboratory, an obsolete one?"

Suprin: "Yes. I think it is somewhat out of date. Especially around a place like the M.P.I. where we have so many hot-shots. But there are still a very large number of doctors, you know, who are uninterested in anything other than treating their patients and developing their practice. For instance, at the [local] district medical society, it is unusual for a little more than a handful of the members to show up at a meeting.

"Many people join because they think it is the right thing to do, because it will be good for their careers. They intend to take some interest in matters, but something always seems to come up. So that, anybody who does show some interest or willingness to work on these matters, before he knows it, he is snapped up to work first on this, then on that. And before he knows it, he has more than he can possibly keep up with.

"People want somebody to talk to them who has a name. They are not interested in anybody who does not have a name. So they get somebody who has a name, and the more he talks, the more he becomes a name. And the more people come to him, asking him to do this, that or the other thing. It's perfectly ridiculous, but on the other hand, it's perfectly sensible. Because a person has a name, that doesn't mean he is better than somebody else who does not have a name. It just means that he has developed a name of himself. You have to work to develop a name. People who think that a name develops naturally are wrong. You have to go out and work on it. But it is perfectly reasonable for people who are spending public or government funds to build some psychiatric unit, or something, to want to deal with nothing but names. If some skeptical politician comes along and wants to know why the hell they spent so much money on such-and-such, or why they built it in the first place, then they can say, 'Well, so-and-so told us to do it that way.' And that stops the argument, if they have been dealing with well-known people."

Dr. Suprin's advice to the residents and the younger members of his staff frequently centered around the process of building their professional names. He had definite ideas as to the strategy one should follow in doing so. He thought of himself as having followed this strategy, and having been successful thereby. He repeatedly expressed concern that many of the younger professionals around him were following alternate routes that he thought would prevent them from realizing their full professional and administrative potential.

Molding the Future Through Group Action

Having developed his own name, Dr. Suprin was actively and enthusiastically engaged in the network of associations in which the business of a profession is conducted, and which since the time of de Tocqueville has been considered a singularly American approach to progress. Dr. Suprin viewed himself very much as a *builder*, one who could put things together and make them run. He talked of his many activities and commitments in terms of their instrumental value in building the future of psychiatry. His professional memberships as well were not only of interest or value in and of themselves. They, too, were part of Dr. Suprin's larger design to assist and to influence the unfolding course of his profession.

Rapidly, and with considerable gusto, the superintendent recited the following list of his memberships. This he did almost completely from memory. The organization of this list was his own.

1. The medical school. Outside of his job as the superintendent of the M.P.I., Suprin's affiliation and faculty standing with the medical school was the most time-consuming. He was a member of:
    (a) the curriculum committee
    (b) the fellowship committee
    (c) the appointments committee
    (d) the committee of professors

    (e) the library committee

    (f) the endowments committee

2. The only other affiliation that was as time-consuming was the American Board of Psychiatry and Neurology. Dr. Suprin served in the administration of the board, which functioned to examine candidates seeking certification in psychiatry and neurology.

3. Federal agencies:

    (a) The National Health Survey Advisory Committee

    (b) Committee A of Federal Agency X

    (c) Committee B of Federal Agency X

4. Governors' advisory committee on mental health

5. International organizations:

    (a) Committee on mental health of the World Health Organization

    (b) Advisory committee for the World Federation for Mental Health

6. Medical associations:

    (a) The American Medical Association

    (b) The American Psychiatric Association

    (c) The Pennsylvania Medical Society

    (d) The Philadelphia District Medical Society

    (e) The Eastern Psychiatric Association

    (f) The Pennsylvania Society for Research in Psychiatry

    (g) The Philadelphia Society of Neurology and Psychiatry

    (h) The Group for the Advancement of Psychiatry

    (i) The American Hospital Association

    (j) The Philadelphia Psychoanalytic Institute

7. The National Mental Health Commission

8. The American Academy of Arts and Sciences

9. Sigma Psi

10. The American Association for the Advancement of Science

It was interesting to note, later in the field work, how different were Dr. Suprin's affiliations with outside organizations, and the quality of his response to these affiliations, from the equivalent attributes and manifestations of the clinical director and the assistant superintendent. The clinical director cited fewer memberships, and neither he nor his secretary was sure exactly what they were. In the observer's work with the assistant superintendent, the topic of membership in professional organizations outside the hospital never arose. The hospital assumed a more dominant role in his professional life and career development than was the case for the other two executives. He restricted his travel away from the hospital, so that he could get done what he considered to be his work. He also did not like to "hit the road."

"I let Frank do that," he explained half humorously, and then went on to point out, "If Frank didn't do as much as he does, then I would have to do more, and I would not like that." Thus, one dimension of role complementarity in the executive group was denoted; this one addressing the issue of primacy of one's orientation toward internal organizational phenomena, or toward external events and situations in the organization's environment.

The Future as Worth Working Toward

Perhaps the first impression Dr. Suprin communicated to newcomers in his organizational audiences was his driving and optimistic approach to his many activities and affiliations. This contrasted occasionally with the more enervated and cynical response that could be detected among others in the hospital toward such great involvement in professional memberships and group action. It seemed that, when one was experiencing the insults of subordinacy in a particularly direct way, one readily focused the resultant hostility on an individual—Dr. Suprin—who utilized his superordinacy with such palpable gusto. When the mood became sufficiently hostile, it was easy to type the man as an "organization man," whose work was entirely devoted to "playing the game." Needless to say, this was not Dr. Suprin's own attitude toward himself. Nor was it that of the people who worked closely with him.

Dr. Suprin's own views of his wide-ranging activities were

simple and positive. They were very much directed toward the future. They were permeated by an optimism based on his judgment of people—himself and others—as ongoing and constructive. He did not talk much about such matters, and when he did, he took care to convey it with as much "hard talk" as the topic would bear, from which a listener could easily draw an imbalanced inference. Both characteristics—optimism and toughness—were manifested, for instance, during a discussion between Suprin and Asche, about civil defense preparedness at the hospital.

Suprin: "Well, you know my theory. All they have to do would be to drop a couple of bales of hay on the parkway, and that would be the end of your evacuation routes. As far as I'm concerned, everything stays right here." He recounted a plan that had been devised while he had been superintendent at another hospital to evacuate that hospital in the event of atomic attack. It involved the transporting of patients and staff to some other place, using the trucks and employees of a commercial transfer company.

"Now, how the hell could they do that?" asked Suprin. "Except if they happened to be right there at the time [of an attack]. And then where the hell would they go? I said, 'No go.' I have found that if you keep the patients and the staff in the hospital, they remain calm. In fact, they think up things that would be useful to do, and then they do them. It's amazing the things you will ask them to do, and find they have anticipated it already. Damn, there's no telling what would happen if you let them go chasing off all over the country. So they may fry, but at least they will fry quietly. . . ."

Asche: "Are you going to build a shelter at home?"

"No," Suprin replied. "I don't fancy crawling into a hole in the ground. That is not in my usual character. Besides, I'm only home at night, and if anything came up, the first thing I would do would be to try to get back here."

Another expression of this essential optimism occurred in response to several statements about existential meaningless-

ness and the plight of modern man that had been made in
Dr. Suprin's hearing by a European psychiatrist visiting the
city that summer. One afternoon, when events were not
pressing too closely on Dr. Suprin, the observer explored
Suprin's obvious impatience and disagreement with the
visitor's thesis. His pragmatic optimism was not hard to
detect in his response. It was interesting, also, to note the
diminution of frequency and intensity of "tough talk" in this
response, and to consider that it was given privately to the
observer, in a relaxed moment, when no others were present.

The observer remarked that the picture presented by the staff
and the residents—intelligence, hard work, good intentions, pur-
posefulness—hardly fit into the moral decay, meaninglessness, and
anomie portrayed by the visiting psychiatrist on a T.V. panel
discussion the day before: a position that seemed popular with
many literary intellectuals in the U.S., but one that Dr. Suprin
had taken the psychiatrist to task on.

"That's correct," Suprin replied. "All that business about moral
decay is just so much nonsense. The search for 'meaning'—whatever that is—with all the feelings that go with it of being lost, of
being in an existential sort of a vacuum, may apply to a small segment of the population. Maybe two or three percent. But it certainly doesn't assume the proportions of a national problem.
Even if everyone at college were to suffer from feelings of meaninglessness—and I don't believe this for one minute—it would still
be relatively unimportant at the national level, because of the
small number of citizens who are at college. I believe I've got the
scientific facts to back my position, and people like that [psychia-
trist] do not. In the study we had done, the findings were that on
a representative sample of the American population, there was
only a very small portion who were worried by anything like
meaninglessness. Only one in ten, if I remember correctly, was
worried about the international situation and the possibility of
nuclear war. It showed that most people were concerned with putting Johnnie through school, or getting Sally's teeth straightened,
or something like that.

"Perhaps the nation is a little over-fond of refrigerators and things like that, but it is hard to take this too seriously. It's only a very small proportion that are troubled by any lack of meaning in life. I can't see building a whole theory on that basis.

". . . I'm constantly impressed at what a fine bunch of people [the young people of today] are. You could hardly say that was moral decay. Maybe one in twenty goes wrong, but that's a good average. There's much less drinking and whoring around than there used to be. I can remember going down to bail out residents who had been arrested for drunkenness and disorderly conduct. I can remember bailing out a resident and his wife who were arrested for assaulting an officer. He had been trying to arrest them after their car had knocked down a post. They started to beat him up. They were drunk, of course. You don't get much of that nowadays."

Teaching versus Other Commitments

The superintendent liked to teach and emphasized the teaching function of the hospital. Nonetheless, his commitment to other activities, such as the ones outlined above, often made it difficult for him to devote himself as much as he would have liked to teaching. One day, while the clinical director was in Suprin's office, Dr. Suprin received a phone call concerning the date of an engagement that had been changed, or that had not been recorded in his calendar. Suprin discussed with the caller the new arrangements, and then with some apparent consternation wrote the particulars down on a jot pad on his desk. Hanging up, he turned to Dr. Cadman and exclaimed:

"Damn! That was news to me. Now I'm going to have to call old —— and see if he will take another of my classes for me. I've already called him several times. If things go on like this, I'm going to have to give up this teaching business. I'm not living up to the obligations I made to these students."

Dr. Cadman shook his head and stood there in silence by Dr. Suprin's desk. After a brief pause, Suprin made a face and

reached forward onto his desk. He flipped through his calendar, telling Dr. Cadman of some of the events coming up.
Cadman smiled sympathetically at the comments that Suprin
made as he went through this review. "Things are tough," he
said when Suprin had completed his review. Suprin leaned
back in his chair, put his hands behind his neck and stretched.

"Yes, well anyway . . . ," he replied, and left his response
unfinished, as was often the case when a remark was directed
affectionately toward him. Then he initiated a brief discussion about the person he was going to phone to take over another of his teaching sessions. "That old ——. He must be a
tough old bat. I hope I'm as spry as he is when I'm his age,"
observed Suprin, changing the tone of the conversation.

INTERPERSONAL TRANSACTIONS AROUND WORK: PERFORMANCE AND RESPONSE

WE HAVE OUTLINED the nature of the superintendent's work
in the hospital. In so doing, we have conveyed something of
the nature of the man. Now we turn the focus of our analysis
to a more explicit assessment of the individual who was superintendent, the manner in which he performed in that position, and how he "came across" to others in the process. Our
change in analytic emphasis is more transitional than discontinuous. Obviously, the superintendent's role performance
cannot be described except in relation to the work he was
doing as superintendent. We make no attempt to divorce
work style from work content. Instead, we attempt to highlight *both* elements of the total performance of the man who
was superintendent.

Teaching Rounds and the Communication of Professional Role Models

One of the principal teaching devices of the Institute's residency training program was comprised of the teaching rounds

that took place every day on each service in the hospital. Every day each service had two rounds: administrative rounds and teaching rounds. Most of the staff of a ward—residents, nurses, social workers, attendants, occupational therapists, psychologists—attended administrative rounds, during which the head nurse from each ward would read the report of overnight happenings on her ward, and the chief resident would then review the content of the report with those staff people whose patients were involved. Teaching rounds usually took place right after these administrative matters had been reviewed. Many of the nonmedical members of the staff did not attend teaching rounds, during which an experienced psychiatrist on the staff would review a case with a resident, interview the patient in question, and then take up for discussion with the group whatever issues the resident, the chief, or he wished to raise. This experienced person, whoever it happened to be, was sometimes referred to as "the consultant," because ideally he was rendering professional opinions, not giving orders to the ward staff. Sometimes this distinction was difficult to maintain.

Dr. Suprin was not often able to visit the services for such teaching purposes. However, he did sometimes substitute for some of the senior members of the staff when they were away and he had the time available. Such a confluence of events occurred in the latter half of the summer in which the observer had begun his field work. The clinical director was away on his vacation. Dr. Suprin took Dr. Cadman's place in teaching rounds. This was of some importance within the residency training program, since it provided many of the residents who were new to the hospital with their first opportunity to see how Dr. Suprin worked with patients, how he acted in their presence, how he talked with them, and what he thought about them. It was the residents' opportunity to gain some knowledge about the diagnostic and therapeutic skills they had come to the hospital to learn about, and it was their opportunity to form some of their own opinions about a man of whom they had already heard a great deal. This they could do in relation to the skills and abilities that had been demonstrated to them, also in teaching rounds, by other senior members of the staff who visited their services, with whom they had already either been impressed or been unimpressed.

The superintendent realized the important nature of the teaching rounds as a communications medium. Having a number of things that he thought were important to communicate to the residents, he entered into whichever teaching rounds he took with considerable vigor and dynamism. That in itself was communicable, but in addition he sought to convey more explicitly to the residents what he thought were the proper attitudes for a psychiatrist to adopt toward patients, and what were the most effective habits of mind for a psychiatrist to apply to his treatment and management of his patients.

Dr. Suprin substituted for Dr. Cadman as a consultant in a teaching round in which a first-year resident presented his case work-up of a 26-year-old woman who had recently been admitted to the hospital after having slashed herself around the face, wrists, and abdomen. The situation in the teaching round was a little out of the ordinary, in that the patient's private doctor—the one with whom she had been in therapy prior to her commitment to the hospital—was also present at the meeting. The resident presented the information he had gathered about and from the patient and his diagnosis of her condition. The outside doctor complimented the resident on his work and agreed with his diagnosis. Dr. Suprin smiled and asked, in effect: Well now, what is the patient really like as a person? In the discussion that ensued, the resident and the private physician together developed the theme that the patient was immature, hostile, dependent, and unwilling to take responsibility for leading her own life. Dr. Suprin sat hunched in his chair with his arms and legs crossed, looking around at the people in the room. When the discussion was over, he nodded and asked, "Well, now, shall we see the patient?"

The resident left the room, and returned with the patient. Dr. Suprin stood up and offered her the seat next to him. As they both sat down, he told her his name. She sat listlessly beside him, her head bowed, taking occasional puffs from a cigarette she was holding. Her cheeks and mouth were loose and expressionless, and it was impossible to see her eyes or the expression around them since she wore very large and very dark sunglasses.

The two of them sat there a while in silence, Suprin looking at her from his position hunched up in his chair, now leaning slightly forward from the waist, and she slouched back, flaccid and expressionless.

"Do you know who I am?" he asked in a very quiet voice. (He always seemed to speak very softly in his demonstration interviews. Any significant amount of noise in the room, the corridor, or on the street often caused one to lose something of what had been said.)

The patient did not respond.

"Do you?" he asked again softly, after a little silence.

The patient nodded her head ever so slightly.

Suprin smiled a bit and leaned a little closer to the patient. "You do?" he asked. Another silence followed, Suprin inclining slightly toward the patient with a little grin, while she lay back in her chair with cigarette smoke curling up her motionless fingers and hand.

She nodded again, somewhat more perceptibly.

Suprin smiled outright, and asked "Who *am* I?" (He asked it almost as though they were having a little game together.)

The corners of the patient's mouth twitched. "The superintendent," she replied in a strangled sort of way, as though she had not spoken for some time and was having difficulty finding her voice.

Suprin nodded. "Would you like to talk with me?" he asked.

The patient shrugged.

"Would you?" Suprin persisted. (He did not continue with the next statement that seemed natural at that juncture, namely: you don't have to, you know.)

The patient cleared her throat. "Yes," she said.

"What would you like to talk about?"

"I don't know."

"Surely you must have something you want to talk about." The patient shrugged.

"*Well?*" queried Suprin pointedly.

"What makes me sick, I suppose," the girl replied.

"You *suppose,*" Suprin pointed out to her.

The patient shifted in her chair, and then sat up. "What makes me sick," she said. She lit another cigarette.

"What *does* make you sick?"

"I don't know."

"You must have *some* ideas."

The patient shrugged.

"Well," Suprin prodded.

The patient nodded.

"You do?"

"Yes."

"What are some of them?"

The patient began slowly to review some of her experiences. Suprin listened without ever taking his eyes off her, asking questions, requesting more information on certain points, comparing and contrasting some of her statements as she went along, pointing out incongruities in what she said and asking her what she thought of them. They spoke softly together, so that most of those in the room were leaning forward to hear what was being said. It was as though Suprin had forgotten everyone else in the room, and was unmindful of their needs. Suprin would smile sometimes as he made certain points to the patient. Although he spoke gently, he was not overly gentle with her. "Well now, that's not what you said before, is it?" and, "That doesn't make too much sense to me," were two instances in which he did not permit the patient to wander off certain points that she appeared to want to get away from.

Pursuing that last statement in response to an earlier statement she had made, he queried, "Does it [make sense] to you?"

The patient smiled.
"Does it?" Suprin asked again.
"No," the patient responded.
"Well, what does?"
"I don't know."

Suprin went on to help the patient work toward some clarification of the issues that had thus been raised. When this had reached something of a terminal point, Suprin changed his position in his chair and told her that it was customary for patients to leave the room at this point, after which the doctors would discuss their case.

"Do you want to go?" he asked. Several of the people in the room looked at one another in some surprise at a somewhat unusual procedure. The patient also did not seem to understand. "Do you want to leave the room?" Suprin continued. "How do you feel about leaving?"
"I don't want to."
"You don't?" asked Suprin.
"No," replied the patient. "I want to stay and hear what the doctors are going to say about me."
"Do you want to stay?"
"Yes, I do."
Suprin smiled and turned to the group. "That's perfectly acceptable to me if it is to you people."

The resident and the outside doctor looked at each other, and several of the other residents exchanged glances. There was some restlessness in the room.

"That's all right with me," replied the patient's doctor, looking at the patient. The patient bent her head forward and smiled. The resident eagerly nodded his approval to Dr. Suprin.

There was another pause, both awkward and amused.

"I don't want to put Dr. —— on the spot," said the patient, referring to her private doctor.

"Oh no, you won't be," replied the doctor.

"O.K." said Dr. Suprin, glancing over to the patient. "That means you can stay." The patient lifted her head up and smiled at him. She sat up in her chair and removed her sunglasses as Dr. Suprin turned away from her to deliver his analysis to the assembled doctors. Seeing her do this, several of the nurses exchanged glances.

Dr. Suprin's analysis might have been more incisive had not the patient been present. Nonetheless, it was not overly gentle. Words like "psychosis," "sado-masochistic relationship," "genital," and "pregenital," "dependency," "suicide," and "hacking herself" were used as Suprin felt necessary. The gist of the analysis was that the patient, contrary to the previously expressed psychiatric opinion, *was* capable of entering into a therapeutic relationship with her doctor; that the hospital would keep her until he returned from the vacation he was about to take, at which time she would then be released to re-enter therapy with him. Her doctor agreed to take her back into therapy if she was ready for it. The forcefulness of Suprin's exposition indicated that in his opinion she was ready for such a relationship and that she had been underestimated by the other doctors who had dealt with her.

When these arrangements were agreed upon among the doctors, Suprin turned to the girl and said, "There. That wasn't so bad. Was it?"

The girl smiled and shook her head.

"O.K.?" Suprin inquired quizzically.

The girl nodded. "Thank you, doctor," she said in a small voice. Suprin smiled at her and stood up, and the meeting ended.

Everyone present seemed to feel slightly euphoric. (It is difficult to describe the visually obvious unfolding of this girl during the interview.) Many people left the room with wide grins on their faces. A few appeared a little moist around the eyes. The patient was the same way. She was smiling as she left the room. She turned and again thanked Dr. Suprin, who was walking behind her to the door. Then, as she walked down the corridor toward the ward, she put her dark glasses on again.

Dr. Suprin walked down the stairs toward his office. The observer asked if what he had seen was an unusual procedure. Suprin replied very gruffly:

"It's not too unusual for me. I believe in being open with the patients. I don't believe in all this secrecy crap."

Interpersonal Style as Communicated in Teaching Rounds

The directness and openness of the superintendent came across in most of his interactions with people, including patients. This style of his was not infrequently perceived by others as having a bluntness that was little short of brutality. Both his style, and this evaluation of his style, were operational in an interview he had with a patient in the teaching rounds of another service and in the subsequent discussion of that interview. In the teaching round in question, a first-year resident presented his description and diagnosis of a female patient with whom he had been working. Dr. Suprin then interviewed the patient. The verbal context alone will suffice to communicate the main process of this teaching round.

"Will you tell me what you hope to accomplish by being in the hospital?" Suprin asked.
"I hope to get well," the patient replied.
Suprin: "What does that mean?"
Patient: "To become more mature. Take more responsibility for myself."
Suprin: "What else would you like to do?"
Patient: "I'd like to get my hair fixed."

Suprin: "Yes, it looks like it needs it." He paused. "What else?" he asked.

Patient: "And clean my dress. There's a spot on it. Out, out damned spot."

Suprin: "You know a lot about Shakespeare?"

Patient: "Yes."

Suprin: "You got it from your parents?"

Patient: "Out, out damned spot. Spot . . . spot . . . cream . . . jelly . . . oil."

"Now, stop all that nonsense," Suprin insisted. "You're trying to say something, but I don't know what it is. Talk to me."

The patient smiled. "You're a psychiatrist," she said. "Psychiatrists know what it all means. Spot . . . cream . . ."

"You're not making sense," Suprin interrupted. "Say something sensible."

The patient stopped smiling. "What do you want to know?" she asked.

Suprin: "What do you think about?"

Patient: "I think about a bridge." (Subsequent questioning revealed that the bridge represented a relationship between the patient and her parents.)

Suprin: "What *is* your relation with your parents?"

The patient inhaled sharply. "I'm sorry, Doctor," she said. "I've got to go."

The patient rose and left the room.

After the surprise over the patient's hurried and unexpected departure had subsided, the residents began discussing Suprin's observations and tactics in the situation. One first-year resident seemed particularly taken aback by what he had just witnessed. He entered into discussion with Suprin, and persistently held to his point until Dr. Suprin became quite emphatic about what he had done with this patient.

"Dr. Suprin," said the resident, "You made the point to us previously that patients will do what they think you expect them to do. I noticed that you cut pretty fast into that patient's problem, and perhaps this is why she jumped up and left. Yesterday,

I was very impressed by Dr. Cape [a clinic director] who was here interviewing [at teaching rounds]. He made the point, very well I thought, of letting the schizophrenic set the pace during the interview. You go along with him at this pace whatever it may be. How does that compare with your approach?"

"I know that's Cape's approach," Suprin replied, "and he is very successful with schizophrenics. However, each person has to work out his own way, and we're very different people, he and I. Cape's sort of slow and easy-going, and I'm not. I just went straight to the problem area, that's all. She [the patient] knew those associations were a lot of nonsense. Did you notice the way she grinned when I told her to stop? I don't think you should fool around with those things. I always think there is a lot of time wasted around here with therapists participating in their patients' hallucinations and defenses."

The resident appeared to be unconvinced. He was leaning forward, staring at the floor, shaking his head very slightly during most of Dr. Suprin's response. Then in a quiet voice, without looking up from the floor, he pursued his point of view.

"But how fast should one knife into the significant areas?" asked the resident.

Suprin replied with great emphasis. "It's not a *question of knifing in*," he said. "Just don't fool around! Don't waste time. I'd start by asking her about this thing with her parents."

The resident paused, and then continued, "I guess it's a question of how fast you go deep."

"*Getting to the significant areas is not going deep!*" Suprin replied loudly. "She's got problems with her parents, and she's going to have to go into them if she is going to get better. That's *all*."

The discussion moved to other aspects of the case. Several minutes later, the patient did return. She opened the door, walked deliberately across the room, and sat down beside Dr. Suprin. Suprin looked at the skeptical resident and tapped his heel on the floor. Then he turned to the patient who did not wait to begin. Dropping all the delusional material, she asked for and received clarification as to what was being done by the staff, and what would be done by the staff, about her going home and getting her former therapist back. Suprin informed her that there was some doubt about getting her former therapist back. She nodded her head. She thanked him, and left the room, mumbling so that only those close to her could hear, "I hope I don't have to come back in here again, although who knows? They say the third time is lucky."

Professional Opinions and Role Performance as a Teacher of Therapists

As can be seen, the superintendent had definite opinions about the work of a psychiatrist, and he had his own methods of going about this work. With these opinions and methods, he confronted those about him with the task of reconciling the acerbity of the man with the benignity of most of his statements about mental patients in particular, and people with problems in general. Sticking with the particular one step further, Dr. Suprin was once asked by one of the first-year residents whom he supervised: "How do you treat schizophrenics? What's the best way to help them?" Dr. Suprin's initial response to this very seriously put question was given jokingly.

"There is more than one way to Rome," he replied. "For the first, Cadman would be the best. He would just grunt. Old Cadman is the most empathic person in the world. He's all heart, so to speak. He's got love in his heart for everyone in the world."

Then he responded in a more serious vein to the content of the questions.

"This is number one. You have got to care for them [the patients]. I talk to them like I talk to the staff and to my friends.

It's Mr. Smith, not a case of schizophrenia. It's not a case, it's a person you are dealing with. Have you ever worked around horses? My father owned horses. He had a lumber business. So I got a lot of practice talking to the lower economic classes. I learned to speak straight and forward, better than in a purely academic background. When I want to swear, I swear. Similarly, when I don't want to swear, I don't swear. I let my patient know I care for him, and am interested in him. I talk simply. I say exactly what I mean. I pay attention to the patient, and don't gaze out of the window or try to read a letter that happens to be open on my desk. You should not be struggling with other issues when you should be paying attention to the patient. That's what I meant when I said you should be comfortable when you are interviewing a patient. If you have to go to the bathroom, go before the patient arrives, otherwise you may be fidgeting around in your chair and the patient will interpret it as your not being interested in him, or being angry at him. Sometimes when I have something important like a trustees' meeting coming up, I'll tell the patient, 'Look, I have this trustees' meeting coming up this afternoon, and it's very important to me. So I hope you will excuse me if my mind happens to wander.' Usually they will say something like, 'That's quite all right, Doctor. I will leave a little early to give you more time.' "

The superintendent went on to talk about a therapist's contract with his patient, and about the psychoanalytic theory of schizophrenia. Then he made his fourth point.

"Fourth point. This business about delusions. I don't pay any attention to those. I hear them through for the first time, but if they start again, then I say, 'Stop all that nonsense, I can't understand you. Talk to me in English.' "

The superintendent went on to tell a story about a man who had recently "got by" his secretary—"She's usually pretty good at keeping these sorts of people out of my office, but this one must have smooth-talked his way around her"—and into Dr. Suprin's office. When seated, the man had proceeded to pour forth a very tense story about himself, and had concluded, "What is the matter with me, Doctor?"

"I told him, 'From what I have just heard, I'd say you were a paranoid schizophrenic, and you should get yourself a doctor.' As soon as I said that, the man sat back in the chair with the biggest smile you ever saw. He said, 'I already have a psychiatrist, and that's just what he told me, but I didn't believe him. So he told me to go out and get the diagnosis checked.' " Suprin smiled.

Resident: "You had no trouble telling this man he was a paranoid schizophrenic?"

"No. None whatsoever," Suprin replied.

Resident: "You must feel very comfortable with schizophrenics."

Suprin: "Yes. I do. I like schizophrenics. I treat them as I treat my friends. I guess you could say I care for them. You have to feel comfortable with them. You can't do anything with them if you don't."

Resident: "Weren't you a little worried about coming right out and telling the man he was a paranoid schizophrenic?"

"You know," Suprin replied, "the patients are confused, and since they are confused, they have trouble knowing what is right and what is wrong. It makes it worse if they feel their *doctor* doesn't know either. I think the patients like to know there is someone steering the boat."

The Melding of Position, Performance, and Personality

There were several gradations of the superintendent's involvement in the hospital's operations, from the purely medical and psychiatric to the completely administrative and political components of his role. Our observations indicated that, except in a face-to-face interview with a patient, the professional and the organizational elements of the superintendent's role were often difficult to differentiate. It is customary to think in terms of the opposition between organizational and professional elements in this kind of job, but little understanding of Dr. Suprin and his work in the hospital could be achieved without thinking of the two as positively interrelated: that is, administration as an instrument for professional contribution and professional competence in the conduct of administration.

The personal element also infused itself into this equation. Dr. Suprin enjoyed the "take charge" nature of his administrative involvements. Also he was personally disinclined to engage in the multitudinous interactions with subordinates that some others around him felt were a corollary of taking charge. Dr. Suprin believed his obligations to those in the hospital were best fulfilled by cultivating his relations with the larger professional world beyond the boundaries of the hospital.

Observer: "You do spend quite a bit of time [in your office] undisturbed."

"That was the way I planned it," Suprin replied. "I have been fairly successful. Theoretically, there are only three persons I need see: Cadman, Asche, and [the business officer]. I can't help a certain amount of informal contact, however. Still, I don't see as many people as Sherman [Suprin's predecessor] used to see. He used to see all sorts of people: the head painter, the housekeeper. People like that. I don't see how I can do what I am supposed to do for these people, unless I have more time alone."

After observing the wide variety of contacts that the superintendent initiated or received during the course of most work days, it became clear that "time alone" actually denoted time that was occupied with affairs that were directed more to matters outside the hospital than in it. This time was spent writing, reading, discussing plans and making arrangements over the phone, arranging schedules, and some just plain thinking. The telephone was constantly in use, so that the superintendent was often interactively engaged in his work while physically alone.

The range of the superintendent's activities and contacts was such that it sometimes became difficult to discern what

central organizing principle was at work. Dr. Suprin's clarification of the matter stressed the underlying professional
themes of therapy and pedagogy.

"It is hard to say what my over-all goal is," he said. "To make
sick people well, and in the process, to find out something about
them, to help us make them better faster in the future. For education, it [his goal] is to teach people how they work; psychologically, sociologically, and physiologically together. As you know,
Cadman and I stress the psychological and the psychoanalytic.
Asche stresses the physiological. Nadel and Jerome [two other
staff people] stress the sociological. The residents have a chance
to work with them all."

These were the goals that gave direction to many of the superintendent's activities. It has already been indicated that
Dr. Suprin found it difficult to realize these goals as much as
he would have liked. He often expressed discontent over the
existing state of the art in psychiatry, and his concern over
lack of teaching time has already been mentioned. However,
the conflict of limitations between the goals he held and the
commitments he had developed was held in check by the satisfaction he derived from the liaison and coordinative work he
performed as an administrator. This is indicated above, for
instance, in the rapidity with which Dr. Suprin moved from
thoughts about his goals to thoughts about the organization of
people around him for the accomplishment of these goals.

This came up more clearly in another context. In chatting
about some observations that had been made about him by
the writer, the superintendent reported the following source
of satisfaction.

"I think the thing I pride myself most about in life, if anything, is my ability to get good, high-caliber people working for
me and with me, such as I have here in the hospital."

In this and in other ways the distinction between the man
as a psychiatrist with professional aims and as a superintend-

ent with organizational objectives was impossible to maintain. From Dr. Suprin's point of view, these two functions of the superintendent's role should not be distinct. They should, by necessity, overlap. He stated that point in the following manner.

"Dr. Bolen [a clinic director] is an administrator from 8 to 1, and a practicing clinician from 1 to 6. This is a good thing. Even the superintendent of a state hospital should carry two, three, or four patients a day, depending on how long a day he likes to work. It keeps his hand in clinically. He gets out of date.

"When I was [superintendent at another hospital] there was a patient scalded in a bath. When I got there, I found the patient, a nurse, and the surgeon on the ward. The clinical director was not there. He was down with the plumber looking at the pipes. What the hell does he know about pipes and gauges? He should be up on the ward, helping the surgeon to get the wherewithal to stick into the patient's blood.

"A hospital with an all-visiting staff can have a lay administrator, but a hospital with a permanent staff needs a medical man at the top; otherwise the staff gets to thinking he doesn't understand them, that he doesn't know what's going on. That's my opinion, anyway."

Much of Dr. Suprin's thinking and behavior as a psychiatrist was reflected in his thinking and behavior as superintendent. His approach to mental patients and to psychiatric theories, and his manner of expressing himself on professional matters, set the stage for many of the attitudes and interactions that comprised much of the administrative context of his job. As he said of himself, "I talk to them [patients] like I talk to the staff and to my friends." Issues of interpersonal style, directiveness, and decision making existed in settings that were both professional and administrative. An example of such a setting occurred when one of the staff doctors asked the superintendent to read and comment on several abstracts that the consultant had written. These abstracts dealt with clinical and theoretical matters, and the superintendent addressed them as the professional psychiatrist that he was. However, in communicating his comments about the abstracts, he was communicating to a subordinate within hospital organization, and the difference in their points of view was one that diverged from the strictly professional into differences that were outwardly of an administrative nature.

The superintendent read through the abstracts with the service consultant in question, and commented as he went along.

"This business about," Suprin read, " '. . . permit a meaningful growth . . .' That is inaccurate. Nobody *permits* somebody else to grow. In fact, they usually do quite the reverse. The kids *take* it. (Vigorous grasping motion with the hand and arm.) That's the whole thing that culminates in adolescence. . . . you can't *permit* someone to have a bowel movement. If he is a kid, and you are the teacher, you can *permit* him to leave the room in order to have the bowel movement, but he's going to have it anyway. . . . *Permission* is not the right word. You can't *permit* a patient to get well, or not to get well. You can aid, abet, or impede, but you cannot permit. That is all any doctor can do. Getting well and getting sick are not in the authoritarian, administrative area. *Permission* is a bad word."

The View of Life Underlying a Patterned Role Performance

The above statement contains the gist of Dr. Suprin's view about the nature of personal growth and development in the circumambient subordinacies and superordinacies of social existence. The struggle for *autonomy* was a theme he sounded, and an issue he raised, in many of his teaching and administrative interactions in the hospital. He felt strongly about such matters as these, and he made no secret of his feelings in the several audiences that made up the whole of the organization below him in the hospital hierarchy. He was an assertively individualistic person in his manner of speaking, in his behavior as senior administrator of the hospital, and in his approach to psychotherapy. He preferred to operate in settings in which there were either few people or very many. He did not like small groups as work or as therapeutic settings, although he recognized that good work was being done by others of his staff in these settings. He detested the unctuous, id-less attitudes that seemed to him often to arise from people and settings devoted to small group work.

His view of man gave more room to assertive behavior, individualistic styles of life, and latent destructive motivations than seemed to be encompassed in the conceptual scheme of many of those interested in small groups. He considered that one of the problems faced by mental patients was a "lack of love," but he also stressed the reality, the persistence, and the unavoidability of the phenomenon of hate. More than once he stated his thought that the problem of aggression was what faced modern man, much as the problem of sexuality had faced the mid-Victorian society in which Freud pioneered. He pointed to the evolution in Freud's thinking, moving from an interest in sexuality in the life of the individual to an interest in the aggression and destructiveness in the life of society. In his opinion, psychoanalysis had tended to go back rather than forward in this trend of interest and concern. He pointed out that, according to his observations, a group could tolerate a high level of free-floating sexuality, much more than was possible in the past, and much more than could presently be tolerated when it came to disagreement and hostility. "If it weren't for television and the turnpikes," he joked, "I don't know what people would do with their aggressions."

Dr. Suprin communicated these notions with some facility. One morning he was writing a speech during his "quiet hour." The speech was in commemoration of a colleague of his who had died. The model that Dr. Suprin was going to use for the speech was that of the identification, selection, and fostering of talent. To this end, he was reviewing a paper on creativity that summarized the relevant literature. At one point he chuckled and read aloud the findings of one researcher to the effect that the technique of brainstorming was found to produce nothing in the way of new or creative ideas. In fact, there was evidence that group processes hindered creativity. Dr. Suprin laughed.

"That's what I've thought all along," he remarked to the observer. "This [group dynamics] business is just a lot of horse shit, if you want a mild word for it. There have been more murders committed in the name of group process! Of course, I am very opinionated in this matter. I know that. But it is like most things. There is a basically worthwhile idea there, but it gets twisted all to hell.

"It is like what happened to Freud's ideas. You know, he was a stern and really rather rigid individual, and people took what he described and twisted it to mean something that he never meant in the first place. Free expression and all that. Unblocking all your frustrations. It's just so much nonsense. That's not what he meant at all.

"With this groupy business, they've taken the idea that people sometimes find certain other people stimulating, and that people are a little bit interdependent, and have blown it up to this [group] stuff. I don't think people are creative in groups. It's nice to read research that supports all your private ideas.

"I think that discussions are a fine thing. It is good to keep the pot boiling for a while, like I am doing with the research discussions we're having these days in the hospital. I think biologists and mathematicians are inclined to make decisions too fast. I don't think that is good. If things get set too fast, then the chances are that people will get hostile or defensive toward the original decisions. I like to keep the pot boiling a while in these discussions. I don't mind holding off a decision. I believe there has to be an adequate interchange of information, but sooner or later someone is going to have to make a decision. So at some point, I say, 'Here is what we are going to do.' Everybody can't be boss, and it is the boss's responsibility to make the decisions. That is what I think anyway. If you don't make the decisions, you are not filling your responsibility, and you should not have become boss in the first place. I tell them, 'This is how we will do things.' If someone has a violent objection, we discuss it. But it is amazing how people can work with a decision, even if they disagree with it. At least they have something to work with."

"You distinguish between communication and decision making in groups," the observer remarked.

"Yes, absolutely," Suprin replied. "It's good to know where everybody stands, but somebody has to make the decisions. Imagine foreigners coming to this country to see what the United States is like, and going to Bethel to find out. What a screwy picture they would get!"

Dr. Suprin related an experience on a WHO committee, where another American doctor had tried to use his Bethel experience. "The two Englishmen on the committee—just typical Englishmen, if you know the English—they got so mad at him, I thought they would kill him. Well, they settled it by not letting him be chairman any more, which was too bad, because I thought he had some good ideas. . . .

"But there are a lot of good people interested in this group business. Take Paul [Cadman]. He's interested in working with groups, and damn good at it. But he's got the same problem, too. He can't make decisions. Sometimes I have to beat him over the head to make decisions. He will come in here and talk things over with me, and I will listen, and sooner or later I'll have to say, 'Now Paul, you should do this.' Four times out of five, he has thought things out and has reached the same conclusions as I have, but he just won't make the decisions. You have to push him a bit."

The superintendent succinctly described his own attitude toward groups in the above-mentioned interaction with one of his staff. The doctor asked Dr. Suprin about group psychotherapy. Suprin replied:

"You better see Paul about that. He is interested in that area. I don't know anything about group therapy. My concept of group therapy is getting a group to do what I want them to do."

The Superintendent's "Philosophy" and His Style of Interaction

Dr. Suprin's communication of these personal opinions and characteristics often elicited interpersonal dynamics that were quite disruptive of purpose in group settings. A statement he made about his relations with people—in this particular instance, his relations with patients—highlighted the difficulties he experienced in certain of these settings.

"I'm not particular about passive characters," he told a resident. "I get annoyed at them. I can't help feeling they need a good boot in the rear. I don't treat them myself. I know they annoy me."

In group meetings with his professional peers—medical executive committee meetings, for example—Dr. Suprin handled this communication of affect and hierarchy deftly and with considerable light humor. In such a setting, people tended to respond to him with relative equanimity, and a subtly democratizing joviality.[1] They also received definite comprehensions (as it turned out, not always the ones Dr. Suprin had in mind) of the purposive thrust of his statements. However, in meetings with subordinate personnel, people in positionally submissive relation to Dr. Suprin, his communications and superordinacy tended to be more ponderous, and the otherwise mitigating humor was often absent or quite misplaced. In these settings, people not infrequently became upset, finding his communications anything but constructive, informative, or amusing; the purposive aspects of Dr. Suprin's communications thereby tended to be over-

[1] In meetings of people who held positions of some superiority over him, Dr. Suprin tended to be polite, deferential, and quietly businesslike in a way that was not frequently to be observed in the settings outlined above. "My," he exclaimed to the trustees of the hospital during one of their meetings, "I never cease to be impressed by the large amounts of work you gentlemen can dispatch in such short periods of time. I wish we had more like you."

looked or misconstrued in the undercurrent of upheaval that ensued. For example, in the course of a meeting with the heads of nonmedical departments in the hospital, Dr. Suprin gave forth with a series of abrupt statements and caustic remarks, the nature of which can be illustrated by three short excerpts.

Nurse: ". . . the nursing service has made several suggestions about the pool table, Dr. Suprin. We have that area covered all the time."

Suprin: "Hell, nobody's ever covered that area. Why I've been through there lots of times and couldn't find a damn person anywhere."

Nurse: "Oh, it's covered, Dr. Suprin."

Suprin: "Well, I guess it's just been my misfortune to be there when nobody was around."

Nurse: "But, Dr. Suprin!" She interrupted herself, perhaps deciding not to take the matter any further.

Silence. No one stirred in the room. No one took up the subject, or turned to another.

Dr. Suprin looked around, appeared somewhat surprised and a little ill at ease. "I'm sorry," he said, "I didn't mean to imply. . . ." His voice trailed off. He did not finish the sentence. He turned to one of the papers before him on the desk, and read out the next topic on the agenda. . . .

Later in the meeting, Dr. Suprin looked at one of the women sitting at the side of the room. "Are you Jones or Smith?"

"I'm Jones," she replied.

"It's your damn first names that get me mixed up," Suprin observed as he wrote a notation on a piece of paper. There was another awkward pause. (The paradox here was that Dr. Suprin was *trying to help* the observer, who had requested the names of the people attending the meeting.)

Further on in the meeting, the business officer suggested to Dr. Suprin, "Do you think we could start a program to check everybody's keys?"

Nurse: "The nurses have already checked their own keys."

Dietician: "Ours were too."

Dr. Suprin turned to the dietician. "How long ago was that?" he asked. "Twenty years?"

The two of them stared at each other briefly. "Something like that, I guess," she replied, looking away.

These interpersonal dynamics were not confined to transactions across the boundary between medical and nonmedical personnel. Similar incidents arose within the medical-psychiatric hierarchy that, perhaps because of the violation of something approximating a code of professional unity, were more unexpected and more electric in their effect throughout the hospital. One of the service consultants described a difficult patient management situation that had arisen on one of the services, into which Dr. Suprin's name and influence had been introjected.

"I don't know how Suprin put this to the resident," the consultant concluded. "Whether he stated it as an opinion, or whether he gave it as an edict. But anyway, the way it came back to us was as an edict. You know the way Suprin is, or at least the way most people hear him. Anything he says, even if it is only an opinion, he says so vigorously that most people can't help hearing it as an order. At least, that is the way it is with the residents. I don't know the way it is with the rest of the staff. Would you know?"

Observer: "He certainly seems to have a powerful way of presenting himself. I guess this comes across in meetings, doesn't it?"

Consultant: "I know he has executive committee meetings, but they seem to be getting fewer, I think. And I think he used to hold some sort of meeting with the nonmedical department heads. You know, the plumber and the dietician: people like that. I understand they have been dropped altogether. I guess it's because he scares people more than he realizes. I mean, they were supposed to get together to discuss things, and express their own opinions. I presume he would expect to give them his opinion and have them give him back their own, but he does it so *forcefully* that they just get *scared* and won't talk."

Notice how the service consultant turned the direction of attention away from the medical hierarchy. It was easier to talk about these phenomena outside the boundaries of one's own group. To return to such occurrences within the medical group, another event will illustrate the impact that Dr. Suprin sometimes had on people. A senior resident entered Dr. Suprin's office to inquire whether one of the patients could be allowed to stay on in the hospital. He entered the office diffidently, stood uneasily at some distance from Dr. Suprin's desk, and spoke softly in almost a mumble, so that it was difficult for the observer and presumably also for Dr. Suprin to hear what he said. Of the several ways of approaching Dr. Suprin that the residents were observed to use, this was the surest way of eliciting a rough answer.

"He's been living here for nothing," Dr. Suprin cut in. "The answer is *no*. *N.O.* I don't blame them for sucking on a tit for as long as they can, but it's gone on long enough. He can go to an outside psychiatrist. . . . What's that? No, he may *not* come in here, and if he becomes acutely ill again, he'll probably go to [a state hospital]. Tell him that! He's a custodial patient. . . . What? . . . Nuts. We have been providing him with a hotel room, and have for the last two years. Let him go to the Y.M.C.A."

Not all, or even many, of Dr. Suprin's communications of affect and hierarchy were as forceful and as explicit as this, but even the more fleeting ones were effective and remained long in people's memories. One day, at noon staff conference, Dr. Suprin introduced one of the service consultants to the assembled residents as the speaker of the day.

Dr. Suprin sat on the table at the front of the room. "Dr. Stanley is going to talk today," he said. "He's behind the blackboard right now." He laughed. "He's hiding." (Laughter)

At this point, Dr. Stanley poked his head out from behind the movable blackboard that was also at the head of the room. He had put some notes on the board, but one of the cleaning men had wiped them off before the conference. He was writing them up again.

Dr. Stanley finished putting his data back on the blackboard. As Suprin took a seat at the front of the room, Stanley turned the board around so that the audience could see what he had transcribed. He was about to begin his talk.

Suprin took a good look at the board and said in a voice audible to all, "Well, the cleaning man showed rare good taste, I would say."

Loud laughter greeted his remark, and Stanley shifted around uneasily, waiting till he could begin.[2]

Affective Specialization of Response to the Superintendent's Role Performance

It was also interesting to note what came into the residents' minds to talk with Dr. Suprin about. He perceived them as coming to him with "tricky legal problems," and several instances of this were observed. However, there was also another theme that occurred more than once in what the residents talked with Dr. Suprin about. Dr. Suprin usually stayed after a staff conference such as the one cited above, and spoke with those residents who approached him. On one such occasion, a resident recounted the following story. A burglar alarm had gone off early one hot Sunday morning across the street from his apartment. That evening, after a ratty day—the baby would not go to sleep—the resident looked up the

---

[2] This incident also illustrates the danger of any attempt to remove interpersonal styles of behavior from the purposive contexts in which they occur, and in which they are observed. Dr. Suprin's communications of affect and hierarchy were not divorced from the purposes he wanted people in the hospital to address. *At the end of this particular conference,* Suprin stood up and with great emphasis of voice and gesture, said, "My usually benevolent attitudes which apply in so many areas" (laughter) "do *not* apply to teaching. Teaching is *the* No. 1 responsibility of this outfit. I don't want any sloughing off or skipping of teaching responsibilities. That is why we are all here. If it comes to my attention that somebody is not fulfilling his teaching obligations, he will have *me* to deal with."

owner of the building. The landlord was an immigrant, extremely fearful of authority, and would not enter the tenant's premises to turn off the alarm. The landlord maintained that the tenant "owned" the store. By this time, the resident was reaching the limit of his patience. He became extremely angry and threatened to enter the store himself, whereupon the landlord called in the police. Eventually the tenant arrived upon the scene and turned off the alarm. However, the incident was reported in the newspaper and was causing the resident some problems with patients.

Another resident then recounted the story of his driving home from the lake—where the tenant in the above story had been—with his family. On the way home he had stopped at a roadside restaurant and had received some very rude service from "an ugly little man." The resident had wanted to hit the man, but he got himself and his family out of the restaurant instead. Nonetheless, he was for some time thereafter "almost giddy" with the desire to go back and punch the man.

A third resident in the group around Suprin then told another story. One of his colleagues, while a medical student, had on his way out to the suburbs picked up two young men who were hitchhiking. These boys had attempted to take his car and his money, but he was an extraordinarily powerful person. (The resident demonstrated with his hands the girth of his friend's musculature.) He beat up both the boys, inflicting broken ribs and dislocated shoulders. He then brought them into court on charges of assault and battery, and the judge had found in his favor.

It was not often that such a clear-cut chain of associations got expressed by those interacting with Dr. Suprin. The incident illustrates what was usually a more covert dynamic in many of the interactional networks surrounding him. He opened up for other people the aggressive component of his psychic energy, and their own. He accomplished this with a directness that only the most obtuse or defensive of people could overlook. He usually did this with such control that his listeners were prompted to come to grips with their own aggressive feelings and energies, from whose potential uncontrollability they had shied away. "He's the sort of man," said one resident of Dr. Suprin, "who, if I hadn't eaten for two weeks, and he told me to eat supper, I wouldn't eat supper." The resident delivered this statement unsmilingly, but with a relaxation noticeably different from his more usual affability and excitability. Here was a man upon whom this resident, along with his storytelling peers, could try out the burden of considerable aggression without having to be overly anxious about that person collapsing under the load. Here also was a man who could demonstrate some of the productive uses of these feelings, both by deed, as a role model, and by word, as a teacher. The pedagogical aspect often arose in Dr. Suprin's supervision of residents.

Dr. Rothstein, a resident, said that he had had a fight with a patient over her rejection of the medication he had prescribed for her. He had forced her to take certain pills, and had stayed with her to make sure she did not throw them up.

Dr. Richards, another resident, added with a smile: "A fight? I'll say it was a fight. And I thought I heard shouting before! There were three of us in the next room—you know, three first-year residents, just new to the hospital. Boy, did we jump!"

Dr. Rothstein: "Yeah. Well, it got pretty loud, I must say. From both sides, too, I might add. Since that, she has been calm."

Dr. Suprin: "Sure. The S.O.B. cares for me after all."

Dr. Rothstein: "What's that?"

Dr. Suprin, in a louder voice: *"The S.O.B. cares for me after all.* That's what she's saying. . . . Be normal. You were afraid of her anger."

Reinforcement of an Affectively Specialized Self-Concept

Dr. Suprin's self-concept had strength and definition apart from the responses of others in the hospital to him. However, other people's responses to him did set the stage for him to elaborate further the dominant elements of this self-concept, and he often availed himself of this opportunity. He jokingly stated to his residents that patients returning to find out how he was, "find me just as thin and mean as ever." He referred to a constituent element in his conception of himself as "cutting throats all over the place."

These were expressions of one highly visible aspect of the superintendent's personality and his role in the organization. It would be easy, however, to give disproportionate emphasis to this one facet. Dr. Suprin usually did so himself. There was a compelling forcefulness to his feelings and thoughts about this issue. He often made—and others believed—statements about his toughness that were extreme and that were later recognized as such by those who knew him, and by himself. A further indication of their extremity was the sense of injury he sustained in situations where it became apparent to him that his statements on this issue had been taken at their face value.

The statement, "He was a very good hater," denotes the pattern implicit in many of these data. As the observation of Dr. Suprin progressed, however, it appeared that he got more enjoyment from his perusal of this model of himself than from actually living as a cynosure of enmity and abomination. As the reader will see, the superintendent was not alone in this situation. The clinical director liked to think of himself as a man of peasant-like simplicity, but he was no "hick." The assistant superintendent was highly attracted to forms of athletic expressiveness, but he himself was "worried . . . about getting into a sweat." This contradiction in self-concept seemed applicable to the superintendent insofar as he was a "good hater."

Dr. Suprin was aware of this distinction between (1) how he liked to think and talk about himself, plus the role model that he thereby helped to create around himself, and (2) the sort of interpersonal transactions that he was really comfortable with on a long-term basis. Now and then he would make statements to people to signal to them that their conception of his specialized affective role in the organization should not be carried too far. In a variety of contexts, for instance, Suprin would half-humorously point out that if residents wanted to keep patients in the hospital, they should consult Cadman. If they wanted to get rid of patients, they should come to Suprin. Cadman always recommended that patients should be "kept on." Suprin always recommended that they be "thrown out." However, in case the observer or anyone else should over-extrapolate such remarks, Dr. Suprin not infrequently made statements containing corrective implications. On the occasion of the admission of a particular patient to the hospital, Dr. Suprin turned to the observer and remarked:

"That Crosier is a tough nut. I don't know whether he would have let the patient in. He probably would have. I'm soft on patients. I always take them in."

Thus, without any explicit statements about himself, Dr. Suprin did the unusual. He spread some of the toughness around the executive system, and accepted some of the softness for himself. But it was treated very much as an aside, a necessary footnote in Dr. Suprin's over-all presentation of himself in his everyday world of work in the hospital.

The Resulting Balance

What was the over-all balance of costs and rewards that the superintendent experienced as the result of doing the work he did, in the manner he did it? How profitable in his psychological economy were his dealings with other people, and their dealings with him? How productive were his administrative relations with others, and what were the consequences of these relations in his own personal development? What mixture of integrity, disgust, and despair appeared to be emerging in the superintendent's continuing development? These are the questions we address in attempting to delineate Dr. Suprin's balance of sociopsychological profits and losses.

Dr. Suprin described in the following terms his understanding of the reasons why he was elected to the presidency of a professional organization, this particular organization meaning a very great deal to him. In fact, he referred to his election in the superlative: "The greatest honor," he termed it.

"They needed someone who could tell people what to do. They needed a troubleshooter sort of a guy. Somebody that could take things apart and put them back together again. So they elected me. That's the sort of work I am good at, and that's the sort of work I enjoy doing."

There was an aura of concreteness and daring about the superintendent. He was a man who was able—skilled enough and daring enough—to take things apart and put them back together again. This was observed more in an organizational sense than in any immediate physical sense. The superintendent moved with adroitness and economy, but the manipulation of the physical world around him was never seen to give him any particular enjoyment. He joked about his distaste for such things as cutting grass. He preferred to do "real" work instead, and for him real work was not primarily physical or concrete. Nonetheless, the superintendent enjoyed the aura that permeated the view he and others held of the man who was Dr. Suprin. He devoted a certain amount of effort to fostering this image of himself. He drove a cream-colored foreign sports car, and he enjoyed chatting with his colleagues in the hospital about sports cars in general; his own in particular. Such occasions did not often arise, but when they did, these men sometimes kidded him on the manner in which they fancied he drove to work. "The Parkway Sweepstakes," one called it. Another mused about the police trying to give him a ticket, but not being able to catch up with him. Had he ever driven his car at top speed? No, he was getting too old for that, but he had had it up over 100 m.p.h. He continued.

"There's a newer model that's being built now, though it hasn't got to the American market yet. When it does, I'm going to turn this one in for a newer model."

"Have your interests taken you under the hood of a sports car very often?" asked the observer.

"Not any more," Suprin replied. "I don't have the time. I used to build racing engines, though. Did you know that? I used to build the engines, and then hire a driver and a mechanic. We toured the country [to participate in various auto races]."

This concreteness—being able to take things apart and put them back together again with his hands—was a theme that recurred in his account of the development of his career.

"When I was doing my internship, I looked up to an ob-gyn man. Many of the problems in gynecology are psychiatric, and the reason so many of this man's patients got well is that he was a good practical psychiatrist. I was interested in doing research. I had done some research in physiology on the side as a medical student. I thought that the psychiatric outfit didn't know a thing about research, so therefore it would be a good area to get into. Perhaps I could teach those guys something about research. Then one day I met [the director of the organization in which Suprin was working] standing in line at the cafeteria, and he mentioned to me a fellowship in psychiatry, and asked me why I didn't apply for it. It was quite a thing to have offered to me, right there in the cafeteria line! So we talked it over. I had decided that surgery was not very exciting, although I liked it. I like to do things with my hands. And gyn work is mostly psychiatric, so I decided to move in on a provisional basis. Then I got into things, and never got out."

The variety of things into which he had gotten himself was considerable. His interests, involvements, and commitments were such that Dr. Suprin was often extremely pressed for time. If disagreements arose, or misunderstandings persisted, they could well be carried on for weeks without any adequate opportunity for their discussion. This required a considerable amount of basic agreement between the superintendent and those who worked closely with him in the administration of the hospital. It also required sufficient maturity on the part of these people that they could hold such disagreements and misunderstandings—and the feelings that went with them— to themselves and not spread them throughout the organization, developing allies and enemies for whom the disagreements would then become matters of principle. Such basic agreements and such maturity, except for relatively isolated incidents and individuals, prevailed. However, Dr. Suprin's schedule regularly required him to move from one engagement to the next, without attaining closure on the first. Sometimes he appeared to decide on issues largely because there was no further time to talk about them. More often, however, the resolution of issues would be postponed, the superintendent expecting the others involved to work on the issues in his absence. It was not uncommon that these others had only a hazy notion of what was expected of them, or what exactly had been delegated.

From a different point of view, Dr. Suprin also experienced the same phenomenon. He saw this as one of the long-standing constraints on the development of his interests.

"There's never enough time for me to do all the things I've wanted to do. I wanted to be an engineer, and I wanted to be a lawyer. I had a hard time to make up my mind to go to medical school, but after I was there for two weeks, I was sure it was the right thing. I like diseases of the heart and chest very much, too. I wish I were quadruplicates or octoplicates to get all the things done that I have in mind. I wrote a lot [about the] laws for mental health . . . , so I have fulfilled my legal ambitions. I also became quite a well-known court psychiatrist, because my boss didn't like to go, so I went in his place. And . . . I've helped build so many buildings that I got plenty of that. I didn't get to build them. I just got to plan them, that's all."

Whatever the reason, the superintendent worked a long day and a hard day. This was such a distinguishing characteristic of Dr. Suprin's behavior in the hospital that the question arose as to how typical this level of activity was for him. This question was raised during one of the tours of inspection he took by himself occasionally, unannounced, through the wards of the hospital.

"Have you always worked as hard as I see you working these days?" asked the observer. "Are you working less or more than you are used to?"

"I've always worked like this," Suprin replied. "It's my rural immigrant background. I learned my work habits in those days, and have stuck to them since."

"So you don't feel you are pushing in any way?" asked the observer.

"Oh, no," Suprin replied. "There are so many things I want to do that I don't get time to do them all. I can't stand sitting around doing nothing. Sometimes though—like mowing the grass —I have to be pushed.

"Cadman works just as hard. He doesn't get in as early as I do, but he has often seen one or two patients at his home before coming in, and he's usually here to seven, eight, or nine at night."

Sometimes the hectic nature of the superintendent's world of work did seem to get the better of him for fleeting periods of time. The occasions when it appeared this was happening were only seconds long. Then, the superintendent would "play a little trick" on himself and re-attach himself to the on-going flow of events around him. Usually during such periods of time he was mute, perhaps not even thinking of what was going on. On one occasion, when the presence of the observer coincided with this tenuous state of detachment, the superintendent mellowed his stance toward work and activity.

"Perhaps I have too many interests," he said. "It has been fun for me, but maybe I didn't get as much accomplished as if I'd drawn a bead on something and really worked on it."

But such ruminations were not typical of him. A statement he made about his interest in cars reflects his great immersion in work.

"Cars are my only hobby," he said. "Otherwise there is nothing I like better than to work."

In another context, he stated his continuing and open-ended engagement in the development of psychiatry in a way that clearly denoted his attachment to professional endeavor.

"I always have something more—about three or four different projects—to do," he said. "When I get them done, maybe I'll go into surgery next."

CHAPTER 5

The Clinical Director: Building the Motivation, Skills, and Insights of Future Therapists

THE OVER-ALL FRAMEWORK of analysis of this chapter is the same as that of Chapter 4. We shall begin by establishing the purposive orientations that underlay the clinical director's observed behavior and then move on to an analysis of the personal dynamics and interpersonal consequences of that behavior.

THE PURPOSIVE CONTEXT OF ADMINISTRATION

THE ACTIVITIES of the day had for Dr. Cadman, the clinical director, as for the other executives, both the immediate objective of maintaining hospital operations and the longer-term vectors that characterized the individual's professional interests and his personal idiosyncrasies. Our analysis will move from the activities of the day through the professional interests expressed therein, toward the personality that was being expressed as the clinical director went about the business of managing the clinical services and the residency training program.

A Long Day's Journey into Life

Dr. Cadman also began work early in the morning. At 6:30 A.M. he began seeing patients in his office at home. He usually arrived at the hospital around 9 A.M., read over the morning reports, phoned the chief residents on the services to clarify points in the reports when this was necessary, and then went in to make his daily report to the superintendent. After the report, he would often return to his office, open his morning mail, and look through some of the papers accumulating on his desk. Frequently, residents would pass down the corridor at this time, and finding him alone in his office, they would drop in to talk over a variety of difficulties with him. He would then go off to take a teaching round on one of the services, and this would take over an hour. After rounds, he would sometimes take a cup of coffee in the cafeteria, chatting with residents or whoever else could find a place around the table.

Returning to his office in the latter part of the morning, Dr. Cadman would attend to a few details with his secretary, and would spend the time from then till 1 P.M. teaching medical students, in supervision with residents, or sometimes take a patient. At 1 P.M., after a brief lunch, he would often see another patient.

The early afternoon was another time when residents would frequently drop into his office. Then, as the afternoon progressed, there was sometimes a meeting to be attended, an interview with patients as requested in consultation by other doctors, or a session or two with patients of his own. Around 5 P.M. any resident with matters of pressing importance to discuss was often able to see Dr. Cadman briefly between patients. In the evening Dr. Cadman would see one or two more patients, or perhaps attend a professional meeting.

"Open Door" Interactions with Residents

The two points that Dr. Cadman stressed most strongly about the organization of his workday were (1) his work with patients and (2) his accessibility to residents. The first was beyond the scope of this study. On the second, he volunteered, "Why don't I see more patients at home? I see them here at the hospital so that if a resident really wants to see me, if something really important comes up, I can always make myself available."

Instances in which this was put into practice were not difficult to observe. One morning, after Dr. Cadman had returned from Dr. Suprin's office, a second-year resident dropped in to see Dr. Cadman. The resident reviewed his thinking on a difficult case he had been trying to treat. Dr. Cadman listened to the resident for about 20 minutes, interjecting an occasional question. After this, the resident concluded by restating his desire to continue his patient in treatment. Dr. Cadman smiled and nodded. "You've got a lot to give," he observed. The resident thanked him and left the room. Dr. Cadman turned to the observer.

"That was an example of my open door policy," he observed. "What suffered here [during his time with the resident]? My paper work. This is probably a reversal of what would go on at a larger hospital like the [hospital he worked in before coming to the M.P.I.], where individual patient care is—I wouldn't say sacrificed—has less priority than administration. That is largely due to Dr. Suprin letting it be that way, because he wants it that way. He and I agreed on it, and if I don't get this work done for him by tomorrow [concerning residency applications for the next academic year], he won't chew my ass off."

Preferred Mode of Interaction: Therapeutic and Didactic

Dr. Cadman's approach was sometimes a little surprising to residents who brought their difficulties to him. This was particularly the case with new residents. Dr. Cadman attempted to make clear his wish for *them* to assume decision-making responsibility for the patients they were dealing with, and this was sometimes at variance with any expectations on the part of residents that they would be told what to do. These issues were usually worked on early in a resident's career in the hospital. One resident, new to the hospital, came into

Cadman's office after his return from his teaching round of that morning.

Resident: "I was wondering, since you are one of my supervisors, whether you want us to bring to you, as supervisor, all our major problems before they become problems, or should we only bring the cases in which we are actually beginning to have some difficulties. For instance, if a patient of mine starts making acute suicidal statements, should I let you know the moment he does so, or should I carry it along on the hopes that he will get over it, and only let you know if he actually makes an attempt on his life? As a supervisor, what would you want us to do?"

Cadman: "Do it any way you want."

Resident (Pause) : "I don't get you."

Cadman: "As a supervisor, my only function is to be helpful to you."

Resident (Nod) : "O.K." (Exit)

That was one of Dr. Cadman's main themes in presenting himself to his residents: that he was in the hospital to be helpful to them, not to tell them what to do. In this, he was setting aside some of his prerogatives as the clinical director, but an interesting paradox existed in that he was not averse to utilizing the prerogatives of his position in his *support* of residents. This was demonstrated in an interaction with one of the chief residents. The chief entered Cadman's office on this occasion, looking considerably less carefree than was his custom.

"How's it going?" Cadman asked.

"Badly," the chief replied. He put a piece of paper on Cadman's desk. Cadman signed. This paper was apparently a request for special nursing services for a patient. "We presented —— [a female suicidal patient] to Dr. —— [a staff doctor] today. He said that the therapist should accept no responsibility for keeping the patient alive, and that he should tell her so. That's better for the therapist, because now he can do some work, but of course the responsibility falls on someone else."

Cadman: "Your shoulders look broad."

Chief: "They are getting narrower."

Cadman: "They look just as broad to me. It just *feels* that way."

Chief: "Well, anyway, I feel pressure from the 'administration' to cut down on Specials, but I want to put this woman on Specials because I think she needs it."

Cadman: "Your clinical judgment comes first."

Chief: "I can feel comfortable with her on Specials, but I would not feel comfortable with her not on Specials."

Cadman: "Don't sacrifice your clinical judgment for money. You can always get more money, but you can't get a life once it's gone. You can quote me on that."

Chief: "Fine." (Exit) [1]

Facilitating the Work of Others versus Directing Others

Dr. Cadman's desire to help residents take full command of their own clinical work was perfectly genuine. However, his position in the organization did make it difficult for him to communicate unequivocally along such nonhierarchal lines. His own responsibilities for the care and treatment of the patients in the hospital made his stance on this issue unclear.

---

[1] That chief's name was mentioned in another context in the superintendent's office. It illustrated something of the difference between the superintendent and the clinical director insofar as their interpersonal reflexes of control were concerned. Dr. Suprin was advising a resident about a patient.

"Till you've made up your mind," he said, "don't go deep. Character disorders will play their doctors like violins. If [the chief] won't administer her [the patient], I will."

Dr. Suprin was trying to help the resident to do what he wanted (to treat the patient). His intentions were the same as those of Dr. Cadman in the incident to which this is a footnote. It is more than superficial differences in interpersonal style between these two men—differences that Dr. Suprin referred to on a number of occasions as being superficial and unimportant—that were highlighted in this crystallization of events. Cadman was attempting to help by getting someone else to take responsibility. Suprin offered to help by doing it himself.

When things were going well, he could do what he preferred to do. He could help other people to do the things *they* thought best. When things were going poorly, he had to try to step in and institute a few remedial actions that *he* thought best. The residents often responded to these ambiguities by selectively perceiving one aspect of his role *or* the other. Some perceived him as *therapist:* helping them to clarify their thoughts and emotions. Others perceived him as *administrator:* indicating, however indirectly, what they should do. Those in the latter category viewed Cadman's nondirectiveness with some disbelief. We have seen one instance of this already. Those in the former category found it difficult to listen effectively to what he had to say when he was trying specifically to get them to do something. An interesting instance of these mixed signals occurred one day shortly after Dr. Cadman had arrived for work at the hospital. He reviewed the morning report sheets, then phoned to the chief resident of one of the services to clarify a situation that had been reported. In seven minutes, the chief was down at Cadman's office, accompanied by a second-year resident from the service.

9:07 A.M. The chief and a second-year resident entered Dr. Cadman's office to discuss what they were going to do with a patient with a history of repeated escapes from the hospital. This patient had just been returned to the hospital by the police, suffering from starvation and dehydration. After the descriptive and explanatory phases of the meeting had passed:

"What are you going to do about it now?" Cadman asked.

Chief: "I used to think that these [attempts on the part of the patient to get jobs] were flights into health, but now I think there is very little health in them."

Cadman: "Is she asking to be taken care of completely for a while? Have you thought of sending her to a state hospital where she can get more complete security for a while?"

Resident: "That is quite possible." He described the family conferences he had been holding, and the family's attitude toward the patient. "Perhaps she could live outside, and be treated on an out-patient basis."

Cadman: "You can't do that until the inner decision is made by her. You guys have got to get together and make sure you present the issues to her. Find out how long she thinks she will need to decide."

Chief: "I knew we were taking a risk on her, and I thought it might pay off. But now I've changed my mind. I don't think it will pay off."

Cadman: "It's just like a surgeon. Every time he touches a patient, he is taking a calculated risk that the patient will die. He has to decide that the probabilities are that the patient will die if he doesn't touch her. You two will have to get together and thrash it out with her. (Smiling) Tell me what she needs." (With that the meeting ended.)

Thus, within the context of having called the residents into his office and making it pretty plain what he thought they should do, Dr. Cadman phrased his participation in this treatment and management situation in such a way that it was the *residents* who were to take the initiative, and then to inform their superordinate of the requirements of the situation.

INTERPERSONAL TRANSACTIONS AROUND WORK: PERFORMANCE AND RESPONSE

WE HAVE OUTLINED the nature of the clinical director's work in the hospital. In so doing, we have conveyed something of the nature of the man. Now we turn the focus of our analysis to a more explicit assessment of the individual who was clinical director, the manner in which he performed in that position, and how he "came across" in the process. The clinical director's role performance cannot be described except in relation to the work he was doing as clinical director. We attempt to highlight *both* elements of Dr. Cadman's total performance.

The Underlying View of Life

In those interactional settings that did not involve the above-mentioned ambiguities, Dr. Cadman's preferred interpersonal style was communicated effectively and with great emotional impact. This was based largely on an almost organismic, "first things first" view of life that manifested itself in a simple, sometimes wordless way in most of his interactions in the hospital. This view could be detected in his approach to a variety of concerns. One day Dr. Cadman's secretary interrupted him to say that one of the first-year residents wanted to see him on a "semi-emergency" basis. Dr. Cadman dropped what he was doing and told her to show the resident in.

The resident entered the office and looked around uneasily. She perched herself uncomfortably on the very corner of Dr. Cadman's couch, sitting with her back straight and her books and handbag clasped against her chest.

Resident: "Dr. Cadman, my father is dying in Pittsburgh, and I would like to go to him."

Dr. Cadman had been leaning back in his swivel chair, scratching his scalp in an absent-minded way. As soon as he heard what the resident had to say, his face wrinkled in concentration, and he swung forward rapidly, placing his elbows on the desk. He leaned forward toward the resident, and looked at her intently.

Cadman: "Of course. You go right away." He and the resident looked at one another. After an instant, Cadman looked away. "Have you asked your chief?"

The resident described the arrangements she had made.

Cadman: "O.K." The resident got up to leave.

Cadman: "Stay with it." The resident turned back to look at Cadman. "Stay with it, as long as you feel you need," Cadman continued. "See it through. (Pause) It's very important."

The resident nodded and left the office. Cadman sat shaking his head.

Cadman: "It's a terrible thing. Everybody has to go through it, but every time it happens, it is as bad as the last. (Pause) Our residents are going through more than their share, this year."

There were many instances in which Dr. Cadman's approach cut through the more conventional, unpersonal view of life to dwell on the elemental, orectic significances of common happenings and events. This view was sometimes expressed in humor. "First things first," he would say with a smile as he went off to the men's room, even though important events were waiting for him. Likewise, it tinged his responses to such events as car accidents, to whose consequences he gave a particularly personal significance, highlighting the potential and immediate impact of such events on everybody.

8:50 A.M.   Dr. Cadman informed Dr. Suprin about the new admissions to the hospital. Then Suprin asked Cadman if he knew that [a colleague's] son had been killed. Cadman replied that he did not know, and inquired as to how the boy had been killed. Suprin informed him that the boy had been killed in an auto accident. There was a pause. Cadman shook his head.

Cadman: "With accident rates what they are, it's bound to strike every home sooner or later. It's too bad."

Dr. Cadman's "Philosophy" and His Style of Interaction

Dr. Cadman reflected the importance that disappointment plays in the life of every individual. Frequently, he seemed to be indicating to whoever would listen his belief in the vital necessity of addressing issues of loss and disappointment in one's life, of working them through to some functional resolution rather than sweeping them away from one's attention. Just as the superintendent's views as a psychiatrist permeated his thinking and behavior as an administrator, so it was for the clinical director. In a variety of settings he communicated his view that life is sad: that a good psychiatrist is a man who knows what suffering is, who knows what grief, sadness, loneliness, disappointment, and indecision feel like, who can empathize with these feelings in his patients. For him, a good psychiatrist's principal asset was his maturity: that is, his having experienced these feelings and mastered them. "Do you know what suffering is?" he asked a group of residents, who sat in hushed silence as he spoke. "Have you suffered?" He smiled at the motionless group. "I have."

This oneness with all life—good and bad—permeated all Cadman's interactions with those he sought to instruct.

A second-year resident came in to discuss his plans for the next year with Dr. Cadman.

Resident: "I'd like to talk about my plans for next year."

Cadman: "Don't I already know what you want to do?"

Resident: "Yes, but one does not always get what one wants in life, and I'd like to talk to you about some of my second choices."

Cadman smiled. "Oh, so you've found that out already," he said.

The resident laughed. "Yes, I found it out early in life," he said.

Cadman, still smiling: "Well, you are way ahead of the game."

Charisma

The imagery that was in this way communicated and received in the interactive settings surrounding Dr. Cadman was that of a man possessed of an extraordinary richness and profundity of inner life, and with a great capacity for resignation in the face of the unavoidable crises in the life cycle. Here was a man keenly aware of the drama and pathos underlying events conventionally considered unworthy of such sustained and concentrated attention. This man not infrequently conveyed, particularly to those in an apprentice-like relation to him, an almost mystical and sometimes prophetic insight into the sentient core of the human condition. "Do you know about the art of this profession?" he inquired of a group of medical students after he had demonstrated an interview with a patient.

"Do you know the shovels we use, and what we shovel?" (a ripple of laughter from the group) "No, really," Cadman insisted.

"It's the crap of life. The crap of life. As I said to our observer over there, psychiatry is a sad profession. We psychiatrists live off the troubles of the world. If there were no troubles, we would be out of business. Hunnh? And I am not saying this because I feel sorry for myself, although there are times when I have asked myself if there wasn't an easier way of making a living."

The occasions on which Dr. Cadman could exercise his persuasions were many. In leading another group of medical students, Dr. Cadman interviewed a divorced female patient whom one of the students had presented as his case work-up. After the interview, Dr. Cadman presented his thoughts in his simple, straightforward manner which appeared to affect three of the four medical students quite forcefully. In his characteristically emotional style, he presented his often-repeated theme that patients are people who have problems they cannot manage, who have come to a psychiatrist for help in managing them.

"What is it that she couldn't stand?" Cadman asked. (One of the students observed that the patient's difficulties went back to 1945, when she was first married.)

"Sure. She was looking for something, hunnh? She was looking for something, but she didn't know what it was. She still doesn't (pause) because it is easier for her to act than to think. All she knows is that it isn't working. (Pause) It never has, really. (Pause) Instead of thinking, she went out lookin', and if you are out lookin', you can always find other people who are out looking too, hunnh? She doesn't love ——. She *knows* that. (*Pause*) And —— doesn't love *her*. They were both lookin', and as soon as they got married, they found out that that wasn't what they were lookin' *for*.

"What brought her into the hospital, hunnh? Why is she here? (Silence) She's here because she's been trying and trying, and she has found out that it doesn't work. So she comes back to her family, and what does she find out? She finds out that they don't want her *either*.

"What troubles one human being is other human beings. Did you ever notice that? It's with other human beings that people get into difficulty. Everybody is routinely capable of getting food, of getting enough to eat, and of finding some sort of shelter. They've been adequately trained in this. But not so much attention has been paid to relations with other people. We're not trained about it in as systematic a way.

"She has a terrible time thinking. It's painful to her to think. And then she broke her arm. That was the last straw. That was what made the camel finally sink to its knees. It made her burden more than she could tolerate. So she came into the hospital to get some help with it. Then what happens? She loses her therapist."

Student: "That was her other arm."

"That's right," said Cadman. "Only now she has learned that she can get another therapist to help her with her problems.

"Did you notice how she thinks? It's slow, and she's taken all the feeling out of it. You give a stimulus and—what do you call those mechanical brains? Yes, computers—all the lights go on, and all the wheels turn 'round, and gradually it works itself down to one answer, characterized by its nonspecificity and by the removal of all emotion from it. But she feels it. She feels defeated. She feels hopeless, although she denied it. That was getting too hot for her, but I bet she felt it when she first came in here. She feels lonely. She feels confused. That's what patients are. They are people with problems—defeated people—and you are there to help them."

On this occasion, the meeting went 15 minutes longer than scheduled. Instances of this nature repeatedly threw Dr. Cadman off schedule. As the students left the room, one hung back behind the rest. As they exited, she turned to Dr. Cadman. "Thank you, Doctor," she said. Cadman nodded.

"Sure," he replied, and the student turned around and left the room.

Observer: "She seemed quite moved by what you had to say."

Cadman: "Of course. And you know why? How many times do you think a girl like her has been back and forth over the same problems herself? She knows what it means. That girl *knows* what I was talking about."

Modal Response to Cadman's Role Performance

It would be easy to oversimplify the nature of the responses that Dr. Cadman elicited in those who came in contact with him, and who experienced something unique in his way of thinking and acting. To say that there was a modal type of response is not to say that there were no other types of response. However, at the risk of oversimplifying the situation, a brief indication of this modal response will be presented here. Variations and complexities will be presented more fully in due course.

Even before the observation of the clinical director began, the superintendent had demonstrated what this modal response would be. The superintendent was asked if he had any information on Dr. Cadman's likes and dislikes that would be of help in not interfering with his "modus operandi" during the period of observation.

Suprin: "Oh, you won't have any trouble with Paul. He's a lot nicer guy than I am. You brought that out in your [interim] report. The residents all think that Paul hung the moon. (Pause) Maybe he did at that."

Half way through their first month at the hospital, the following conversation was overheard between two first-year residents working on one of the hospital services.

Dr. Rand: "What did you think of that?"
Dr. Ragolski: "It was magnificent! Marvelous! I just sat there." He demonstrated by slouching into a nearly horizontal position in his chair, opening his eyes wide as though he were staring in amazement at some stupendous phenomenon.
Dr. Rand: "I know. I never saw anything like that. I just sat there in awe."

At this point, the observer interjected himself and asked Dr. Rand if they were discussing a case demonstration they had seen. Dr. Rand replied that they were discussing an interview that Dr. Cadman had held with a patient that morning on teaching rounds.

Observer: "Was it good?"

Dr. Rand: "Good? It was *marvelous*. I have never seen anything like that in my life. I have seen other psychiatric sessions in my life, but nothing like that before. It was amazing! He got to the heart of that girl's problem just like that— (a jab of the forefinger) —just like that, with a problem that's been going on for ten years. He had her crying in the group, when she saw it, which is a very difficult thing to do with all those people present. If you want to describe him, I would say he is a God-like figure. That man has *uncanny* skill. It's just amazing."

Role Management: The Conduct of Simplicity, Stubbornness, and Anger

Observing Dr. Cadman going about the business of his day's work, one was constantly witness to his manner of presenting himself to those around him. The deep-feeling and direct-thinking quality of the man, and the manner in which it was communicated, has already been presented. He also liked to view himself as a simple person: "A hick from the country," was one expression he used in this matter. "My development is based entirely on my peasant background," Dr. Cadman explained in establishing the relation between this aspect of himself as a person to the style and content of his professional role as a psychiatrist. In this, the superintendent was one who was pleased to associate himself with his clinical director.

Dr. Suprin was fond of remarking to many people in the hospital that he and Dr. Cadman were "country boys." A frequently used vehicle for transmitting this allegiance based on a felt common heritage was the superintendent's weekly staff conference, at which he would not infrequently make such casual asides as the following.

"Paul [who was present at the meeting, sitting and smiling in the front row] and I are both from the flatlands, from squarehead country. That is why you'll probably find that we often look at a problem the same way, and have the same goals of treatment."

But there were limits to this unanimity, and the superintendent was quick to point them out.

"But," he continued, "our mode of operating in that situation would be quite different."

A simple man with simple thoughts: that was the main implication of much that Dr. Cadman had to say about himself. "When they ask me how I think," he laughingly referred to hypothetical researchers somewhat overfond of complex methodologies and electronic equipment, "and they find out, then they say: 'That's too *simple* for machines.'"

All was not simple, however, in the causes and consequences surrounding this image of peasant-like simplicity. Although this manner was endearing to many, it was not infrequently quite frustrating to those working closest to Dr. Cadman in the organization. One morning during the summer, the secretaries closest to the work of the superintendent and the clinical director were chatting about how quiet things were at that time, and what a lack of trouble there had been recently. Dr. Suprin at that point came out of his office, put something on the desk, and overheard the women's remarks. He observed that the reason for the quietness and lack of trouble was that so many of the staff were away on vacation. Then, one of the secretaries replied with a laugh.

"Yes, that's right. Cadman is away, and he's the cause of all the troubles around here."

On another occasion, the same secretary jokingly chatted with Dr. Cadman about his anger and what he did with it.

Secretary: "I don't think I've ever seen you mad, Dr. Cadman."

Cadman: "That could be. When I get mad, I'm just like a stubborn old woman. I dig in my heels, and nobody can move me."

Secretary: "Oh, yes. I remember Dr. Suprin calling you a stubborn old so-and-so. (She laughed.) He said it was from your Polish background. I told him I thought you were Hungarian."

Cadman: "I guess it doesn't make much difference."

Secretary (laughs) : "You are stubborn, anyway. Is that it?"

It was not often that Dr. Cadman was to be observed openly expressing aggression against his residents, but when such occasions arose, it often took the form of a contest as to who was more simple—less effetely sophisticated—than who. In such contests, who would win was never in question.

Cadman took a teaching round, during which there were several quite conspicuous (though wordless) altercations between himself and the chief as to which two of the three main actors—the clinical director, the chief resident, and the patient—were going to sit at the head of the room. Dr. Cadman had removed one of the three chairs at the head of the room while the chief was out of the room, in order to sharpen the issue and make sure he got his way. When the chief returned to the room, he found only two chairs at the head of the room, so he was forced to sit on the side, as close to the front as he could manage. As soon as the interview was over, and the patient had left the room, before anything else was said or done, the chief got up and took the seat next to Dr. Cadman.

Dr. Cadman began to comment on the case.

Cadman: "We're still in the age of Hippocrates in this business. The uterus still gets blamed for a lot of things."

Chief: "Yes. The Greek word for it was 'hysteron.' "

Cadman turned to speak directly into the chief's face, "I'm not that educated."

Loud and general laughter followed that remark.

Chief (trying to retrieve his point and his position) : "Hysteron, you know. The root of the word, hysteric, . . . hysteria? . . ."

Cadman conspicuously did not respond, leaving the chief to sputter to an uneasy silence, to the continued amusement of many of the service personnel.

Dr. Cadman's role management of simplicity, stubbornness, and anger did not often take this openly aggressive form. Usually they occurred in relaxed and mutually supportive interactions with residents who had worked under his tutelage for some time, or with psychiatrists who had once been his residents. These communications were usually received with fondness and appreciation, and also with some tangible element of disbelief on the part of those who felt they knew him well. For instance, in a discussion with the psychiatrist who was later to become his assistant, Dr. Cadman received the following response of friendly incredulity to his customary "ploy" to establish himself in an inverse hierarchy of worldly sophistication.

Cadman: ". . . The trouble with this place [the hospital], you know, is that everyone wants everyone else just for himself."
Researcher: "Is that any different from anywhere else?"
Cadman: "I don't know. I haven't traveled around much, like you. I'm just a small-town boy."
Researcher (laughing) : "Oh, I don't buy that stuff any more."
Cadman leaned back in his chair (frequently a gesture of relaxation for him) and smiled. He did not pursue the matter further. The researcher then turned the discussion to the theory of neurasthenia, and studiously asked about Dr. Cadman's thoughts on the matter.

Offstage and Onstage Performances

Such was the manner in which Dr. Cadman presented himself within the hospital. Other information, both separate from and related to the emotional and conceptual image that has been outlined, was to be gathered from his less deliberate behavior in other settings. These were settings in which the communication of his personal and professional structures of belief were not at all uppermost in Dr. Cadman's mind. This situation obtained either when he was alone, or when he was interacting with others around such routine matters as filing, scheduling, or correspondence. Dr. Cadman expressed some feelings of oppression about the routine "administrative" work—as it was called in that setting—with which he was constantly confronted.

11:00 A.M. Scheduled meetings of the chiefs, the service consultants, and the assistant clinical director in Dr. Cadman's office. No one had shown up. Dr. Cadman chatted to the observer about the routine that characterized so much of his life at the hospital, again emphasizing his often-repeated theme that nothing new was happening there.

Cadman (shaking his head) : "Chronic, chronic."

Observer: "You mean, none of it is new?"

Cadman: "Just the same old stuff. It's like your business executive, at least as I see him. He comes to work in the morning. He sits at his desk all day, shuffling papers from one pile to another. Just like this." He demonstrated moving a sheaf of papers from a stack on the left-hand to a stack on the right-hand side of his desk. "From one pile to another. Then he leaves at 5, goes home, and can't remember for the life of him what he did all day. How's he going to tell *that* to his wife? And it's the same thing, day after day."

A service consultant had entered while Cadman had been speaking.

Consultant: "What's this?"

Cadman: "I'm giving our observer here my stereotype of the business executive." He went on to restate the extensiveness of routine in his day.

Consultant (expressing surprise) : "But I thought new things were *always* coming up."

Cadman: "Yes, but they are all much the same. You've seen them once, you've seen them all. Every day is about the same, and you get involved in a lot of little things, a host of administrative detail, and the next thing you know, the day is over and you can't for the life of you remember what you did." He laughed. "Unless you've settled in your own mind the fundamental question of life, you are going to spend the rest of your days feeling like you have done nothing."

With Dr. Cadman's view of life, and with his skill and fluency in practicing it, it often seemed as though the flow of events around him regularly interrupted not only his preferred style of interacting, but also the train of thought that meant most to him. The concrete little details of running his part of the organization distracted him from what he considered himself best at, and what he most wanted to do; namely, clinical teaching. From these distractions arose frustration. "America's No. 1 scut boy," Cadman used to grumble as he worked his way through the accumulations of paper work on his desk:

"That's what I am. America's No. 1 scut boy. If I ever get an award (in a loud voice), or a distinction, or an honor, or anything like that, it will be for all the *paper* (!) work I do around here." He laughed and turned to the observer.

"Every organization has its scut boy," he said, "and in this organization . . ." (he left the sentence unfinished).

Observer: "You're it?"

Dr. Cadman turned back to the work on his desk without replying.

The frustrations of such work reinforced, and were reinforced by, some ineptitude on Dr. Cadman's part in coping with the external world—physical and social, as well as bureaucratic—which contrasted somewhat with the superintendent's deftness in this regard. Even such an unremarkable event as opening the door to his office in the morning often took on the aura of a battle between man and the refractory forces of nature. A composite picture of Dr. Cadman's work day will convey this to the reader.

It was with some awkwardness that Dr. Cadman opened the door to his office the first thing in the morning. He must have unlocked and opened that door many times during his term of office as clinical director, but the following procedure was the one he was observed to use. Around 9 A.M. he passed the superintendent's office, walking down the corridor to his office, wearing a battered soft grey fedora and a billowing top coat that was either old or needed dry cleaning. He usually carried something in one or both hands—a brief case and perhaps a bundle of papers tied together with twine—and sometimes he was gripping something under his arm as well. He reached his office and stopped in front of the locked door. He put down what was in his left hand, and searched through several pockets to find his keys. Finding them, he searched to find the right key. Selecting the correct key, he inserted it into the lock.

He turned the key in the lock, pushed the door with his knee, but the door would not give. Letting go the key, he turned the door knob, and again pushed the door with his knee. But the lock must have slipped back into position, because again the door would not give. From this point on, he customarily followed one of two procedures. Either he stepped back from the door, put down what he was carrying in his right hand, took the key in his right hand and the door knob in the left, and turning both simultaneously, would again give the door several pushes with his knee. Or else he leaned against the door with his knee, exerting steady pressure on it so that neither the lock nor the catch would slip back when he let go of either the key or the door knob. Then he shifted his left hand rapidly back and forth between the key and the door knob, giving each a twist in turn, and each time bucking the door a little more with his knee. The door flew open. Dr. Cadman pushed it back against the wall, picked up whatever he had deposited on the floor during this process, and entered his office. He deposited his brief case on a chair, hung up his coat and hat, and turned to his desk.

His secretary entered the office. Dr. Cadman fished in his

pocket and gave her some change to get him a package of cig-
arettes.

Mrs. O'Toole: "Only one package today? You cutting down on
your smoking?"

Dr. Cadman felt with both hands in his jacket pockets for more
money. "I've got to keep some money for carfare if I don't get
picked up tonight." At this point, he extracted a rumpled one dol-
lar bill from his left-hand jacket pocket, held it up, and looked
at it.

Mrs. O'Toole laughed. "That's enough. It only costs 15 cents to
go on the bus."

Cadman handed her the bill. "I never know whether it costs
15 or 20 cents for carfare."

Mrs. O'Toole (leaving the room): "Imagine you paying 20
cents for a 15 cent bus ride!"

Dr. Cadman took off his jacket, hung it up on a peg on the
wall, and sat down at his desk to open his morning mail and
read over the ward reports. He rubbed his hands together
briskly and smiled.

Cadman: "We got an early start this morning. Maybe I'll get
some work done for a change, and not just tread water. In this
business you're doing great if you just . . . you know?"

Observer: "Keep your head above water?"

Cadman: "It's hard."

He started to open his mail. "I open all my mail. It's a specific
peculiarity of mine. I like to see what's coming in," he said.
He opened several circulars, looked them over, and threw
them in the waste basket. He opened a letter and began to
read. Presently he was shaking his head. As he finished the
letter, he explained.

"This is a letter from that medical student I saw in consultation. You remember?" He read, " 'Thank you for showing me
that it was my attitude that was holding me back in therapy.' "
Cadman shook his head. "What a lowly profession this is." He

read, " 'I have come to see that I was making my therapy a failure by trying not to make it a success.' " Again he shook his head. "And people have to *learn* this!"

As he opened his mail, he came across an item that prompted him to point out that there were several organizations to which he belonged because they were so much a part of his work at the hospital, and that because of his interest in the hospital he was called upon to perform certain duties not directly connected with the hospital's operations. In this instance, his statement was in reference to an announcement bearing the date of a meeting of a local psychiatric association. The example he gave of activities required of him due to his position in the hospital was that of consultation: consultation with doctors in the community who are in "transference binds" with their patients. Cadman referred to this as "a sort of public relations activity."

What outside organizations was Dr. Cadman a member of? Dr. Cadman listed three organizations and six committees. He was confused as to exactly which committees he was on, and referred the matter to Mrs. O'Toole. She produced a list of committees of which Dr. Cadman was a member, but this list was a year old, and she did not know if he was on the same committees again this year. Cadman said he was a member of other organizations, but when asked which ones, he replied in general terms about "professional and local organizations" and did not name names.[2]

Cadman turned to a pile he captioned, "things that don't have to be done right away." Some of this material consisted of notes he had written to himself on small index cards. He threw several of these in the wastebasket.

---

[2] Notice the difference between Cadman's apparently muddled knowledge about his memberships, and the clarity, precision, and extensiveness of Suprin's recall on the same topic. Obviously, membership in such bodies had different meanings for the two men.

"Usually," he said, "these reminders can be thrown away if you wait long enough. Things have a way of taking care of themselves, if you don't complicate matters.

"Most of my administrative work is done between teaching, supervision, and consultations. I guess, perhaps, because I don't get too much gratification from it. I could easily use two secretaries to do all the necessary foot work, if I were administrative. Take these reports. [Data on overnight events on the wards, and on patient turnover.] I boil them down and tell Suprin just the briefest amount. Very briefly I give him information on two points. First, points of danger, and second, points of administrative or public relations interest. For instance, if a senator calls, Dr. Suprin will at least have heard of the patient."

Dr. Cadman gathered up his papers and got up. "Let's go," he said. He left his office, walked down the corridor and into Dr. Suprin's office. Without ado, he prefaced his remarks with the phrase, "nothing unusual," and informed Suprin of the new admissions to the hospital. Suprin inquired about two patients whose progress appeared doubtful to him. Cadman said he would look into their cases. Cadman then brought up the matter of a fourth-year resident wishing to apply for a position as chief resident for the next year. Suprin reiterated his stand that these positions were open only to residents in their third year in the program. He stated his thoughts about more senior residents.

Suprin: "It's time they got out on their own. When do they think we'll stop supporting them?"
Cadman: "I certainly don't know. You've had more experience in the matter than I've had."

He then read out a list of names of residents who were applying for positions as chiefs in the following year.

Suprin: "Boy! That's going to be hard to choose from."
Cadman: "Yes, they're a good bunch."

The two men turned to a discussion of the doctors who were leaving the hospital and the resulting vacancies that were to be filled.

Cadman: "Will you clear up my impression that staff positions are not negotiable by me?"

Suprin: "House staff positions are negotiable by you, but only house staff. Not the clinics. They aren't negotiable by you."

Cadman: "That's very comforting. Now there won't be so much bouncing back and forth with the people that come in to see me."

Suprin: "Not the clinics. Not the outpatient units." Suprin glanced intently at Cadman, apparently to check his reaction.

Cadman nodded: "I understand."

As Cadman rose to leave, Suprin inquired whether he would be attending the meeting of a particular committee that evening.

Cadman: "I didn't know that they were to meet tonight. I'm not sure if I'll be attending, although I doubt it, because I'll be attending another committee meeting tonight."

Suprin: "You better check and see whether you're supposed to be attending this one. I've a hunch you are."

Cadman: "I'll check. (Pause) I will have to rearrange my schedule. I didn't schedule it. At least Mrs. O'Toole doesn't have it down here. (He was examining his pocket calendar.) Thanks for reminding me."

Suprin: "Maybe you don't have to go." Cadman shook his head as though he did not believe that encouraging statement and exited.

Flipping through the pages of his pocket calendar, Dr. Cadman walked back down the corridor and into his office.

Cadman (to the observer): "Did Suprin say 6:30?" He clicked his tongue against his teeth. "That's some inconvenience." He paused, still scrutinizing his little black book. "I'm going to have to rearrange two patients. I could have done so a lot easier if I had known earlier. I can't understand why Mrs. O'Toole didn't tell me earlier. I'll try to schedule the patients for earlier in the day—2 or 3 P.M.—these meetings come out of hospital time—otherwise I'll have to cancel. My patients understand this when they come to me."

Dr. Cadman turned and lifted a sheaf of papers off the top tier of a five-tray "in-and-out" basket. He shuffled through these papers, searching for a notice of the meeting in question, but to no avail. He gathered the papers together again and returned them to the tray. He pressed the buzzer that sounded in Mrs. O'Toole's office. When she entered, he informed her of the meeting Suprin had told him he must attend. Did she know anything about it? Mrs. O'Toole expressed surprise. That was the first she had heard of it. Cadman asked if she had received a notice of the meeting. She replied that she could not recall receiving such a notice. Cadman asked her to look around in her office, nonetheless. He and Mrs. O'Toole went through his black book together, to check whether she had written the notice of the meeting on the wrong day, week, or month, but they were unable to find any notation of the meeting at all. Dr. Cadman then gave her the black book, and asked her to reschedule his two patients for earlier in the afternoon; if they could not make it, the appointments were to be cancelled.

At 9:15 A.M. Dr. Cadman went off to take a teaching round on one of the services. After Cadman had interviewed the patient presented that morning, a resident asked Cadman for his diagnosis of the case. Cadman sat in silence for a moment, and then replied.

"As far as diagnosis is concerned, I'd call it a depressive reaction in a very narcissistic character. It so frequently looks like schizophrenia that that's what it is called."

After the residents' laughter had subsided, Dr. Cadman continued in his quiet way.

"Why do we hate schizophrenics? (Silence) Because they disappoint us. Because they violate our expectations of what is good for them. We don't love them enough to help them with their expectations of themselves.

"What we call 'decisions' is an integrative activity. (Pause) A lonesome activity. (Pause) A lone activity. (Pause) You have to give them the opportunity of choosing over and over again, choosing the right things and the wrong things, but having the security enough for choosing. That's the only way for them to get beyond the pleasure component, and on to building onto the reality component. That's the way they can begin to take into account the reality element."

Dr. Cadman returned to his office at 10:30 A.M. Mrs. O'Toole was in his office, looking through one of his two filing cabinets.

Mrs. O'Toole: "You have that meeting tonight, Doctor."
Cadman: "I *do?*"
Mrs. O'Toole: "Yes, you do."
Cadman: "How come you and I missed it?"
Mrs. O'Toole: "I don't know. I can't figure it out. I've rescheduled one of your patients, but I can't get hold of the other."

Several people had phoned to make appointments to see Dr. Cadman. He and Mrs. O'Toole discussed these calls, trying to come to some mutual understanding as to who, exactly, had phoned. They got into an argument as to whether two particular people had been scheduled to see Dr. Cadman. Mrs. O'Toole took Dr. Cadman's black book from his desk and looked through it.

Mrs. O'Toole: "You see, *you* put them in your book some days ago." She pointed to a page in the book.
Cadman (looking at the spot indicated): "I guess I haven't seen them."

Mrs. O'Toole cracked a joke about people not knowing what they are doing and left the office.

Cadman (to the observer) : "It's murder to have a secretary who doesn't keep track of things. Some secretaries can keep everything organized. I had one such in my life. It was a pleasure. Yes, it was a pleasure. She was young and intelligent. And beautiful, too, like that swimming woman, you know?"

Observer: "Esther Williams?"

Cadman: "Yes, that's the one. She was just like that, only smaller. I used to boast about her all the time. She would write down on a list everything you would have to do in a day, and you'd come in in the morning, and all you would have to do was to read it to know what you had to do that day. You didn't have to think about it at all. You could just go ahead and do it."

Mrs. O'Toole entered the office again. Cadman asked her if she had "the plans." She replied that she had.

Cadman: "Well, where *are* they?"

Mrs. O'Toole: "They are on my *desk.*"

Cadman: "Well, will you *show* them to me, please? (Mrs. O'Toole left the office.) I've reminded her three times to show me those plans in her book."

Mrs. O'Toole returned to the room with some papers, and placed them in front of Dr. Cadman on his desk. He leaned over, scanned them briefly, then looked up.

Cadman: "What have you been doing with them?"

Mrs. O'Toole: "I've been holding them for Mr. ——. I thought he'd be along any time."

Mrs. O'Toole then informed Dr. Cadman of a phone call she had received from "a woman who knew a woman" who might be interested in typing up transcriptions of a number of tape recordings that Dr. Cadman had stored in his office. Cadman asked about this person, but Mrs. O'Toole did not know about her.

Cadman: "Goodness me. Why didn't you *ask?*"

Mrs. O'Toole replied to the effect that she had not felt at liberty to ask.

Dr. Cadman got up from his desk, and left the office. He went downstairs, through the main lobby, along the corridor toward the cafeteria, and turned into the business office. He spoke with the business officer about getting the woman in question to do the typing that he had in mind. He explained that his secretary was "having trouble mobilizing herself to take the necessary steps." The business officer replied that he would take care of the matter. Dr. Cadman thanked him and left the office.

On his way back to his office, Dr. Cadman stopped at the mail boxes in the main lobby, and picked up his own mail.

Observer: "It must slow you down to look after all these details."

Cadman: "It slows me down and raises the blood pressure." He amplified this theme until he had reached his office. Mrs. O'Toole was inside, and when Dr. Cadman saw that she was there, he raised his voice as he continued to address the observer.

"The only way to survive in this profession is to ask people to do only what you would do yourself, because that's the way it usually works out. (To Mrs. O'Toole) Did you find the notification?"

Mrs. O'Toole: "Yes, I found it in my room." She explained where in her office she had found it.

Cadman: "Will you *get* it for me, please?"

Mrs. O'Toole left and returned with the paper. Dr. Cadman looked it over, showing it to the observer at the same time. It was a schedule of meetings for that night, the meetings being set up in such a way that Cadman could only spend about 15 minutes in the first meeting if he was to attend both the meetings he was supposed to attend. Dr. Cadman asked Mrs. O'Toole to find out if the schedule had been set up that way knowingly.

A resident came into Dr. Cadman's office to confer with him about plans for next year. The discussion lasted for several minutes.

Resident: "I want to talk about my plan for next year."

Cadman: "I have to inform you that Dr. Bolen is not taking you into his clinic. Can I help you arrange something? Something in the way of a staff appointment?"

Resident: "I'm sorry that Bolen won't take me. I'd be interested in staying around here, but I think I should look into [another hospital] first. What does one have to do for a staff appointment?"

Cadman: "Well, the thing to do is to see the top man in each unit. Dr. Cape, Dr. Parker, or myself for the house. I'm sorry, but I don't see any vacancy coming up in the house for next year. How about Dr. Asche?"

Resident: "That would be for research?"

Cadman: "Yes."

Resident: "Well, I don't think I am ready for the staff yet. I think I should go to [the above-mentioned hospital] and get some experience with children. Maybe I could come back later. I'm disappointed that Bolen won't take me. I'll contact you when I have something worked out."

Cadman: "Good." (Exit the resident.) "He's a good man. I'd like to keep him here if I could. Suprin likes him too. Dr. Suprin would be in his perfect legal right to tell Dr. Bolen to take him, but he didn't. It's different here from a business, say, where one man owns everything. Maybe there is a different sort of people here, but here the boss isn't the boss. He's just one of the boys, trying to get along like the rest."

When the resident left, Mrs. O'Toole re-entered the office. She and Dr. Cadman worked through the arrangements for a trip he was to take. They were getting the blocks of time for the trip sorted out. During this process Dr. Cadman glanced up at Mrs. O'Toole. "I need six hours for sleep," he said. He grinned and added, "I don't sleep during the day."

At 11:00 A.M. Dr. Cadman turned to the next piece of business on his agenda: a second-year teaching group. Several of the residents had entered his office and taken seats. Others were still coming in. After some searching around for a topic of interest to the group, there seemed to be tacit agreement that Dr. Cadman should continue with his presentation of concepts he considered therapeutically useful.

Cadman: "What did you decide to use me for in this time? (Silence) Have you discussed it with each other? (Another silence) We've gone through the three patterns of defenses [content of last week's discussion], haven't we? (Long silence) Any ideas?"

Rizzo: "I thought we had worked this out last time. Certainly last time was to my satisfaction. I just assumed that you would continue presenting to us some of your thoughts and experiences in a lifetime of treating schizophrenics." (Long silence)

Cadman: "I'm not trying to turn this into a group meeting. I just want to make sure you know what we're doing, so that by next spring you won't feel you have wasted your time."

Reid: "Well, I thought this would more or less be a seminar that could be called 'A Seminar in Psychosis' and that we were going to have the benefit of your experiences in treating psychotics, in which we would take an active part contributing."

Remick: "I'd be interested in having you interview a patient in front of a one-way screen, and we could discuss it."

Cadman: "I do so much interviewing in front of people. I suppose that's the only way you people get to know me; when I'm interviewing."

Remick: "No, what I meant was actually interviewing a patient behind a one-way screen, so that the audience could not be seen. Then we could discuss the interview afterwards." (Silence)

Reid: "I suppose a common wish of all of us is, 'What is Cadman *really* like in psychotherapy?'"

Cadman: "That depends on the patient."

Reid: "Does he really say those things when it's *his* patient?" (Silence. Several more residents enter.)

Cadman: "Well, if you are interested in the theory of psychosis, we can get right at it."

He opened a large loose-leaf binder that already lay on his desk, flipped through the pages, gave the residents several references that he recommended they read, and proceeded with the substance of his talk: his thinking on the concept of *Einfühlung* or empathy.

"*Einfühlung.* You know what that is? (Silence. Then several of the residents attempted to reply, but Cadman cut them off.) It's knowing what one feels like by feeling it in oneself, but knowing the feeling in oneself is not the same feeling as the feeling the other has. Some of you theoretical big guns will shudder at this attempt to understand a clinical experience by using a clinical idea, but you'll have to forgive me for not progressing further. (Pause) It is a characteristic of what has been thought of as religious psychology, or esthetic appreciation, et cetera. It's when the feeling of what's inside feels as though it is coming from the outside, and not from the inside, and it feels as it does *because* it feels as though it were coming from the outside. It's the feeling of being 'at one' with the outside. It's a very useful feeling in therapy, and at the same time it enlarges the need for correctives on the part of the therapist. Empathy. That's a much misunderstood word. It's not the same as sympathy. It's knowing what is *you,* and what is *me,* and what the difference is. It's very important, but that is all it is. Part of the mess we are in today in psychiatry is that we don't keep our tools straight. We extrapolate too much.

"That's the trouble with many of the research studies I read: well presented and carefully analyzed, but the conclusions they draw don't have anything to do with the experiment. They extrapolate too much, or the conclusions they draw have nothing to do with the research, and the only reason they did the research was so that they could publish their conclusions. At my age, I can afford to be cynical. It's you guys who are going to have to work with it, that is, if you want to live with yourself."

This session lasted till noon. Dr. Cadman was scheduled to lead a staff conference at noon. He straightened up his office before leaving. He moved the microphones he had been using in the preceding hour back to their place at the side of the room, turned off the recording machine that had been running since the beginning of the meeting, and straightened out the chairs. Under one of the chairs, he found an ash tray brimming with cigarette butts. As he left the room, he stopped and picked up the ash tray. "Notice," he said as he placed it on the corner of his desk. "It is the Chief [meaning himself] who picks up the ash trays."

He left his office and headed toward the library, where the staff conference was scheduled to be held. On the way, he dropped into Mrs. O'Toole's office. He inquired about the arrangements she had made concerning his patients later in the day. The arrangements were still up in the air. She had not yet been able to get in touch with one of the patients in question. Shaking his head, Dr. Cadman went off to the staff conference.

There were few residents in the library when Dr. Cadman entered. Dr. Cadman took his accustomed place at the head of one of the tables and waited. Dr. Crosier, the admissions officer, entered the library, looked around in surprise, then walked over and sat down next to Dr. Cadman.

Crosier: "How are you?"

Cadman: "I'm puzzled at the moment."

Crosier (glancing around the room, then up at the clock above the door) : "You mean because it is five after 12?"

Cadman: "Yes, it's a question of whether these meetings should be obligatory or not obligatory." He explained to Crosier some of the thinking that had gone into the decision that year not to make attendance at staff conferences obligatory. "The residents have six hours of scheduled supervision already."

Crosier: "What are you going to do about it?"

Cadman: "I'm discussing it with the chiefs these days."

Crosier: "That's a good thing to do. I sometimes get the feeling that we have no chiefs anymore."

At 12:07 Dr. Cadman turned to the resident who was to present the case.

Cadman: "Well, Dr. Rush, it's your decision. Do we meet, or do we not meet?"

Rush: "I'm really ambivalent about that. I hoped to present this woman, and I scheduled it, but on the other hand this patient is a real problem for me, and I don't think we are getting anywhere, and it's going to be painful for me to talk about it. Therefore, I'm quite ambivalent about it. (Pause) But I did prepare." (Pause)

Cadman: "All right. Let's all move around one table."

Returning from the staff conference to his office, Dr. Cadman poked his head into the office of the assistant clinical director. Dr. Ackroyd looked up from his desk and greeted Dr. Cadman.

Cadman: "There was a skeleton crew today."

Ackroyd: "Not many people there today."

Cadman: "No. We had to decide whether we were going to meet or not."

Ackroyd: "That's what you get for making it optional. We advised you against it, remember?"

Cadman: "I know. I'm just feeding something back to you."

Ackroyd: "Oh, yes. And I'm just letting *you* know. . . ." His voice trailed off into an unended sentence. He and Cadman smiled at each other.

This is a fair example of a very interesting but difficult phenomenon that had to be contended with during field work among the executive ranks of the hospital. Dr. Cadman was here referring to the attendance at the staff conference, and Dr. Ackroyd understood this. However, neither of these two men actually mentioned the point of reference of their discussion. There were many such discussions, in which the central points of reference were debated and decided much as in a family setting; through allusion and innuendo, rather than through any explicit statement of the issues in question. Much of the dialectic process in such decision-making settings was carried by incomplete or grammatically meaningless sentences.

Unfortunately, this characteristic of the administrative interactional processes of the hospital cannot be conveyed in the oral data reported in this study. This distortion raises to the manifest level much of what was more frequently latent in such settings. It also attenuates what was a powerful evaluational criterion used in relation to who among the larger medical executive group in the hospital were "in" and who were "out" of the subsytem of information and intimacy that existed around those in formal decision-making positions in the hospital's medical hierarchy. The criterion was that of *discretion*. Who could be trusted to listen without rushing inappropriately into action? Who could utilize information sparingly, both in deed and in communication? Who could handle the latent content of interactions implicitly, without driving toward embarrassing clarifications of underlying issues? Who could refrain from impugning the motives or the characters of those whom one did not like within the organization?

It was not a question of keeping one's ears open and one's mouth shut. A shut mouth symbolized one's detachment from, and disdain for, the "politics" of the organization. It elicited nothing to hear. Rather, this matter of discretion was closely related to one's interpersonal style in handling one's involvement in administrative issues. It comprised a deftness and fellow-feeling that countenanced certain privacies and intimacies as opposed to a querulous or hatchet-like insistence upon laying everything open to "public" scrutiny.

Thus having still another problem turned back upon him, Dr. Cadman continued on his way back to his office. He entered Mrs. O'Toole's office next. He picked up his little black book that was on her desk, and saw that he was scheduled for patients from 1 P.M. onward (it was now 1:05) with two meetings in the evening, the first starting at 6:30. There was still some doubt about one of the patients. Mrs. O'Toole said she had been unable to contact him.

Cadman: "Did you try?"

Mrs. O'Toole: "Oh yes, I tried." She described her efforts to contact the patient.

Observer (seeking to establish whether he should leave or not) : "So you'll be seeing patients from 1 o'clock on, Doctor?"

Cadman (examining his notebook) : "Yes, it appears that way."

Observer: "O.K. I'll catch up on my notes this afternoon and be back tomorrow morning."

Cadman: "That's what administration's for, so that everybody can fit their schedules to their needs." [Interpretation: that is what I am here for, to arrange to help everybody satisfy their needs, except my own.]

The next morning, the observer inquired about the un-scheduled meeting that Dr. Cadman had been at such pains to attend. Dr. Cadman appeared indifferent to such queries as: how did it go? Or, what was it about? Then he was asked what time it had ended.

Cadman: "Well, the meeting ended around ten last night. So I did not lose too much sleep."

Observer: "Was it worth all the trouble of rearranging sched-ules?"

Cadman: "No. Not a bit. It was more or less of a formality. It was more a question of letting people get to know one another, rather than getting any work done."

Observer: "In what capacity did you attend?"

Cadman: "Gee, I don't know. I'd have to look it up for you, if you want to know."

Observer: "No thanks. Why did you go?"

Cadman: "I guess because Suprin and I are supposed to be in charge of part of the program."

Active and Passive Responses to the Environment

Here again was Dr. Cadman's lack of forcefulness in reaching out, grasping and dispatching the concrete external events that comprised the administrative realm around him. Despite the energy and inconvenience attending the reshuffling of his schedule so that he could go to that meeting, he was still manifesting a vague sense of confusion about its structure and purpose, and a detachment and disinterest in his role in it. He appeared more acted upon than acting, but as in other instances it was never clear how much this was "real," or how much it was yet another facet of Cadman's role-taking in the hospital. There was some indication that the preponderance of reaction over proaction in Cadman's administrative style was a phenomenon of fairly recent origin, perhaps related more to a growing conception of himself as an elder statesman, leaving the fighting to his younger colleagues, than to how he "really was" as an individual. That such an enigma should surround him was in itself a force in the charisma that was Cadman.

There was evidence that such a stylistically passive mode of response had not always been such a distinguishing characteristic of Dr. Cadman. The middle management group occasionally swapped stories among themselves about the way Cadman "really" was back in the "old days": that is, in a period of time of which they had little or no direct knowledge. Then, so it was rumored, he was "a real Napoleon" who "really ran things." In those days, so the story ran, he was a distinctly brutal man who "terrorized the staff and the patients. People really jumped when he toured the wards. Why, I heard that he once fired an attendant on the spot for sleeping on the job. Can you imagine that?"

Cadman had certain thoughts on how he used to be, and how he was during the period of observation reported here. This was not a topic on which he spoke at all frequently, but

in connection with his midwestern background and his similarities and differences with the superintendent, he had this
to say.

"And then, he [Dr. Suprin] is from Missouri, and so I knew
what he was like; I know people from Missouri. I was like that
myself, but I've changed more than Frank has."
Observer: "In what way?"
Cadman: "Oh, the frontal attack. I used to be more like that
than I am now, but I've learned that, in this district, to get what
I wanted to achieve with other people, I could get it better by
being like I am now. So I changed. I learned to change."

The Resulting Balance

WHAT WAS THE OVER-ALL balance of costs and rewards that the
clinical director experienced as the result of doing the work
he did, in the manner he did it? As in Chapter 4, we close our
analysis of one executive's organizational behavior by attempting to delineate the psychological profitability to Dr. Cadman
of his dealings with other people in the M.P.I., and the consequences of these transactions in relation to his own continuing personal development.

Costs and Rewards of a Specialized Role Performance

Dr. Cadman attributed much of his professional and organizational success to the very interpersonal style that is being
described. He summarized both the style and the success with
graphic humor: "So there you have the passive Cadmanian
way of falling into a shit pot and coming up with a rose." He
continued:

"Take my advice. If you are ever going to take over an organization, take over a shit pot. Everything you do makes it a little
bit better. That's the way I made my reputation."

However, Cadman's interpersonal style also introduced certain irritations into his life as an administrator that were not

as readily apparent in the superintendent's existence in the hospital. The events that were observed to occur during field work with Dr. Cadman may not have been typical, but they seemed to build up a level of frustration that prompted Dr. Cadman to re-examine explicitly his reasons for remaining in the hospital, for sustaining the burden of "scut work" and face-to-face impositions that his style of interaction seemed to elicit, or at least did little to discourage.

10:35 A.M.   Dr. Cadman entered his office. Mrs. O'Toole entered and told him that Dr. Conn, chief of the emergency service, wanted to see him. He replied that his morning would be taken up with Dr. Suprin. He picked up his papers and headed for Dr. Suprin's office. On the way, he paused to speak with Dr. Suprin's secretary.

Cadman: "Has Dr. Bolen sent in the list of names yet?"

Secretary: "Names? What names?"

[Yesterday Dr. Bolen promised Dr. Suprin that he would have a list of names ready of those he would accept for training into his clinic next year. He promised this list, in Dr. Cadman's hearing, for 11 A.M. today. Suprin and Cadman needed this list before they could determine the number of residency applicants they could accept for the next year's program. They had held up their selection for approximately one week in order to get this information. During this period, Dr. Cadman had received a number of phone calls—some of them long distance, and some of them irate—from residency applicants who wanted to know, one way or the other, how their applications to the M.P.I. had been decided on.]

Cadman: "Bolen said he would have some names up to us by 11 o'clock."

Secretary: "That's the first I've heard of it, Doctor."

Dr. Cadman returned to his office. Dr. Conn entered and chatted briefly with Dr. Cadman about his career plans.

10:50 A.M.   Dr. Conn left and Cadman went into Suprin's office. Cadman asked Suprin if Bolen had sent in the names yet. Suprin's reply was interrupted by a phone call. Suprin took the phone call. Cadman stood and waited. Suprin concluded the phone call, turned to Cadman, and replied that he had not received the names. He took out his black pocket calendar. He leafed through it and gave Cadman the times when he, Suprin, would be busy. (11:30 to 12:00, 1:00 to 2:00, and after 4 P.M. with the faculty.) Cadman took out his little black book and looked through it.

Cadman: "Could we meet at 11?"

Suprin: "Yes."

Cadman: "I'll get someone to take my rounds. [That is, Dr. Cadman was scheduled to take a teaching round at this time, but would get a substitute in order to attend to his business with Suprin.]

Dr. Cadman returned to his own office. Mrs. O'Toole entered.

Cadman: "Will you get someone to take my rounds?" (It was now less than 10 minutes before these rounds were scheduled to begin.)

Mrs. O'Toole: "I'll try." (Exit)

Cadman: "We'll wait for Dr. Bolen. We'll see what happens with him."

He sat down at his desk and reviewed the papers he had drawn up for his selection of residency applicants.

Observer: "Your principal project this morning has been waiting for Dr. Bolen, has it not?"

Cadman: "Yes. He is holding up progress, and my saddle sores will be getting deeper."

Observer: "You do for the patients, you do for the residents, you do for people like Dr. Bolen. What do you do for yourself?"

Cadman: "I do it all for myself. Really, I do it all for myself. When I was in first year of medical school, I made the discovery that I didn't know how to study. I realized that if I didn't take charge of myself, I wouldn't be able to get through it all. So I assigned myself a task, and I carried it through, and I've carried it right on to the present. I work at the tasks I've assigned to myself. I'd rather do this than cut the grass.[3] (Pause) I've always

---

[3] Note that the superintendent made a similar reference to cutting the grass. Concordances such as this may have been coincidental. They may also

had a good deal of say in what I do. There are compromises, of course, as there are bound to be. But it's *all* pleasure."

10:55 A.M. Dr. Cadman phoned Dr. Bolen.

Cadman: "Kirk? Cadman. Can you tell me anything on . . . Yeah? (Laughed) O.K." He looked at the phone receiver in his hand, shook his head, and hung up. "Jesus Christ! 'It's not 11 o'clock yet.' "

Observer: "Is that what he said?"

Cadman: "Yeah. 'It's not 11 o'clock yet.' (Laughed) As long as I've got enough papillae, I can hold down this job."

Observer: "Papillae?"

Cadman: "They are the taste buds on the tongue."

Observer: "I don't understand."

Cadman: "They are for kissing all the asses that I have to do around here. (Low voice, apparently to himself.) F—— it." He sat for a while, then spoke. "You know, my wife answers the phone at home, where I see some of my patients. I have an office there. She tells me I'm crazy not to go into private practice. I have consultations—I would say 50 or 60 a year—that I refer to other physicians, so there would be no dearth of private practice. I would miss the associations that I get here, though. That's what I worry about now. It would be a lonely job." (Pause)

Observer: "What associations do you like the most here?"

Cadman: "With the students."

Observer: "Does 'students' include the residents as well?"

Cadman: "Yes."

Observer: "In other words, all the 'learners.' "

Cadman: "Yes. The young ones coming up. They are the life blood of this organization. They are the future of our whole area."

11:05 A.M. Cadman glanced at the clock on his wall.

Cadman: "Maybe I should phone him up and say it's five after 11."

Observer: "He asked for it in a way, didn't he?"

---

have been symptomatic of the microcosmic elaboration of thoughts and feelings that comprised the relationship between the clinical director and the superintendent.

Cadman (laughed) : "That would be enough to start a life-time feud. . . ."

Mrs. O'Toole entered the office with a letter in her hand. She placed it on Dr. Cadman's desk.

Mrs. O'Toole: "Dr. I. withdrew [his application to the residency training program]."

Cadman: "That's too bad." He looked at his list of names which represented his ranking of the candidates he considered acceptable. "I ranked him fifth."

11:10 A.M.   (Cadman glanced at the clock on his wall.) "Jesus Christ! Where's that bastard Bolen?"

Cadman picked up his papers and went into Suprin's office. They began to go through the listing of acceptable candidates, each having drawn up his list independently.

Cadman: "I. withdrew. He accepted a residency elsewhere, although he didn't say where."

Suprin: "That's good.[4] That'll make things more comfortable." He crossed the applicant's name off his list, and suggested another that he put in its place.

11:17 A.M.   Dr. Suprin received a phone call from Dr. Bolen. Bolen read off the names of the residents he would take for training in his unit during the next academic year. Suprin copied them down.

The actual rewards that Dr. Cadman achieved in working with students and residents was unclear in the above context, so several days later, the issue was broached again. In the context of a much more peaceful day, Dr. Cadman still spoke with conviction.

". . . I have a very selfish motive in choosing the people I work with. I take in and work with only those I think I will get something from. Either I can learn something from him, or get something out of him, or else I think that he will carry a little

---

4 The reader will see this difference between Cadman and Suprin develop, Suprin's specialization being around a rational, unloving emphasis on getting people out of the hospital; and Cadman's around an emotional, supportive emphasis on letting people stay on in the hospital.

bit of me into the future. I tell the residents: 'If you got something from me, pass it along. If you didn't, destroy it.' Some of the residents feel some hostility toward me, and they thank me profusely. Others thank me for what it was worth. It's a very sentimental thing. I hope that someone will do the same thing for my kids. . . . If you want to get grandiose or delusional about it, I'm looking after my posterity. That's what I get out of it."

Rewarding as it was, this orientation toward training and trainees also had its frustrations and ill temper. Dr. Cadman preferred not to dwell on this subject, but he pointed to it by example—"It's the Chief who picks up the ash trays"—on a number of different occasions. After an attempt to prompt an advanced resident into actively assuming responsibilities incumbent to his position in the hospital, Dr. Cadman remarked as follows.

"We are a training organization. That is our principal objective. We try to get them [the residents] to do it themselves, to think it out, and to sweat it out themselves. They always want us to decide. Believe me, it would often be easier to do it ourselves than to try and get them to work it through on their own."

Latent Roles and Latent Issues

There was a widely recognized familistic component in this, Dr. Cadman's cardinal orientation to the hospital and to his participation in it. Like a parent, he fondly watched over the "young men coming up" and supported them in their tribulations as neophyte therapists. But like a parent, he often experienced considerable stress and strain in working administratively to produce the best possible clinical environment in which these young professionals could grow up. These analogies were certainly not lost on him, and there were times when, like most parents, he seemed to ruminate about growing old, and about the inevitable consequences that accompany the process of aging. There was more than one face to these ruminations. It sometimes appeared somewhat as though Dr. Cadman liked to feel trapped by the fact he was growing older. He mused about this with a colleague of approximately the same age.

Cadman: "I'm past the stage of moving. I only have 13 years to go. No one would want to invest big money in me at this point. I thought I could spend the last 10 years of my life here playing around in the clinical research area. But as I grow older, I find I can do less of what I want, not more. You can only do research when you're young."

Then, having set the stage for the next remark, Dr. Cadman stepped back and let his colleague have the last word on the subject.

Colleague: "Yes, there is always something to do. Somebody always wants something."

It appeared to the observer that this phenomenon was more one of wanting to feel trapped—wanting to feel victimized—than one of actually being trapped or victimized. Dr. Cadman obviously had too profound an appreciation of his unique skills and attributes to hold any firm conviction that he could no longer be master of his fate in the professional realms of psychiatry and psychoanalysis; if not in the hospital, then outside of it. Such easily verbalized resignation to the inevitabilities of the life cycle and to the inexorabilities of life in organizations must be understood in terms of the psychoanalytic culture of much of the hospital. People in the hospital often talked, sometimes jokingly, to each other about their personal problems. In so doing, they revealed issues that were apparently genuine, but also not too problematic. A function of these casual, controlled intimacies was that each conversationalist could use his listeners to practice the conceptual scheme of his profession, to share personal insights, and to develop solidarity with people whose view of life was the same.

Dr. Cadman experienced, in fact, a freedom in his position

in the hospital that he was able to contrast with his perceptions of the personal subjugation required of business executives by the organizations of which they were members.

"Most of the men in my neighborhood are businessmen," he told the observer. "They are the transients of the neighborhood. I couldn't live as they do. One of my neighbors works for [a well known corporation]. Our kids pal around together. I met him through our kids. He's a skilled engineer, and a very good executive. Well, his company wanted him to move to the West Coast, so he did. He moved his whole family out there. I mean, the company pays all the removal expenses and all that, but he still had to pull up and move his whole family out there. The thing that gets me is he didn't want to go. He likes it here. He would like to stay here. But he didn't say no. He's a talented executive, but he didn't even feel free to *discuss* the matter! I get the feeling he's a victim in his own organization. He can't feel part of it. There are always others just as smart as he is who would go in his place. The boss probably knows this, and plays one off against the other. Everybody is always waiting for promotions and transfers.

"You know, I sometimes go to one of their cocktail parties. I usually refuse, but sometimes I can't think up a good enough excuse. You know why I refuse? I can't stand them. They wear me out. I can go and just look, you know? But still they wear me out. Everybody's sweating it. The husbands are sweating it with the boss' wife, and the wives are sweating it with the boss. You know what I mean? Shining up to them, being nice, saying nice things, letting the hands be a little free, perhaps. And all the while not giving a damn for that other person. Can you imagine the difference between that and what the husband and wife must say to each other when they are alone? And think what it does to them! They are scared people. This is a nation of scared people, you know that? A nation of scared people.

"And when you meet someone who isn't sweating it like all the rest, who isn't making up, a collected person—you know what I mean?—one who's quiet and confident; then you can know for sure that he's a guy who can do something nobody else can do."

A Sense of Identity: Oneness in the Person-Position Encounter

The data have indicated that the clinical director was indeed an actualization of his own model of the inconspicuously self-assured individual, secure in his realization of a rare skill, and dedicated to unimpeachably altruistic goals. It is difficult to communicate the forcefulness with which he dramatized this to those around him. Again using himself as a teaching instrument, he would sometimes muse aloud to those around him about the developmental issues he had faced in his professional career, in a way not unlike the following.

Observer: "Would you say that one of your basic hopes in training the residents—your posterity, as you called them [in a conversation of the preceding week]—is that they will go into your field of work?"

Cadman: "Yes, it is. And they do. Of the people that were with me at [another hospital] there are [he listed several names] who are still doing this sort of work. . . . I don't heistate to seduce people to work in this field if I think they can take it. Of course, I don't seduce people into the area if I don't think they can stand it once they are in it. It takes a particular type of person to do this sort of work. I had one man who was just asking to be seduced, but he wouldn't have made out. He wanted to see results too quickly, and if anything went wrong, he got to feeling very blue."

Observer: "So the payoffs are a long time coming in this area, is that it?"

Cadman (smiling) : "The payoffs are very small indeed, and far apart. Sometimes they never come at all."

Observer: "What holds you to it?"

Cadman: "It's a wide open area. Not much is known, and there is so much to know."

Observer: "The frontier, again."

Cadman: "Very much the frontier. And at a more personal

level, I'm afraid of death. . . . And there's more than one type
of death. There's death when your body gives out, and there's
death that goes on every day, day after day."

Observer: "Sort of a living death."

Cadman: "Sure, when they're dead on their feet—When a guy
can't live, and give a little bit to others, and get a little bit back.
When he can't transact a little bit of the business [of life].
That's a schizophrenic, you know.

"It goes back to when I was nine, during the first World War."

Observer: "In the midwest?"

Cadman: "Sure. And people were dying like flies, of influenza
—you know, in a small town with inadequate medical facilities—
and I had responsibility thrust on me, much more than I could
bear at the time, and I was terrified. That's when I decided to be
a doctor. I wanted to become an internist, and then a diagnos-
tician, you know? So I could tell what was wrong with people.
Only, all the time I was learning these things, I felt vaguely
dissatisfied. . . . I'd take a patient and work him up, and put
him through all the machines, and then I'd look at all my data
and have to diagnose him as organically sound and healthy.
So I'd take it to the neurologist, and he'd say, 'Sure. He's a psychoneurotic.' Well, we'd have this tag on him—psychoneurotic
—so what do we do with him now? 'Talk to him,' he'd say. So I
started talking with him, and pretty soon I found out that they
wanted to talk with me. I found out that I was the sort of person that people wanted to tell their troubles to. I even did a
little study with 100 patients diagnosed as psychoneurotic."

The immediacy and forcefulness with which Dr. Cadman
related his current professional and organizational commitments to the developmental experiences of his entire life—his
childhood, his studies, his internship, his experiences in this
and other hospitals, in the army, and in private practice—
conveyed the impression that here was a man who was making
use of everything that he possessed and had experienced. Here
was someone who did not believe in "sunk costs," who had
not written off or blocked out segments of his life, who had

taken it all and achieved a well-integrated personal system. This produced a consonance of person, position, task, and role in the organization that carried forward, almost inertially, through situations in which Cadman's role was quite obviously out of line with the duties and privileges thought by others to be incumbent upon the man who was clinical director.

The stresses and strains that Cadman experienced resulted, in part, from his role specialization. They came, so to speak, from *outside* his role. He did not experience as much stress arising from *within* his role as did the superintendent, who faced the inside-outside issue mentioned earlier, or the assistant superintendent, who faced the researcher-administrator dilemma to be described. There was a unity, a sense of permanence, about Cadman's role that did not adhere to as great an extent to the other two executive roles. Throughout most of his interactions in the hospital he was perceived, and perceived himself, almost unidimensionally as simply "the sort of person that people want to tell their troubles to."

There was no talk of what Cadman would "do next." The tacit assumption was that he would continue to do in the future what he had been doing in the recent past, that he would continue to act as he had acted, and continue to be what he had so successfully been to those who had studied under him. All this, despite the fact that the growth of the hospital and the increased size of the residency training program was making it increasingly difficult for him to maintain this role. Occasionally he talked of the necessity of changing his role, but never that he was planning to change it. Occasionally he mused about private practice outside the hospital, but only in moments of administrative turmoil, or "collective desperation," as he termed it. In calmer periods, he told the observer:

"My primary commitment is to the hospital. Why do I see patients in my office here at the hospital, instead of in my private office at home? I take patients at the hospital so that I can remain available. If the court letters don't happen to be available before 3 o'clock, I can pick them up between my 3 P.M. and my 4 P.M. patients. If the residents, after their evening rounds, want to confer about something with me, they can catch me between my 4 P.M. and my 5 P.M. patients.

"My commitment here has slowed down my progress in other organizations, you know. For instance, I became a member of the Institute in 1948. If I'd been in private practice, I could have accumulated enough experience to be a teaching analyst in four or five years. Instead, I became a training analyst only two years ago.

"I take several training analysands now. In two or three years when my present patients have wound up their business with me, I'll be taking only training analysands. Then, this too, becomes part of the clinical training picture."

Career Development Beyond the Early Adult Years

A reading of the literature on career development indicates, by default, that the dynamics of career development terminate in the early twenties. Such an accent on youth implies that from age 25 or 30 onwards the individual merely consolidates certain immutable career resolutions and repeats certain activity patterns that bring him continuing success or get him more deeply into trouble. According to this conception, beyond the early adult years the basic decisions and involvements are "given," and any sort of reappraisal, agonizing or otherwise, is implicitly surrendered as a prerogative and a burden of the late adolescent and immediately post-adolescent period.

The data gathered in this study, pertaining to men who were in their late forties and mid-fifties, indicate clearly that this view of career development is incomplete. These executives were still very much involved in working through a continually evolving series of person-position resolutions, the performance of which constituted their careers.

The "clinical training picture" was the purposive *Gestalt* of Dr. Cadman's work life, and it was meaningful that he should return to it so forcefully and explicitly in reflecting on his probable course of future career development. The clinical training picture was Cadman's major orientation in his pedagogical and administrative engagements within the organization. It was the "ball," so to speak, on which he kept his eyes during the interpersonal "game" that the writers are describing. Returning to it near the end of the observer's time with him, Cadman re-established the ascendancy of clinical learning in his work within the hospital.

His statement also denoted certain long-term differences in patterns of career development between himself and Dr. Suprin. The latter had built his career through constant utilization of the role-themes of builder, legalist, administrator, and teacher. Holding these constant, so to speak, he had varied his position-settings in order to get the maximum utilization out of his highly cathected role-themes. For Dr. Suprin, this lesser embracement of position-settings had produced many internal rewards and external results, because it freed him from the necessity of having to cut down on proven role-themes in order better to fit into a given position-setting. Dr. Suprin held tightly onto this personal freedom from the Procrustean bed of position-settings, and he demonstrated this forcefully to those around him. It was important to him to have this freedom, and to have others realize that he had it. This he communicated formally by his antibureaucratic stance on patient administration, and informally by many jesting remarks such as the one he made to the observer: "Maybe I'll go into surgery next."

In *comparison,* Dr. Cadman's greater embracement of a given position-setting was manifested in his statement about his planned future activities: "This, too, becomes part of the clinical training picture." Over the course of his career, Dr. Cadman's range of position-settings had not been as great as

Dr. Suprin's. Put more positively, Dr. Cadman preferred to go more deeply into a narrower range of commitments in position-settings. For him, clinical teaching in psychiatry and psychoanalysis was more all-encompassing than it was for Dr. Suprin. Within that position-setting Dr. Cadman appeared to be readying himself for a change of role-themes: from charismatic inspirer of younger medical students and residents to training analyst of older, less malleable psychiatrists.

There were different sets of cost and reward associated with these different patterns of career development. The professional eminence of both men indicates that each in his own way had utilized himself to very productive and satisfying ends. The undercurrent of costs was much less apparent, but it was there. The variability of Dr. Suprin's position-settings led him to speculate quietly, on one occasion, when he was "alone" in his office with the observer: "Perhaps I have too many interests . . . maybe I didn't get as much accomplished as if I'd drawn a bead on something and really worked on it."

For Dr. Cadman, the embracement of one basic position-setting led him to the necessity of having to live with the realization and the actuality of never being the No. 1 man in the organizational context to which he had chosen to devote himself. Also, the changing of role-themes contributed to his somewhat foreboding sense of growing old. By contrast, Dr. Suprin was approximately the same age—both men were in their early or middle fifties—but he manifested little of this concern about growing older. Perhaps his continued utilization of the role-themes of his early adult years contributed to his aura of youthfulness and enduring vitality.

These issues of role-theme and position-setting were also found to be operational in the evolving career development of the assistant superintendent, and we will return to them at the end of the next chapter.

CHAPTER 6

The Assistant Superintendent: Fostering the Development of Creative People and Their Ideas

AGAIN, the role-analytic framework of this chapter is the same as in the preceding two. We shall begin by establishing the purposive orientation that underlay the assistant superintendent's observed behavior. Then we move on to an analysis of the personal dynamics and interpersonal consequences of that behavior.

THE PURPOSIVE CONTEXT OF ADMINISTRATION

THE ACTIVITIES of the day had for the assistant superintendent, as for the other executives, both the immediate objective of maintaining hospital operations, and the longer-term vectors that characterized the individual's professional interests and his personal idiosyncrasies. Our analysis will move from the activities of the day, through the professional interests expressed therein, toward the personality that was being expressed as the assistant superintendent went about the business of managing the research programs and the nonmedical departments of the hospital.

Work as a Way of Life

The assistant superintendent was also no stranger to hard work. He had worked in the hospital longer than the other two top executives. While in medical school, Dr. Asche had become interested in physiological research and had developed the desire "to go beyond what was in the textbooks," as he put it. Shortly thereafter, he entered the hospital's residency training program and soon became involved in research in the hospital. After his residency, he stayed on at the hospital to combine clinical and research work, and was then appointed director of the research laboratory. The research organization in the hospital was, at that time, quite small. Dr. Asche carried on his research and, as a research administrator, encouraged and assisted others to do likewise. After Dr. Asche was appointed assistant superintendent of the hospital, his primary commitment continued to be to research administration, rather than to the administration of the hospital in any routine sense.

The results of Asche's work were considerable. The list of publications that bore his name amounted to slightly over 150 articles and books in several of the branches of science pertaining to psychiatry. Also, the hospital's summary of research projects, at the time of the study, listed 40 research projects requiring the attentions of approximately 200 people. It was under Dr. Asche's administration that this large and varied program of research came into being.

The observer was rapidly made aware of the reality and the mystique of hard work that surrounded Dr. Asche's life in and around the hospital. The theme of purposeful activity meant much to him. He would talk about his work readily, articulately, and with a great deal of infectious enthusiasm. As with the other top executives, his work was not confined to the hospital setting or to the usual hospital hours. Dr. Asche expressed particular pleasure about the professional activities he performed outside of regular working hours—in the evenings and on weekends—as though these extra efforts produced extraordinary feelings of productiveness and satisfaction.

The observer arrived at the hospital early one morning to accompany Dr. Asche on one of his teaching rounds. Asche approached the ward conference room, apparently coming from his office. The observer inquired about this.

"Yes," Asche replied. "I was tired last night, so I didn't get any work done. I went for a bicycle ride instead. But I came in early this morning and read a couple of hundred pages of a social work manuscript. It's good stuff. I think we are going to be able to make something of it."

Not infrequently, Dr. Asche would enter the hospital around 9 A.M. and walk unhurriedly through the corridors and up the steps to his office. Looking somewhat sleepy around the eyes, he would enter his secretary's office to begin the business of the day by checking out what was on his calendar for that day. The observer came to ask regularly what Dr. Asche had done overnight or over the weekend, since the two of them had last interacted. "Oh, jeez," was one of his not untypical replies. "It was great. Teriff!" He would then proceed to describe his accomplishments during the period of time in question.

Observer: "Did you have a good weekend, Doctor?"

Asche: "I'll say. I had a terrific weekend. I got so much done, I even amazed myself. I read several of these reports. [These were research reports, which he proceeded to specify.] Then I got to work on this drugs and social business, and produced this." He lifted the manuscript. "I spent Saturday afternoon watching my son play football. Boy, you should see those boys play. Not just my son. Do they ever go at it! They throw everything they've got into it, and then some. They sure go after each other. *Crack!*" He drove his right fist into the palm of his left hand, and winced. "You can hear it all the way to the sidelines. My wife and I, we look at one another. We kind of wonder how anyone can get out alive. You'd think it would be almost tougher on the parents than on the kids, but it's not. They're there, yelling and screaming louder than the rest of them. Boy, they sure take it seriously."

Asche's secretary had entered, and Asche handed her the manuscript on "drugs and social" as he talked. "Then, on top of that I bought three pocket books and finished those off yesterday."

Observer: "It sounds like quite a weekend."
Asche: "Yeah, I was feeling great." He turned to his secretary.
"Ready for action?"
Secretary: "Mm, hm."
"O.K. Here it goes," said Asche, and he began to dictate letters.

Dr. Asche's ideas and feelings about work integrated well
with the values shared widely by his professional colleagues
engaged in research and administration. Working hard and
talking about working hard were primary elements in a code
that united Dr. Asche with the shifting nexus of people
around him; persons of varied professional backgrounds,
coming and going about their several careers, but all to a
greater or lesser extent devoted to the expansion of knowledge in psychiatry and related disciplines. Dr. Asche put it in
the following way.

"They're my type of guy," he said. "We're all cut from the same
cloth. We speak the same sort of language."

In fact, the several professional and scientific groups with
whom Dr. Asche had contact had considerably different technical languages, but the theme of work, dedication, and discipline exerted a smoothly integrating effect upon even those
parties whose manifest purposes were potentially antagonistic. For instance, the hospital received a visit from officials
of the Public Health Service concerning the hospital's application for funds to conduct research. The application was for
a large amount of money. Dr. Asche, who was in charge of
the hospital's preparations for the visit, observed to those who
were working with him, "We've got to justify that amount of
money for the next three years. Some of them [the visitors]
might find that swallowing that sum is tough, since it is more
money than most of them will ever see in their own research.
What are we going to say to justify it?" He and the others
proceeded to organize their replies.

At 9:30 A.M. the switchboard operator phoned from the lobby to say that Dr. Hill had arrived. Dr. Asche went down to meet him. They greeted each other warmly, and Asche invited Hill to his office.

Hill: "I don't want to disturb you. Let me go off by myself until some of the others have arrived. I don't want to disturb you unnecessarily."

Asche: "Not at all. Not at all. Come on up and chat till the others get there. I've got some of the boys in the office. They'd like to meet you."

On the way back to Asche's office, Hill mentioned that he had received a copy of Asche's new book. He shook his head and smiled. "I don't see how you do it. Tell me, how *do* you do it?"

"Oh, I just work," replied Asche. "That's all. Just hard work. There is no other way, at least none that I know of. But maybe, that's because I'm too dumb to know any better." The two men laughed, and Asche continued: "My students at the medical school used to ask me what I studied, and when I did my work. I always told them I studied two things: big things and little things. And that I worked only two times: day and night. But I guess you must be working pretty hard yourself these days, from what I hear," Asche observed.

Hill: "Yes, I guess I'll have to allow but what I have, although my family objects. But I do it because I enjoy it, not for success or for monetary gain, which are two motives that have been adequately satisfied. You know, I really believe that people are truly at their happiest when they are hard at work. I don't think that is something people have to learn, either. Just look at the way a child will work away at something that interests him; that joyful intensity with which he attacks an absorbing task, with that wonderful feeling of self-forgetting and complete immersion in what he is doing. We hear a lot about competence and the drive to succeed these days, but I think this engrossment in work is really quite separate from questions of ability and success."

Hill's tone and intensity brooked no logical, dialectical repartee as to the representativeness of his portrayal of childhood, or its appropriateness in considering adult work habits. Asche received Hill's statement enthusiastically, smiling and nodding his head vigorously.

The occasions **Dr.** Asche took to express this ideology of work were numerous. One day, as Dr. Asche set out for one of his regular weekly visits to a municipal psychiatric unit he had helped to establish, the observer walked with him to the bus station near the hospital.

Observer: "Did you work this weekend?"
Asche: "Did I? I'll say! I read some more of that I was telling you about. I did several hours of Johnson's work. . . . My purpose there is, I suppose, first to help him in his research, and to find out what it's like for the poor clinician who would have to rate his patients this way. Then I read several hundred pages of the ABC Project write-ups. Some of them [the researchers] were having trouble with their data, and now I see why. Then I read an excellent monograph on operant conditioning. I worked some more on the Fiezl paper. It's still pretty thin. I got my wife to help me with it. I read a manuscript that Kastner has written up for publication; some sort of potboiler. I don't see where a fellow his age should be writing potboilers. That's for the old guys, like Frank [Suprin] and me. A young fellow like that should be working close to his data—at the creative interface—not turning out potboilers.

"And I had a meeting with Jerome: me and my wife with him and his wife, sort of to re-establish contacts that my work doesn't seem to let me do any more. We had dinner together; then he and I sat down together to talk about our project. We talked about the good papers, and we felt good together; and we talked about the bad papers, and we felt bad together. We talked about how this fellow Pierce would work out. He's still pretty much of an unknown. We have no data on him, but we're going to watch him closely to see how he develops. Then there's Jane Shanks, who isn't turning out quite as we expected, and we've got to figure out what to do with her. . . . Jerrie is not going to let it drag along all winter. We talked about Zahka and how he seems to be working out on the project. Zahka looks good!"

Mobilizing the Work of the Future

This statement by Dr. Asche illustrates the very real concern he experienced regarding the mobilization and utilization of research resources. He was greatly involved in the search for, and development of, the individual creative talents he saw to be the *sine qua non* of research. He was also very attuned to and skillful at the mobilization of the financial resources needed for the complex and long-term research being carried on at the hospital. Most of the money that supported this research came from governmental and private agencies beyond the hospital's immediate sphere of influence. This money was usually granted for particular projects, and for relatively short periods of time. Thus, the continuity of research was often problematic and could only be maintained through constant skilled attention to research proposals that would win against other proposals in the competition for the limited funds that these agencies had to give; through constant attention to the maintenance of high theoretical and methodological research standards, to the completion and publication of research, and to the perpetual writing, rewriting, and submission of grant applications. Dr. Asche's adaptation to the life of "grantism" and his success in the "grant business" were considerable. "We are becoming experts at writing up research proposals around here," he jokingly observed.

The superintendent was more direct and less modest about this skill. "Howie is the best damn grant application writer in the country," he said of Dr. Asche.

"When he finds out that there is money available," Dr. Suprin continued, "he goes out after it, and he usually gets it."

On another occasion, Dr. Suprin developed further on this theme. "Howie's a gem," he said. "He has a way with him. All he has to do is to stand there"—Suprin gesticulated, opening his side pockets with his fingers, and looking upward as to heaven with an expression of ingenuous hopefulness on his face—"and the money falls right into his pockets."

Mobilizing the Workers of the Future

Important as these financial matters were, Asche's concern for the mobilization and utilization of human resources was greater. His interest in the human development aspects of running a hospital and a research organization was manifested in a wide variety of ways: from formal written statements to spontaneous expressions of enthusiasm in casual interactive settings. A particularly direct expression of this interest was found in Dr. Asche's foreword to a synopsis of M.P.I. research studies in which he stated:

"It is apparent that, like Birk,[1] we believe in the 'fecundity of aggregates'—in an assemblage of vigorous minds with diverse points of view, with opportunities for free exchange and collaboration according to their natural affinities, plus progressive enrichment of the company as new disciplines or areas of thought arise which promise to illuminate human behavior in health and disease."

Dr. Asche was active in attracting and selecting people whom he considered talented to work in the several operations of the hospital. He considered himself greatly assisted in this by the richness of professional resources and the climate of activity in the hospital to which he himself had contributed.

"I don't think I could tell you of a more successful group of researchers than the one we have in this hospital," he said to a statistician who was considering a research position in the hospital. "I think you'll find this a very exciting place. You can learn almost anything you want around here—psychology, psychiatry, neurophysiology—anything along those lines. You can go a very long way, just as far as you want. There's always something going on."

[1] Dr. Seymour Birk, first superintendent of the hospital.

Getting people to work in the hospital and getting them to make the most of their talents were two separate issues. Dr. Asche invested his energies in both. He considered the interest of an individual and the interest of the hospital to be in no way opposed.

"I want you to make your own name," he told the above-mentioned statistician. "The better known you become in your area, the more use you are to us. The more publications you get out on your own, or with the persons you choose to work with, because you are attracted to them, or for psychological or intellectual reasons, the higher status you make our operation here. We could hire a high status man right away, but our primary concern is to develop our relationship with Jacob Orlinsky. And if he says hire somebody who hasn't made a name for himself yet, O.K. We can wait it out."

Getting people to make the most of themselves was not always an easy task. Sometimes, Dr. Asche's efforts along these lines took a lot out of him; requiring him to assert himself in ways that did not come naturally to him, in which he was not particularly skilled, and which upset him considerably. One illustration of this is the following:

2:15 P.M.   Asche spoke to a research worker on the phone. He pressed the researcher to hurry up with his rewrite of a monograph.
Asche: "We can't keep them waiting any longer. In case you are worried, it is an *important* work! The students and the residents are turning to it a lot. They think it is a useful monograph with a useful bibliography. It's a vital piece of work. . . . Sure, I know, but it falls more in the category of social action, not in pure research. . . . You *will* get criticisms, of course, but you can't let them hurt you, Ernie. Someone is bound to criticize. Some will like what you did, and others will want you to have done something else. You know that. It happens every time, no matter how good it is. You can't let them hurt you. I know about

you. I know the way you are. . . . *Please* Ernie! You got all the strength you need to withstand that sort of thing. . . . Look. I'll take a chapter and rewrite it for you, if you want it. . . . How's that? . . . I'm willing to take the time. It's worth it to me. I want to see some payoff coming from all this work. . . . No, I don't need the credit. Nobody is going to hold up any grants if I don't get credit. People are very kind to me that way. They think we are doing *good work* here. . . . For God's sake. Let's get it out. I think we are well ahead of the game, but I don't want anyone to beat us to the punch. O.K.? O.K."

Asche hung up and turned to the observer. "I know that guy. He won't let a manuscript out of his hands. He's scared of being criticized. I had to put it to him. That's the only way I know to stir him up."

INTERPERSONAL TRANSACTIONS AROUND WORK: PERFORMANCE AND RESPONSE

WE HAVE OUTLINED the nature of the assistant superintendent's work in the hospital. In so doing, we have conveyed something of the nature of the man. Now we turn the focus of our analysis to a more explicit assessment of the individual who was assistant superintendent, the manner in which he performed in that position, and how he "came across" in the process. The assistant superintendent's role performance cannot be described except in relation to the work he was doing as assistant superintendent. We attempt to highlight *both* elements of Dr. Asche's total performance.

The Personal Appeal to Creativity: Accentuating the Positive

The above incident demonstrated a way of dealing with people that Dr. Asche preferred to avoid. He considered it more productive to address the positive side of people, as he was attempting to do above. But he was having to do it in an aggressive and peremptory manner, and this was a form of interaction in which he was not at all comfortable.

"You have to address the healthy part of the ego," he said
when questioned about his administrative behavior and the
thinking that directed that behavior.

"You can't let yourself get drawn into this stuff," he said, pointing to the contents of an angry letter. "Otherwise there'd be no
end to it. We'd *never* get anything done. . . ."

Dr. Asche tried always to emphasize the positive elements
in any purposive setting in which he was involved. He often
tried *not* to draw attention to weaknesses, and sometimes he
tried to draw people *away* from such preoccupations or insights. Criticism was an activity in which he did not often
indulge.

"I don't try to tear down the things I don't like," he said. "I
hope that if I work hard enough at it, they will drop out anyway and be replaced by the good stuff."

Critical sophistication was not a quality he appreciated in
people administratively responsible for the furtherance of
research. He considered that such a tendency on the part of
an administrator destroyed more research than it produced.
An incident from a research conference demonstrated these
opinions, and the sort of administrative action that resulted
therefrom.

. . . Next, the group discussed the design and procedure of
the project. Several places in which to do the research were suggested. One of the suggested research sites was —— Hospital. The
assistant superintendent discouraged this. He referred to the experience of one of the researchers from another project with
Dr. T. of the —— Hospital.

"T. is a great analyst and critic," Asche observed. "Perhaps too
much so. He raised all sorts of questions. They were good questions, but they were hardly relevant to the project. Why, someone from over there came here to look at our records recently.
All I did was phone the record room and tell them to let him
in. That's all. We gave him a room and everything. They thought
this hospital was a wonderful place to work in."

Such was Dr. Asche's belief in regard both to the administration of specific projects and to the over-all course of the development of psychiatry. He admired those of his colleagues whose administrative behavior reflected a similar positive approach, especially those whom he thought were even more effective at it than he. One day, he picked a letter off the desk of one of his secretaries.

"Here's one," he said enthusiastically after he had read over the letter.

Observer: "One what?"

Asche: "One of the best [administrators] in the country." He showed the letter to the observer, pointing to the laudatory highlights contained therein.

"He's always emphasizing the positive aspects of things," Asche concluded. "I've never heard him say a bad word about anybody. He always has a positive orientation to things, and he's always moving things ahead."

Dr. Asche considered this administrative approach to be the most suitable for fostering research and creativity.

Viewing Research and Creativity as a Life Process

There was a great sense of immediacy in Dr. Asche's interest in research and creativity. In his way of thinking, phenomena such as enthusiasm, dedication, energy, creativity, research, and personal development were so highly interrelated as to be inseparable. It took good men to do good research, he thought, but doing good research somehow made a good man better. Working at the "creative interface" between the known and the unknown, and fulfilling the obligation to "come up with the goods" and to report them in the literature; that to Dr. Asche was what increased a man in stature. This was a major source of Asche's satisfaction as a research administrator. There were several people in whose personal and career development he believed he had been of help. He took great pleasure in their work, but his delight focused more directly on what these people had become or were becoming in the process of their working relations with him; on the release of their creativity, on the realization of their talent, and on a heightened sense of their being. He described the self-realization that one man had experienced in the work that he—Asche—had helped organize. "In other words," Asche concluded, throwing his arm forward in an expansive gesture, "he's becoming more of a *man*."

Asche believed that the proper way to enter into research was to *do* research, as a response to one's curiosity and an outlet for one's creativity. Any system of prerequisite training that was at all elaborate or prolonged met with his impatient disapproval. He was more interested in nourishing a neophyte's curiosity and enthusiasm in the process of doing research, and he was concerned about the stultifying effects of any training program that held a potential researcher away from his field of interest for any period of time whatsoever. Asche expressed his thoughts to a resident in the following way:

Asche: "I think our training program has made the residents happy, and has developed great clinical insight in them. But I don't think the creative side has been cultivated enough. By that I mean imagination, and working on other projects than the ones they are involved in every day. I mean the pursuit of learning outside their own fields; like mathematics, or something like that. I don't think my colleagues would agree when I talk about creativity, and the cultivation of the instrumentalities for its release. . . ."

Resident: "I guess that brings up what we feel. What is it in us that is creative? So much has been routinized; narrowed down."

Asche: "Yes, that's right. Narrowed down. Now in England . . . I have some questions about what they're up to, but they do pay some attention to the inner man. They get it from basic questions, almost down to the artistic vents of self-expression. Now that's what I want to cultivate here. Dr. X says we can't do research until we are trained properly in psychiatry. I don't agree. If Dr. X is right, then nobody is ready for research until they are as old as Dr. X. He says that it takes 15 years of intensive work before a person is matured for psychiatric research. That means the man is between 40 to 45 before he is ready. I think the answer is well given by Max Levin. He says that training for research is like training for parenthood. If we waited till we were properly prepared for parenthood before we became parents, we would be well out of our libido. We would be too old to have children. I believe we should take them [people interested in research] as they are, and move on from there."

The resident's response was less than enthusiastic. He presented an alternative point of view to Dr. Asche's, and it became apparent that neither agreed with the other.

Asche: "Well, that is probably true. But that is the sort of stuff we don't get enough of. Another thing is that we don't spend enough time helping to make the research interesting for the researcher. We don't help the research man to have fun. Research is a hell of a lot of precision work. We should make it more fun for the people involved."

Asche was quick to sense any expediency in a person's expressed desire to do research. It was with considerable skepticism and some distaste that he viewed anybody who was carefully considering whether or not it would be a good thing to do a bit of research, or who was considering what were the avenues of research most likely to pay off in any short-term sense. Anyone who did not express or seem otherwise to have genuine research interests and enthusiasms was not judged too favorably by Dr. Asche insofar as that person's potential contribution to research was concerned. This is illustrated by Dr. Asche's evaluation of the above-mentioned resident. Throughout a lengthy interview, the resident showed no tendency to come to grips with the research alternatives that Asche was forced to propose to him.

The resident dwelt more on what did not interest him than on what did. He expressed what seemed to be his central preoccupation in the following words:

"I would like to find out my limitations. I don't think I am a basic scientist. I was never very good at biochemistry and things like that. I think I'm more of a clinical man. My interest has been rather diverse so far. It seems that I can get interested in many of the peripheral areas of psychiatry, but I don't have any principal interest so far. . . ."

After that interview had ended, Dr. Asche gave his evaluation of the resident in question. He felt that the resident was "well-educated and a very sharp fellow," but that he lacked "the zip and enthusiasm that it takes to be a good researcher." The resident, he thought, was "almost too well-rounded," whose "motivations are based largely on expedience."

"He needs money," Dr. Asche observed, "for an analysis. The need for money seemed to be stronger than the need to do research. He was expressing a typical resident pattern in wanting to do extra work to get extra money for the purpose of analysis. This is almost irrelevant to the desire to do research."

Interpersonal Style in Teaching and Research Administration

This emphasis on spontaneity in research tended to affect the assistant superintendent's administrative and teaching behavior. When Dr. Asche spoke to those around him about creativity and research, his own behavior tended to become expansive and demonstrative. In fact, he demonstrated his sentiments about research with a physical exhilaration that was quite similar to the feelings he conveyed in his enthusiasm and respect for his sons' athletic achievements. He once told his undergraduate psychology class that man was only a short hop from his ancestors, and that he was meant to swing from the trees and exert himself physically all day long. "It's only recently that man has become sedentary, and it gets him into some difficulty," Asche concluded.

This physical expansiveness manifested itself most strongly when Dr. Asche was feeling either in a creative mood or in a creative environment, or both. Then he made statements such as, "This is the search for creative talent" or "We've got to help these guys be *creative!*" He often accompanied these enthusiastic statements with vigorous physical gestures, usually clenching one or both hands into fists and shooting his arm or arms straight over his head, or straight out in front of him in a punching motion. After a chat with a teacher of social work, Dr. Asche walked from his office into the corridor, swinging his arms windmill fashion in his exuberance about facilitating the creative process.

Asche chatted with Miss Patten, head of social work, about one of her social workers who had just presented a paper that day.

Miss Patten: "How do you like how her mind works? I think it is wonderful. It is one of those rare combinations of both the systematic and the imaginative."

Asche: "Yes, she has a very rich association. It's very rare and wonderful."

Miss Patten: "And she can do something with it, too."

Asche: "She's very creative, and that's what we want. This is the search for creative talent!" He got very enthusiastic as he made this last remark, and leaving his office, walked into the corridor, waving his arms about as he finished his statement.

The enthusiasms the assistant superintendent felt for research sometimes, in the presence of sympathetic and equally devoted listeners, developed into an expansiveness about the future in which Dr. Asche indulged pleasantly, in a jocular manner that indicated he meant what he said, but not too seriously.

After a lunchtime conversation with a research-oriented clinical psychologist whom Asche evaluated highly, and during which these two had animatedly discussed some recent research findings and their implications, Asche was asked the following question.

Psychologist: "What do you think the future of psychiatry will look like?"

Asche pointed to the observer. "I'm trying to impress upon him that my work is determining the future of psychiatry. I keep telling him that what Frank [Suprin] and Cadman are doing is just routine. They take what we have now and are working with it. But I'm the future of psychiatry. I'm helping to push things on, to contribute to the things of the future, helping to determine where psychiatry is going."

The Self-Actualizer as an Ideal Type

Dr. Asche felt most comfortable helping and encouraging people to follow their own interests, and he liked best to deal with people who had interests they wished to follow. He and the superintendent were agreed that, if they had to choose between a researcher who was difficult to control because he stubbornly held to his own interests, and one who was difficult to mobilize because he was not sure what his interests were, they would rather deal with the first. Dr. Asche felt very much at ease when interacting with people who, in one way or another, approximated this paradigm of the headstrong self-actualizer. A number of these people he worked with came from outside the hospital, some of them having once worked in the hospital on a full-time or part-time basis. They represented a wide variety of professional backgrounds, and they often ranged widely in age. When such people met in groups, there was a casualness of dress, speech, and deportment that differed from the somewhat more stylish dress and controlled behavior manifested in groups made up of the hospital's staff and psychiatric residents. There was an equalitarian atmosphere in some of the research group meetings, with fewer expressions of hierarchy and less outward deference to professional wisdom than in the meetings of the clinical groups that were more central to the hospital's operations.

To anyone who made the clinical operations of the hospital his point of reference, there was a foreign feeling to some of the research group meetings. At their best, these meetings developed a spirit, an identity of their own, that meant a great deal to the participants. At their worst, these meetings could be dull, depressing, and apparently futureless.

The meeting that Dr. Asche enjoyed most, during the period of observation, illuminates his own conception of his role in developing the talents that would develop psychiatry. It gives a picture of what the reciprocal behavior of others was like in situations wherein Dr. Asche realized this role conception. It illustrates Asche's preferred style of interaction, and the response he liked to see in the people for whom he cared.

Asche met Singer, the director of the XYZ Project; Parker, the principal author of the original XYZ manuscript; and Titlebaum, a professional writer who had rewritten the manuscript in a way that Asche had found extremely pleasing. (Singer appeared to be a man in his thirties, and the other two in their twenties.) They went off to lunch together.

The cafeteria was crowded, and the group was forced to split up to find table space. Singer and Parker sat at one table. Titlebaum and Asche sat at another with two residents, Drs. Rublin and Rottenberg. Rottenberg left shortly, explaining that he had an analytic hour coming up.

Rublin began to tell Asche how hard he worked—how many hours per week—and how little he got paid for it.

"How much *do* you work?" asked Titlebaum pointedly. Asche smiled at this.

"I work between 70 and 80 hours a week," Rublin replied.

"Go on," said Titlebaum. "Nobody works that hard."

"Well, *I* do," Rublin protested.

"What do you do?" asked Titlebaum.

Rublin: "Lots of things."

Titlebaum: "Like what, for instance?"

Rublin: "I like to be here mostly for my patients."

Titlebaum: "Oh. You mean you're in the hospital for 70 or 80 hours a week."

Rublin: "So what?"

Titlebaum: "So I don't call that work."

"Well, I do," Rublin replied, turning to Asche. "Especially for what I get paid for it."

Titlebaum: "Nonsense. Just think of the pots of dough you'll make when you start taking on private patients. You got any private patients now?"

Rublin: "I'm not that sort of guy. I'd never take on patients just to make money."

Titlebaum laughed.

Asche had been smiling throughout this exchange. He interrupted here and said, "I don't see anything wrong with taking on patients when a fella needs some dough."

Rublin: "I'm not that sort of guy."

Asche tried to get Rublin to specify the hours he spent in the hospital, and the activities he spent them on, but Rublin would not supply the data. He maintained that he spent between 70 and 80 hours a week in the hospital, on hospital business.

"I can't see how," Asche observed.

Titlebaum smiled.

"Well, I *am*," Rublin insisted.

"Oh, I believe you," replied Asche, "That's because you are an honest guy. I don't see how you do it, though. I think that is too much work, even for a young guy like you."

"I like to work that much," said Rublin. "I need to work that much."

Titlebaum smiled: "I don't believe you."

Rublin: "What?"

Titlebaum: "I don't believe you work that much. I don't think anybody can work that much. I'm talking about real work, now. Not just sitting around. *I* work six hours a day."

Rublin: "Six?"

Titlebaum: "Yes, six. I get plenty done in that space of time. I couldn't do any more work than that in a day, and really call it work."

Rublin: "It all depends on the sort of life you lead."

Titlebaum: "I lead a very satisfactory life. I enjoy myself tremendously. Every morning in the winter, I skate in the park. I have a better suntan in the winter than I do in the summer. You have to seize life while you have it." He made a vigorous grasping gesture with his right hand. "You only have it once."

The observer looked over at Asche, who was watching Titlebaum and smiling. When Asche saw the observer glance at him, he winked and nodded his head.

Titlebaum continued: "And I enjoy my work. I must be good at it, because I've got a stack of it waiting for me, and it keeps coming in. Up to here." Another vigorous gesture of the hand. "Then there are the plays, the theatre, interesting friends, books, things to do. I couldn't afford to work more than six hours a day."

Asche was smiling broadly.

Rublin: "That's all right for you, but I couldn't live that sort of life."

Titlebaum shrugged.

The conversation turned to writers, writing styles, and writing procedures. Asche said he was interested in how Titlebaum could be a professional writer in scientific and technical areas, and cope with the advanced states of knowledge in these fields. Titlebaum laughed and replied that he specialized in medical texts. Asche said he would like to get Titlebaum to look at some other work that Asche had in the mill. Titlebaum replied that it was a little out of his line, that he was very busy and did not know when he could get to it, but that he would take a look.

Asche: "I suppose we should get back to work."

Titlebaum: "That's fine with me. That's what I came for."

They arose, leaving Rublin at the table.

On the way back to the conference room, the observer met Parker. He, like Titlebaum, had a pleasant, sociable, self-confident and self-assertive manner.

During the meeting, the two younger men did most of the talking. They demonstrated great familiarity with the content of the manuscript that was being edited. They both had strong opinions, and had no hesitancy in expressing them. They went at the work, and at each other, talking loudly and enthusiasti-

cally. If they had some criticism of the other's work on the manuscript, they said it right out. Neither seemed offended or taken
aback by the other's remarks.

Asche enjoyed himself immensely. He sprawled back in his
chair, smiling, nodding his head, and occasionally glancing
"meaningfully" at the observer. At several points in the meeting,
the observer glanced around to see how Asche was responding,
and Asche nodded and facially expressed his approval of what
was going on.

Both he and Singer were quieter, raising questions now and
then, and putting particularly flamboyant statements—particularly some of Titlebaum's—into a better balanced perspective.
Asche enjoyed these statements, nonetheless, and listened intently
to everything that was said.

Personal Response to Proaction and Passivity

Asche's response to this meeting, and to the people in it,
conveys something of his ideal conception of how researchers
and other creative individuals should be: intelligent, articulate, on top of their data, assertive, enthusiastic, and secure
enough to take criticism openly and undefensively. When in
the company of people who were at all like this, Dr. Asche
became relaxed and slangy. As in the above meeting, he
would not infrequently sprawl casually in his chair, a leg
slung over one of its arms and an arm hooked over its back.
Or he would lean far over the table in front of him, his arms
spread widely, as he listened intently to what was being said,
nodding his approval, and tossing off ideas as they occurred
to him. "Geez," was an expression he used. "Wow. Ain't that
the greatest?" Other participants were often addressed, in
these productive moments, collectively as "the gang," or as
"you guys," or affectionately as "kids."

"Dr. Pierce, the gang," he said in introducing a new member. Or, "Are you guys sure of that?" he inquired. Or, slam-
ming his palm on the table, he ended a meeting with, "O.K.,
kids. That's it." After one meeting, he turned to the observer

and asked, "Well now, what do you think of my researchers?"

Dr. Asche's experience of the less successful meetings was very different. Although he tried not to dwell on them, and would say little about them, the feelings they created in him appeared equally distinct.

9:05 A.M.   Dr. Asche entered his secretary's office looking a little sleepier than usual. Upon inquiry, he reported that he had been at a meeting the night before that had lasted till midnight. The meeting had been devoted to the planning of a project that would provide a place for a small group of ex-patients to live while re-adjusting to life in the community.

Asche described the content of the meeting, and concluded, "It's a tough bit of business."

Observer: "Things aren't going too well?"

Asche: "I'm afraid some things have been let slide longer than they should have. It's not an easy thing, but nobody wants to get in there and do the plain, ordinary, unglamorous administrative detail work that has to be done to keep the thing moving along. Another thing is the fund raising. Some of the members of the board have hustled around and gotten promises of money for the project, but we can't get the money until we get the project certified, and we can't do that until we attend to some of the details. If we don't hurry up, I'm afraid that money will have gone elsewhere. For tax purposes, some of it is going to have to go somewhere by the end of the year. I'm afraid we're going to lose it."

Observer: "That's too bad."

Asche shook his head. "It's a small project," he said quietly, and paused. "Only four patients." He shook his head. "I wonder sometimes whether it's worth the effort, really."

Observer: "It does take a lot of effort, doesn't it?"

Asche was disinclined to examine the matter further. He passed it off with a shrug. "Oh, I don't know," he replied noncommittally.

(Later that day another person who had attended that meeting entered Asche's office.)

Miss Patten: "What did you think of the meeting last night?"

Asche shrugged.

Miss Patten did not share Dr. Asche's tendency to remain silent on unpleasant issues. She replied, "Well, I thought it lacked
spirit. I didn't think it was a good idea to meet there, and I don't
think we should meet there again. There was less spirit there
than there would be right here. People were definitely holding
themselves in check."

The Marginality of the Innovator

It was on occasions such as the above that Dr. Asche was
reminded of the looseness of the network of associations he
had built up around him: that is, how far these relationships
extended beyond the organization of which he was an executive, and how little direct control he had over them. His response to such moments, however, redefined and re-empha-
sized his conviction that he had acted effectively in working
for the things he cared about. An instance of this occurred
after a luncheon meeting Asche attended to discuss one of
the above-mentioned research projects. The following conversation took place as Dr. Asche and the observer drove
slowly back to the hospital after the meeting.

Dr. Asche appeared to have enjoyed himself in the presence of a sympathetic and responsive audience. For instance,
one of the researchers had interrupted himself, and had said
to Asche with a smile, "Oh, I forgot. This is the thing you
always do for me, but I never do for you." Asche had smiled
about this for some time. The observer followed this up.

Observer: "They seem to work well with you."

Asche: "Oh, that Singer's a peach. He and I get on well together. I've helped to bring him along, and he helped me too.
I have several I can work with like that." He spoke briefly of his
two secretaries, and how they helped him with his work. Then
he went on. "Kastner is a hard worker. Ginsberg is too, but he's
inclined to argue too much for my liking. There's nothing he
likes more than his own ideas."

Asche stopped there. It seemed to the observer that Asche had not finished enumerating the people with whom he could work closely. If he had, it was a surprisingly small number of people when compared to the profusion of his work-oriented interactions during most work days. Also, his comments about the two last-mentioned people did not really indicate the basis of a particularly close working relationship between them and Dr. Asche. Finally, there seemed to be an aura of lethargy or depression around this disinclination to talk in specific terms about his working relations. During this exchange, the observer felt something to be missing in Dr. Asche's responses: something that related his enthusiasms for abstract phenomena, such as the advancement of knowledge, to the duller tone he more than once communicated on concrete phenomena, such as his administrative relations with other people.

There were data indicating that other people who interacted with Dr. Asche sometimes received similar impressions. One staff member reported, in the following words, what it was sometimes like to talk with Asche: "Sometimes, after you've spoken to him for a while, you begin to wonder if anybody is at home." This was one response to Dr. Asche's quietness in some settings, and around some issues, where a more active style of interaction and greater expressiveness were expected of him.

These settings often involved disagreements and hostility, and one of the issues was how to tell a subordinate about one's disappointment in him without disrupting whatever satisfactory headway he was making in other ways. Asche frequently held much back in these situations. As will be seen, he tended to take more than his share of responsibility for the transactions that took place in these settings.

On one occasion, a researcher was dissatisfied with this response and went to the superintendent. "When will they ever learn," said Asche, shaking his head, "that when they don't

like what I have to tell them, the last person in the world for
them to see is Frank Suprin. I'm real easy on them, compared with what Frank can be."

The observer continued his conversation with Dr. Asche.

Observer: "Is there anyone in the other research projects you
work with like that?"

There was no reply.

Observer: "How about ——?"

"Oh, yeah," Asche replied. "He's a good worker. Smart." (Silence)

Observer: "How about ——? Do you work well with him?"

Asche: "Yes, him too. He's a good thinker. He's got a fine
mind. Does a good profound job. Slow but high quality. But
there's not much follow-up to his work, for some reason."

Observer: "You seem to have a concept of action research, and
that professional writer you like so much [Titlebaum] embodies
a lot of it."

Asche: "Oh, cripes. That was a beautiful job. It was good. *It
moved.* So much of the stuff I read is fascinating, but it doesn't
move. Boy, he really got into the stuff, didn't he? There were
some parts that were pretty rough, and that are going to have to
be rewritten, but that's partly because of the rough stuff he was
given to work with. There were some parts in there that were
so good, they were just lyrical. Did you see what he did to the
title? . . . It's good. It has a ring to it. We're going to keep that.
And then he starts out the book with this quote from a patient,
on how much the students meant to him. It gets the reader's
imagination right from the start. It's so much better, so much
more appropriate to the material, than the slow, stodgy, over-
reasoned stuff that the sociological boys and the people from
psychology feel they have to write, or else they will be open to
the challenge of sloppy thinking. It's all very well but. . . ."

Observer: "You made a little more sense to me in that [lunch-
eon] meeting. I could see where you were getting some payoff in
that meeting. It was not like some of the others I have seen you
in. Some of these meetings are so disorganized . . . but you just
keep plugging along."

Asche: "Yeah, that's right. I just keep plugging along. I never let it go. It's taking the simplest little idea and making something out of it. Just the simplest little idea, as long as it is there. And then keep banging away at it. It's making something out of almost nothing. It takes a lot of determination. It takes some trust in the worth of one's ideas, no matter what people say, and no matter what kind of bastard people call you. I've had enough experience with my ideas to believe that they will pay off, and I keep working away at them, and most of them do.

"That meeting today was the result of seven years' work. Sure, I wonder what we are getting ourselves into right now, but it was the same way seven years ago. We'll have to plug away at it and it will grow. Who knows what we will have in seven years' time?

"It's the creative process. Now you take that Donald Singer. When I first met him, he was buried at [another hospital], doing routine social work. Well, I took him on, and now he's making *twice* what he'd been making there. And not only that, but he is growing and developing. Now it's a Ph.D. he is moving toward, and he has the administration of the project, and applying for grants, and all that. He's a *man*. Why, he must handle $200,000 to $300,000 of grant money every year. That's the sort of stuff I go for, and I've got a bunch of people around me that go for the same sort of thing.

"Of course, you have to tolerate some insecurity. These grants come in like that, and then they end, and you have got to get others. Sometimes they don't come through, and you have to have enough security not to let it throw you. You have to have enough faith in your ideas to know you can get another grant. Just so long as you have enough coming in to eat, and enough security to tolerate this life of grantism.

"Cadman said to me about six years ago that he could never do what I'm doing. It was too insecure for him, he said. He said it was all in my head, and nothing out there to give it any sense, and how could I stand it? Sure, it was all in my head, but that's what creativity is—taking something that is in your head and making something of it—and you have to be able to tolerate a certain amount of insecurity to be creative. Sure it was all in my head, but that was six years ago, and look at it now. It's huge. It's all around me. And it is creative.

"I've had to plug away at it. I try to work with the little things that are good, and build them up. I don't try to tear down the things I don't like. I hope that if I work hard enough at it, they will drop out anyway and be replaced by the good stuff.

"It's all part of the creative process. It's all part of growing and developing, each man in his own way."

Observer: "This seems to fit with your belief that a man doesn't have to have all the right degrees before he can do what he is interested in doing."

Asche: "Absolutely. I got a lot of this from Richard Sherman [ex-superintendent]. He was interested in that sort of thing, even if it did not look quite right from the outside."

Observer: "From what you said about developing your staff, it sort of sounds like your objectives for the staff are the same as your objectives for the patients."

Asche: "That's right. It's all part of the same cloth. It's all part of growing and developing and moving ahead. It's all part of becoming a man; an active, creative man."

Role Strains Involved in Accentuating the Positive

Dr. Asche's administrative behavior reflected the strength of this belief and the tenacity with which he held to it in a variety of administrative-interactive settings. In some settings this behavior seemed appropriate to the situation, and in others it seemed less so. It not infrequently took a palpable amount of effort on Dr. Asche's part to maintain this stance, even in situations that turned out for the better.

Late one afternoon Dr. Asche worked over a manuscript written by a young social worker. Before she arrived for her appointment with Dr. Asche, he told the observer that he considered her manuscript so unorganized as to be unusable in its existing form.

When the social worker entered his office, Asche took the manuscript into his hands and said, "I've read this over, and I'd like to take it off your hands, and do more work on it, if that is all right with you. It will still be your chapter, understand, but we will work with and add to your good work."

The social worker had taken back the manuscript and was looking through it as Asche spoke. Asche was smiling to himself as he spoke, putting his hands over his mouth when he sat down behind his desk.

The social worker said she would like to try again to write the material to his satisfaction.

Asche: "O.K. Let's work with it."

Social worker: "I don't know how this should be handled. When Dr. —— read it, he said it didn't mean a thing." She and Asche looked through the manuscript together. They came to an exhibit.

"Oh, that's very good," exclaimed Dr. Asche. "That's very useful. We could use that. This is a *very, very* useful table to publish."

Dr. Asche worked with the social worker over the manuscript, emphasizing its good points, pointing to the bad points, explaining their weaknesses, and gently presenting ways in which these weaknesses could be removed. He did this quietly and patiently, despite certain nonverbal manifestations of an underlying impatience and annoyance that he was working hard not to communicate to the girl. He went through her categorization of her data, the definitions of categories, *et cetera*. None of them seemed to make much sense. The social worker kept saying so, and she apologized more than once for that fact.

Asche: "Does this mean this is what you went by when you wrote up this section?"

Social worker: "Yes, but I was never satisfied with the way I handled it. I would like to learn what went wrong and how to do better."

Asche: "Everybody has troubles with this at some time. The problem is conceptualization. You've got to set out the headings so that the reader can follow them through—one, two, three, four—so that it is as easy as possible for him. There has to be a complete consistency of numbers throughout. . . . I'm trying to tell you how we work out in writing. It's a lesson, if you will. . . . You've got to aid the reader in every way. You've got to do his thinking for him." (The session continued in this way up to the time of the observer's departure.)

In this instance, Dr. Asche's behavior—his way of inter-acting as an administrator—was rewarded both by the social worker's immediate responsiveness in the here-and-now prob-lem situation, and by her subsequent rewrite of the manu-script. He spoke of its improvement to the woman's super-visor.

Asche: "I've read ——'s paper again. I want to tell you that it is tremendously improved. That girl's got talent, if she wants to use it."

Miss Patten: "That's good. I'm glad to hear that. She has not wanted to use it for a long time. I'm glad to hear you were able to help her."

Asche: "Yea!" He clenched his fists above his shoulders, and shot his arms straight up over his head. "Talent," he exclaimed triumphantly.

This indicates something of the value of Dr. Asche's ad-ministrative style. It points to the sources of external reward relating to his continuance of this pattern of behavior. In the incidents immediately following, the reader will see that Asche was not always rewarded, in any direct way, for be-having the way he did. However, this variable ratio of re-ward perhaps contributed even more to the strength and persistence of his friendly, equalitarian attempts to be con-structive.

In some settings, the extent to which Dr. Asche persisted in his emphasis on the positive was more out of line with the situation being addressed and the response that was elicited. One such meeting began with the distribution of what proved to be irrelevant materials. One of the senior members of the group soon discovered this.

"That's the wrong one," said Miss Patten. "We never used that."

"Oh, I'd better take it back," replied Dr. Asche's secretary.

"That's too bad," said Helen, a social worker.

"We used this, didn't we?" asked Susan.

"Of course we didn't," said Miss Patten. There followed a discussion about the additional data: who worked on them, what was left undone, who wrote up what, and what data were left untouched.

Asche: "I'd like to see all the raw data."

Susan: "I don't have time to write up the data. It must be there somewhere." She got up from her chair and joined Mitzi in searching through some floor-to-waist level cupboards filled with papers and boxes. Several piles of paper spilled out onto the floor.

Miss Patten: "It must be there."

Dr. Ball whistled quietly and glanced at Dr. Asche sitting next to her. He grinned. Meanwhile, the search continued, and the pile on the floor grew larger.

"Dr. Sedgwick had it all organized before he left," Helen observed.

"Well, that's no good, is it?" Miss Patten responded sharply. "If I ask for one thing and I get another, just because nobody knows where anything is."

Susan straightened up from the cupboard. "Well, I give up," she said. "I'll find it later. It must be there."

"It must be there," repeated Miss Patten.

Some time later on in the meeting, Asche observed, "I don't mind telling you it's in good shape. We're better off. . . ."

"Than you thought we were going to be," Miss Patten interjected quickly. The two of them exchanged looks. Asche paused and appeared to modify what he was going to say.

Asche: *"We've got a very rich pile of pretty fair stuff here, although it's uneven."* [The emphasis has been added. This was the most succinct verbal manifestation of Asche's accentuate-the-positive syndrome that was observed.] "Are we all clear on what we are going to do?"

(Silence) Several nod.

Asche: "Alrightie. Let's brainstorm on the last chapter of this book. What did we learn?"

(Silence)

Asche smiled: "All free associations will be willingly accepted."

(Silence)

Asche: "It was research into action, wasn't it? O.K. What action?"

(Silence)

Asche: "Does it fit in with the Commission's recommendations about prevention clinics and the screening of patients?" (Several nod.) Asche jotted a few notes on a pad of paper next to him. "O.K. What are the minimum requirements for service?"

(Pause) "A nurse?" Someone ventured. . . .

Rockland: "That's true. They found it a very hard thing to do."

Asche (writing): "Resistances to home visits on the part of the staff. What were some of the important findings here?"

Susan: "Well, we learned to be firm, and to stand for what we thought was best. We got into some awful situations when we let the patients or their families talk us into doing something against our best judgment. So I would say we learned to be firm."

Miss Patten: "You mean we had to go through this whole project just to learn *that?*"

Susan: "I know it's funny, but that's the way it seems to me. We learned to take a stand on our best judgment, and not be manipulated."

Miss Patten shook her head, and there was silence. . . .

Rockland: "We learned that if we came in with a big team too fast, we scared the patient. Then there was also the business of coming too late with too little."

Miss Patten: *"Once."*

Rockland: "What?"

Miss Patten: "I say that happened just once. You could hardly put that in the last chapter."

Helen: "We had an experience from which we could say that the doctors should do all the screening."

Miss Patten: *"Why?* I presume you are referring to the nurse."

Helen: "Yes."

Miss Patten: "She was just a young thing. I don't think you can say from that that only doctors should do the screening."

Dr. Ball: "Can we say something about the difficulties we got into with not interviewing the whole family?"

Miss Patten: "That's an interesting point, but it's not represented in any of the papers of the book."

Dr. Ball: "It isn't?"

Miss Patten: "Show me where." Dr. Ball shrugged.

Asche: "Use of home O.T.?"

Miss Patten: "Great. We tried that."

Asche: "How about the use of home nursing?"

Miss Patten: "We thought of that, too."

Asche: "Was the day hospital useful to your folks? Was partial hospitalization useful?"

Dr. Ball: "We didn't use it very often."

Miss Patten: "Oh yes, you did."

Asche: "The use of drugs, folks? How about the use of drugs?"

(Silence)

Asche: "Liberally?"

Rockland: "Yes, and there was a great deal of resentment about it at first. One of the directors used drugs a great deal to start off with."

Asche: "Resentment by whom?"

Rockland: "Resentment by the patients. They felt they were getting the shotgun treatment, which is not what they wanted."

Asche: "Any research ideas?"

Rockland: "How about the pre-morbid area?"

Asche: "Pre-morbid? Pre-morbid? How are we going to get into that? That's a little bit out of our area. . . . How about good and bad patients in the prevention of hospitalization? Do we have anything on that?"

Susan: "Wasn't that what the whole study was about?"

Asche: "Do we need to know more? Do we know all about it?"

Susan: "Yes. Don't we?"

Miss Patten: "Noooooo! There's a whole variety of cases we don't know anything about."

Dr. Ball: "That's all right. They are for the next generation. Just as long as I don't have to answer them. . . ."

The date of the next meeting was set. Asche turned to Dr. Ball. "Sara," he said, "I'd like to know who will be the person to write up the last chapter."

Dr. Ball laughed. "I think you'd be *just the man.*"

Asche turned to Miss Patten. "I am going to write to —— today. You should have seen the letter I got from him."

Miss Patten: "Angry?"

Asche: "Oh boy!" He made a face. Turning to Dr. Ball, he said. "You and I will work on it."

After the meeting, the observer asked Dr. Asche if he were discouraged by what had gone on. "No. Why?" he asked. The observer replied that it appeared as though almost no one had learned anything from their experiences on the project.

"They're a smart bunch of people," Asche replied. "They learned a lot. Why do you say that?" He seemed disappointed that the observer had reached such conclusions. The observer pointed out that when Dr. Asche had asked for ideas to be used in the last chapter of the book—on what had been learned from the project—the vast majority of suggestions had come from Asche himself. Then, in reply to his indirect question to Dr. Ball, he had been told jokingly but pointedly to do the work himself.

Asche did not reply. He got up from his chair, walked into his secretary's office, and went on with other matters.[2] He appeared somewhat upset by the observer's disinclination to

---

[2] Asche sometimes went into the office of either of his secretaries to relax after tense interactions. After one such event, he walked slowly from his office and into the next.

"What will I do now?" he asked his secretary.

"Take a deep breath," she replied.

On another occasion, after a tough day, Asche went into his secretary's office where he received a phone call that turned out to be a hot one: *"What?* . . . Sure, I know, but . . . *No.* Absolutely not . . . finish the job, period!" He hung up.

"It's been a hectic day," his secretary observed. He smiled and walked slowly back into his own office where he sat down by himself with his back to the door, gazing out the window.

participate with him in accentuating the positive aspects of the meeting, during which the positive aspects had not really predominated. The observer was more curious about the un-avoidably negative aspects of the meeting, and their relation-ship to the costs Dr. Asche incurred in attempting to advance against a series of obstacles of not insignificant magnitude. The observer, however, had not correctly assessed the force-fulness with which Dr. Asche addressed himself to things positive, or his resistance against dwelling, even briefly, on the unpleasant and unproductive issue of costs to himself.

THE RESULTING BALANCE

WHAT WAS THE OVER-ALL balance of costs and rewards that the assistant superintendent experienced as the result of do-ing the work he did, in the manner he did it? As in Chap-ter 4, we close an analysis of one executive's organizational behavior by attempting to delineate the psychological profit-ability to Dr. Asche of his dealings with other people in the M.P.I., and the consequences of these transactions in relation to his own continuing personal development.

Some Costs of a Specialized Role Performance

We have indicated that Dr. Asche's accentuation of things positive in his administrative behavior was related to his own productivity, and to the productivity of those who worked with and around him. Increasingly, it became evident that this role specialization got Dr. Asche into troubles that he might have avoided had his interpersonal behavior been less specialized. This does not imply that he might otherwise have been free of all administrative-interpersonal difficulties. It means that had Asche—and the same obviously applies to the other executives—played his role differently, he would have elicited a different set of costs and rewards that might or might not have been more to his liking.

Asche's customary refusal or inability to let go his anger,

and to direct it against the people who made him angry, made him a relatively easy target for people with unattached aggressions to express. Certainly he was more serviceable as a scapegoat than either the formidable Dr. Suprin or the lovable Dr. Cadman. People's conceptions of Dr. Asche were not as distinct as those of Dr. Suprin and Dr. Cadman, but to the extent that Asche was imaged by others, it was as something of a "nice guy." His actual and attributed tendency not to "hit back" rendered him liable to a form of punishment that the other two executives were not observed to receive. It was not that the other two executives received no punishment from subordinates. As the reader has seen, they received a different sort of punishment.

The chivying, teasing, and argumentation that Dr. Asche was observed to receive occurred in a variety of organizational settings: in the casual interactions of corridor contacts, in more formal interactions in his office, and in more public settings such as teaching rounds. Much of this took the form of good-natured joshing, to which Asche usually responded in his accustomed friendly manner. When he did not, it was an occasion of some note.

(Dr. Asche and the business officer were discussing a researcher's disbursement of project funds.)

Asche: *"What!* I told him he couldn't spend a penny before September first. Who signed for all that?"

Business officer: "You must have."

Asche: "If I did so, I had no knowledge of it. If I signed anything, I did so completely inadvertently. You know that. Why did you let him do it?"

The business officer said something about the researcher's having the permission of Dr. Suprin. Asche told him to phone the researcher and speak with him. He demurred.

Asche: "All right, *I'll* speak with him." Asche was very excited at this point. His voice got loud and his face took on a somewhat blank expression, eyes glazed. The observer had never seen him so perturbed.

The researcher was out to lunch.

Business officer: "We're always going to have *one* of them." [That is, that sort of person in the organization.]

Asche: "Not if you and I got together on it. If I signed anything that day, I must have been blind. He's got to pay back . . . every damned penny. I'm more careful about the . . . funds than you or Frank are."

Business officer: *"Oh, no."*

Asche: "This guy! He's not going to slip me the business like that. We've spent thousands of dollars on setting up a unit for —— [here Dr. Asche was referring to another ongoing tense administrative situation], and now he's not going to train here. I could get paranoid!"

Several minutes later, Jerome entered, and joked with Dr. Asche. "I've got an eye out for you," he remarked.

"Well, put it back in," Asche retorted as he left the office.

"Ooh, nasty!" Jerome called after him. (Jerome later told the observer that Asche's remark was "quite out of keeping with his usual behavior.")

There were instances in which Dr. Asche had difficulty representing himself, or his position, forcefully enough at his level in the organization. One such occasion arose when he received a phone call from the business office around 10:30 A.M. one morning.

Mrs. O'Toole had a 20-page manuscript that Dr. Cadman wanted typed *today,* and she was too busy. She wanted to know if one of Asche's secretaries could type it. Asche informed one of his secretaries of the request. She told him that neither she nor the other secretary was free to do it.

Asche picked up the phone and spoke to Mrs. O'Toole. "We're busy here. The problem is what to do about secretaries. Is it in his handwriting? That makes it worse. Nobody can read his handwriting, you know. Yeah, I'll look around." He hung up. "God damn silly ideas. Silly, silly problem."

Secretary: "They think that just because there are a lot of us here, we don't have a lot of work to do. They don't know how much work we do around here."

Asche went to Dr. Ginsberg's office and asked him if his secretary could do the job.

Ginsberg: "How do you evaluate the problem?"

Asche: "Taking gas. That's how I evaluate it."

Ginsberg agreed that his girl would work on the manuscript after she had finished her present project. That evening, shortly before 5 o'clock, Asche found out that only two pages of the manuscript had been typed.

Asche asked his secretary: "What's the problem here?"

Secretary: "I don't think you realize how very difficult it is for a secretary to work from that sort of material."

Asche phoned Cadman: "We've got two pages typed. . . . It's very slow going, you know. Nobody can read your writing. Now what do we do?" He listened to Cadman's reply, then hung up. He shook his head. "It's a funny business," he said quietly. "I don't think Cadman works. . . ." He stopped himself before finishing the statement.

Another incident of a similar nature occurred in one of Dr. Asche's interactions with Dr. Suprin. Asche had entered Suprin's office to explain to him a budgetary proposal, whereby some of the funds of one research unit could be applied to expenses incurred in another. The observer did not understand the proposal, and Dr. Suprin appeared to be having some difficulty with it as well. Asche had just begun to explain himself when Suprin interrupted.

"Now wait a minute. You're going to run us into bankruptcy that way."

"No. I don't think so," Asche replied.

"I guess I don't understand, then," said Suprin.

"I guess I don't either," laughed Asche. "I was always sort of an indirect guy. I guess I'm too indirect for my own good." He attempted once more to explain what he had in mind.

"Now hold on," Suprin interrupted after a short while. "It seems to me you are trying to fix one up, and are doing it by screwing up the second grant at the same time. That's not good business, you know that."

"Geez," said Asche jokingly, "I don't know much about business."

Suprin: "You are lousing up the second grant to fix up the first one. Instead of getting one grant in good shape and then worrying about the other, you are going to screw both of them up. You scare me, Howie. You're going to run me right into bankruptcy, if you go on like that."

Asche: "Oh, I haven't run you into bankruptcy yet, have I?"

Suprin restated his opinion another time, and in the course of the ensuing discussion did so again twice more.

After leaving the superintendent's office, Dr. Asche said to the observer: "Frank and I work together O.K. these days. We didn't used to work together so good, but we worked it out between us. He used to jump in, like you just saw; only I'd argue with him, and he'd get mad, and then we'd both get mad, and then it would take us quite a while to work it out. Now I don't argue with him any more, and he knows it. He'll sound off like that, and after it's over, we'll get together and work something out. What that session today meant was that I didn't have my figures worked out very well. Frank's a lot better on figures than I am, and he picked this up a lot faster than I could. He responds quickly to any sort of feelings of fuzziness.

"What it means is I'll do more work on these figures, and then we'll get together again on it. All that business about bankruptcy, that doesn't mean too much. Frank's been around long enough. He knows how I operate. He knows I'm not going to run him into bankruptcy. My plan is to. . . ."

He explained his plan again, but again the observer could not understand it.

"No?" queried Asche. He shook his head. "I guess I'm too sneaky. Even sneakier than I thought."

Asche's adherence to what might be called "positive interaction" and his avoidance of fight,[3] crucial as these were

---

[3] Talking about "creativity," Asche outlined certain facets of his life history to the residents during one of their regularly scheduled noon conferences. Asche stated that, for his parents, physical exercise had been something to be avoided. He was taught that, "breaking into a sweat, shortness of breath,

in his conception of how to facilitate personal development in others, sometimes seemed to stand in the way of his *own* development. "I spend so much time doing for other people that I don't have time to do for myself," was the way he expressed it in a moment of pique. To a certain extent, he created this situation himself, in that he more than accepted the responsibilities of his multiple position in the hospital, but he did not often exert the authority either of that position or of his years of experience as a doctor and researcher. Even people considerably junior to him—residents, in fact—could tease him with apparent impunity; disrupting his work, his thoughts, making it difficult for him to do what he wanted to do or say what he had in mind to say.

During one hour with a resident Dr. Asche was teased about Dr. Cadman's closer relations with residents and about the clinical flair of staff psychiatrists *other* than himself. His own clinical stories, and his obvious enthusiasm about them, were ignored. At one point, a contest developed as to who was more open with patients, Dr. Asche or another staff psychiatrist? Asche became quite annoyed.

"If you ask my opinion," he informed the resident, "I think those [the other doctor's stories] are very bland. I don't think they're completely true, either. And they are certainly not very personal. That's just my opinion, of course."

The resident smiled, but did not otherwise reply.

Asche continued: "I believe I reveal more of myself to my patients in my way than —— ever does with those stories. But you don't have to take my word for it. You just listen carefully next time. . . . You see if I'm not right."

"I'll check on it," the resident replied. The end of the hour

---

and palpitations of the heart due to physical exercise was like getting some sort of disease. This attitude has become considerably weakened in me, but it still remains a bit. However, my wife and I have raised our two children to enjoy physical exercise. You should see them swinging from the trees, like a couple of monkeys." He smiled. "They're not like their old man, worried about getting into a sweat."

had arrived, and with that the resident got up from his chair and left the office.

After the resident had departed, Dr. Asche turned to the observer to comment. The observer expected to hear a few choice words about the resident, but instead was surprised to hear the following.

"You see that man?" Asche inquired. The observer nodded. "He's one smart boy. I'd keep him here if I could. There are so many of these young fellows we would like to keep. He was a jet pilot, did you know that? And he was a doctor to pilots. He's seen A-bomb blasts himself. He says their power is just phenomenal, just unbelievable. He's been around, that boy. He's smart. Interested. Dedicated. He's a second-year resident, and he wants to be chief next year."
Observer: "Do you think he'll make a good one?"
Asche: "One of the best. One of the best."

On another occasion Dr. Asche and a resident had an altercation about the resident's possible interest in a position other than the one he had accepted at the Institute. This was perhaps the most electric session in which Dr. Asche was observed to participate. When it had terminated, Asche turned to the observer and asked, "Did you see what was going on there? Did you get the picture?" He and the observer discussed the session for about 20 minutes. Then Asche sat in silence for about the same period of time, until the observer asked him what he was thinking about. He replied that he was still thinking about the resident in question.

"I thought I had done a great job in setting him up with the equipment he needs. Frank [Suprin] and I think him capable of great things. We thought he would be satisfied, if not pleased, by the arrangements we have made for him, at least in the immediate future. We thought he'd settle down to do some productive work. I'm surprised, even shocked, to see the direction of his thoughts, to see what is still occupying his thinking time; that everything is up for grabs, and that he's taken the time and effort to measure carefully the pro's and con's of both positions along carefully thought-out dimensions, perhaps even playing one off against the other in his mind. Then, too, I'm disappointed he didn't get what I was trying to tell him. He didn't get the message. Instead he behaved in that paranoid manner that you saw. This is a pattern of behavior I find hard to cope with. They always take the best in the system—academic freedom, for instance —and use it against you like a club.

"Boy, I've learned one thing, though. If a person comes to me for a job, and I even smell a hint of paranoia about them, they won't get the job. I'm getting too old for that sort of thing."

The next day Dr. Asche slipped away from a noon staff conference and went to eat lunch by himself in the cafeteria. There he revealed to the observer that he was still preoccupied by the implications of the transaction described above. His statement gave further weight to the interpretation concerning his difficulties in directing his anger outward toward the sources of provocation.

"I'm still worried about ―― [the resident in question]. I feel there is a growing schism there, somehow. I guess I'm too sensitive on things like that, but I keep worrying on them. I don't know whether a good administrator would have that much sensitivity. The trouble with me is that I am either not sadistic enough, or I am too bound up in my own sadism to do a good job at it."

There were other examples, much less blatant than the above, of a continuing undercurrent of muted disparagement that Dr. Asche received mostly from residents, which he professed not to see and against which he did not attempt to defend himself. The patients presented to Dr. Asche in teaching rounds appeared to the observer to be one manifestation of this covert attitude. The "art of roundsmanship" as the residents jokingly termed it, was the process whereby a patient and a staff doctor were matched in a teaching round. This was based on the predicted recommendations of the doctor being in line with the private goals of the resident as to how the patient should be managed. We were unable to trace through the working of "roundsmanship," but the patients presented to Dr. Asche spoke for themselves. At the best, they provided excellent teaching examples of the social psychiatric point of view, of which Dr. Asche was a recognized exponent. But as Asche himself recognized, there was something of a perfunctory response to these cases and that point of view.

"I have to do this," he said. "Otherwise, they [the residents] would get too damned self-satisfied." Then, after a pause, he added, "No one else around here seems to do it."

A few of these cases were refractory, nonpsychologically minded, and definitely antitherapeutic patients whom the residents had despaired of treating according to the methods they wished to practice: for example, a veteran whose only wish, despite his illness, was to leave the hospital. "Tell him he has to stay," recommended Dr. Asche. "He's been in the army. He knows what discipline is." Several of the senior women present at the meeting nodded their approval, while the residents—for whom assertions of authority were largely unattractive—remained unresponsive. Or a patient referred to the hospital from the courts, about whom the resident in charge had "learned a lot of bad language, but little else."

"I'm not interested in taking him further," the resident informed Dr. Asche at the *close* of the session.

Or the young male psychoneurotic whom Dr. Asche interviewed and found to be nervous about the prospect of leaving the hospital and going out to look for a job.

When this issue [about getting a job] became apparent in the interview, Asche suggested that the patient and he *role play* the

situation in which the patient was applying for a job and Asche
was the prospective employer.

There was some laughter in the room at the proposal. Several
of the residents glanced "meaningfully" at one another. Dr. Rous-
seau raised his eyebrows and grimaced, as an aside, to Dr. Rowan
who was sitting next to him. The patient was slightly embarrassed by this proposal, but Asche started acting like an employer
and stuck to it, so that after several attempts to side-step the situation, the patient "got with it" and stayed with it. In the course of
the next 15 minutes, several events and issues in the patient's life
were raised that were not in his medical record, and that Dr.
Rowan had no knowledge of.

After the patient had left the conference room, Asche turned
to Rowan and asked, "You recommend more therapy?"

Rowan nodded.

"I don't think so," Asche responded. "He's had lots of psychotherapy. Five years of it, to be exact. He's got loads of insight."

"Enough to sink a ship," muttered a nurse who was sitting
next to the observer.

"But," Asche continued, unaware of this concurrence, "he
doesn't know what to do with it. He still feels anxious. Have you
done a careful drug analysis on this guy?"

"No," replied Dr. Rowan.

"What do you mean?" the chief resident asked Dr. Asche.

Asche explained what he meant by a careful drug analysis.
". . . as in epilepsy. One of my professors used to say that the
little things are the big things. You vary the drug level a little
each day, and watch at what level the seizures begin to fall off."
With his hand he drew a curve of a hypothetical graph in the
air. "That's the sort of thing I mean."

(Later, Dr. Asche told the observer, "I meant a depth analysis
of drugs, just like a depth analysis of personality. That's something that nobody does around here.")

Next, Dr. Asche stressed the practical management aspects of
the case: how to help the man stand on his own feet and stay on
his feet, without psychotherapy, since that did not seem to be
helping him. Asche then pointed out that role playing and psy-

chodrama could be effective therapeutic devices when used by certain therapists with certain patients.

"There is none of it being done in the hospital now," he said. "I think the usefulness of these techniques tends to get overlooked by the residents now coming into the hospital."

After the conference Asche told the observer that he had deliberately chosen to role play with the patient "to point up other alternatives to the currently accepted therapeutic mode."

The Purposive Intent of Role Specialization

Here again is an instance in which, for the purposes of this study, the personal dynamics of the man cannot be held separate from the purposive organizational context with which they interacted, and in which they were observed. Just as the superintendent's assertive directiveness was oriented toward the realization of his concept of a training hospital, and the clinical director's supportiveness was intended to get residents to take charge of their own clinical responsibilities; so were the assistant superintendent's patient, nonauthoritarian promptings intended to introduce the hospital's trainees to the existence of therapeutic modes other than those then uppermost in their minds. This the assistant superintendent did with deliberation, and with the help of his less deliberate, more natural interactive style. Both of these had the effect of circumventing some of the nonrational turmoil about professional methods that could be elicited easily from trainees by recommendations that sounded like directives.

Dr. Asche's convictions about many professional matters were too great to say that his was a laissez-faire way of teaching. However, a sense of detachment came across in the more strictly pedagogical settings that did not occur in the more research-related settings. The observer inquired about this. Did Dr. Asche teach on a regular weekly basis? (Dr. Asche taught a weekly group of undergraduate students of psychology, but the question was asked in the context of medical-psychiatric education.)

"Oh, no," Asche replied. "They slip one in on me once in a while. Nothing regular, though; I don't want to get tied down with a lot of teaching. It would slow me up in research."

The reader has earlier been introduced to the drive and enthusiasm that Asche often radiated about research and creativity. For him, research could reach "the peaks of creativity; new ideas, breakthroughs, wham!" It could also be "terrible, just terrible." Teaching in its several forms, from the purely didactic communication of knowledge to the more informal sharing of one's wisdom with the young, did not reach either the same "depths" or the same "heights" in Dr. Asche's experience. His transactions with others along these lines permitted a freedom of feeling, thought, and action such that some people overlooked the emotional, intellectual, and behavioral alternatives that Asche was in fact proposing to them. Dr. Suprin tended to startle or scare people into attention to what he was saying. Dr. Cadman loved and charmed people into considering his views. In relation to these two, Dr. Asche tended not to make as distinct an impression on others. As such, there were some who tended unthinkingly to overlook his presence and thereby to be unimpressed by what he had to offer. But there were still others who incorporated what Asche offered, who perceived the thrust of his arguments, who considered his proposals and often agreed with them.

Role Transition: Up and Out

In some ways the nature of Dr. Asche's role in the organization was changing as he grew older. Dr. Cadman referred more often to the issue of growing old, but there were few signs of incipient change in his organizational role. Except for the unlikely alternative of going into full-time private practice, there were no indications that Dr. Cadman would do other than continue his clinical directorship in the same manner as observed. Dr. Asche referred only infrequently to growing old, but when he did, it was in relation to courses of action he was considering taking in the hospital. One aspect of this intended role change has been presented. Dr. Asche intended to take less punishment from subordinate personnel. "I'm getting too old for that sort of thing," he said. He also intended to reduce his direct involvement in the research projects being carried out in the hospital, and to organize these projects to facilitate that change.

"We've got a big screw-up on the data," he told the observer after one research meeting. "The work I did brought that out. It's a good thing I'm on top of the data, or whatever got published would be murder. From now on, every project is going to have a data hawk, someone who is going to stay close to the data. It's too much for me. I'm getting too old for this sort of thing."

Thus, it appeared that Dr. Asche was in the not unusual transition of a researcher, moving successively from direct engagement at the "creative interface," to the administration of research, and on to the administration of even larger purposive aggregates. Near the beginning of field work, the following conversation took place.

Observer: "You seem to be at the hub of a lot of research."
Asche: "Yes, and I love it. It's a wonderful place to be."
Observer: "Research is the big pay-off activity for you?"
Asche: "You bet. The other guys [members of the staff] teach, but I teach them what they are going to teach. There's a tremendous lag between the stuff they teach and the stuff we are working on in research. In teaching, it's still the simple, simple stuff. I think I'm a good teacher! I think I could be good at it, but I don't like the repetition. I can teach something once, maybe twice, but the third time— (he grimaced, baring his teeth and sucking in his breath) —I can't stand it. I have to have something

new. I like to have new stuff, and that's what you have coming
in all the time in research."

"When I get worn out," he added, "I'd like to run a hospital
like Frank [Suprin] runs it. But it will be a long time before
I wear out, I hope."

One year later the observer reviewed recent developments
with Dr. Asche, who had the following to say about himself.

Asche: "One of these days, I'm going to run my own show."
Observer: "You sound definite on this."
Asche: "I am definite on it."
Observer: "More so than last year?"
Asche: "Oh, yes. I'm more definite on this than I was last year."
Observer: "Why?"
Asche: "I don't know why. I just know I want to run my own
show, that's all. I'm running it here anyway, a lot of the time
when Frank is away. Perhaps I want to have no superior—no
immediate superior—for a change. I don't know. It's a challenge
of responsibility, I guess. Putting one's own place in operation.
Perhaps the real reason is that some of my friends—people who
are the same age as I am—we grew up together, so to speak—are
beginning to take on that sort of position. (Asche gave an example.) That's not the sort of place for me, though."
Observer: "Do you have one in mind?"
Asche: "No. I don't have my eye on any one right now. I'd
want somewhere where I can put into practice some of the procedures we have developed here. I'd be willing to go into competition with the Institute any day."

Career Development Beyond the Early Adult Years

It can be seen that Dr. Asche, who was in his late forties,
had by no means given up the task of career planning. In fact,
during the time of this study and immediately thereafter, he
entered into a phase of intensive concentration upon the several career alternatives open to him, and the various internal
and external forces relating positively and negatively to each.
This was not an easy process, as the data have indicated. In

several ways, the resulting balance of personal demands and positional requirements was more costly for Dr. Asche than for his other two colleagues in the role constellation. Dr. Asche had demonstrated a singular constancy of both role-themes and position-settings. He had been a psychiatric researcher at the Institute for two decades. Yet, he was now in the process of changing his role-themes from researcher to administrator to executive, *and* his position-settings from a small teaching and research institute to a larger, more custodial hospital.

The differences between the executives' dynamics of career planning should not be overstated. All three men were planning, each in his own way, to attain in the stage of development that Erikson has entitled "mature age" the sociopsychological condition of *integrity,* as opposed to the *disgust and despair* resulting from the mere repetition of established, obsolete career patterns.

CHAPTER 7

The Concept of Role-Task in Executive Work

WE HAVE OBSERVED each executive as he came to grips with the requirements of his position and with his own work-related preferences and aspirations. On the one hand, there were things that had to be done. On the other hand, there were things he wanted to do. While these were not mutually exclusive, there were yet major disparities in each case. The executive's assessment of the organizational imperatives of his position was not as complete, rational, systematic, and impersonal as a bureaucratic sociologist or an efficiency expert may have wished. His assessment of these imperatives was largely in terms of his own interests and preferences, in terms of what he would like to see done in and by the hospital. In short, the bond between the person and the position was highly individualistic.

This coming together of the person with his position and with other people in their positions was highly engrossing to the men observed. It was an area in which their experiences apparently meant a lot to them, and which they could share easily with younger people, such as the residents, often without being asked. On the other hand, the written formulations of the duties of their positions—their job descriptions—did not enter into any of their talking or behaving. It seemed futile to seek to delineate the superintendency, for example, in terms such as, "to direct, to supervise, and to coordinate." The concept of role-task helped us to get descriptively and analytically closer to the actual way these men actively established themselves as superintendent, as assistant superintendent, and as clinical director, both separately and in relation to each other.

The term "role-task" denotes the linkage between a man's assessment of his personality, his here-and-now conception of himself, and his assessment of the requirements of his position in the organization. The concept of *role-task* is different in kind both from the usual concept of *task* as a concrete activity, and from the usual concept of *role* as expected normative behavior. As the terms are ordinarily used in organizations, a task derives entirely from organizational imperatives: it is what a person must do in a given position so that the organization can realize its goals. A role, on the other hand, is what a person does. This is influenced to a great extent by what sort of a person he is, the needs he seeks to satisfy, the ideas and aspirations he is seeking to express. The concept of role-task envisions a melding of organizational imperatives and personal strivings.

Briefly, *role-task work* is the sustained and directed effort of mind in which a person seeks to synthesize the organizational requirements of his position with his own individual needs, interests, and aspirations. The result of successful role-task work is a set of personal policies, as it were, by which the person strives to advance, or impede, the purposes of the organization, depending on his needs. Role-task work is seen as an active, ongoing process engaged in by the individual. It is a basic requisite of productive membership within an organization. This idea about man-in-organization points to the person-position encounter as highly problematic; it cannot be taken for granted in a theoretical sense, although it may often be conveniently ignored in purposive situations that are functioning smoothly.

An Example of Role-Task Issues

SITUATIONS that are not functioning smoothly can be used to illustrate issues of role-task. A person entering an organization is usually assigned a number of tasks to peform. He is expected by all, including himself, to go ahead and perform these tasks, to "get on with the job." The process by which he gets on with the job—the way he modifies the job, the way the job modifies him—usually go unnoticed, except for situations involving unusual, extreme task assignments or florid, intractable personalities. Role-tasks presented by extreme task assignments have been touched upon in reports of adjustment to prison camps.[1] Role-tasks relating to abnormal personalities have been delineated in studies of the "careers" of hospitalized mental patients.[2]

Just as the psychology of abnormality has contributed greatly to our understanding of normality, so too our understanding of executive role-tasks can be increased by examining the role-tasks of mental patients. What *is* the role-task of a hospitalized mental patient? First, what is his *task?* Put simply, his task as assigned to him by the organization is *to try to get better.* This task implies a host of concomitant activities, interactions, and underlying sentiments, all directed toward implementing the re-establishment of a condition of mental health satisfactory to key members of the hospital staff. But it cannot merely be assumed that each patient will (1) *discern* and (2) *establish* meaningful transactions around this assigned task, or (3) that he will *know* what the concomitant operations are. His inability to do so in other social contexts can be viewed as a cause for his current membership in a mental hospital. In this context, the issues of role-task become highly problematic. They can-

---

[1] See B. Bettelheim, *The Informed Heart,* 1960.

[2] See F. Pine and D. J. Levinson, "A Sociopsychological Conception of Patienthood," 1961.

not be ignored theoretically, nor can they be overlooked administratively in any long-term sense by those in charge of the patient's welfare. Here, perhaps more than in other contexts, each member is different, has a relatively uncommon structure of needs, with hidden strengths and apparent weaknesses.

The role-task of the patient is to establish a working relationship between himself, and what *he* is, and the hospital, and what *it* (i.e., "they") demands. His role-task is, so to speak, to plug himself into the organization, and to plug the organization into himself without blowing all the sociopsychological fuses in the process. To extend this metaphor, the patient is expected to generate enough current (motivation and understanding) to circulate through this circuit between himself and the organization, to make the establishment of the circuit worthwhile. The re-establishment of this circuit is, in itself, one of the major goals of therapy.

An example of the role-tasks of patients is provided in a study of patienthood by Levinson and Gallagher.[3] Using factor analysis, they found that one of the major role-tasks facing every patient in a mental hospital is to decide for himself, *what sort of a hospital is this?* The patient's answer to this question was related both to his personality and to the character of the hospital. Yet there was no provision in the expectations of the hospital staff that indicated that patients must decide for themselves what sort of a hospital they were in. This again points to the difference in kind between a task and a role-task.

The transferability of these ideas beyond the boundaries of the psychiatric ward is immediately apparent. How much time and energy are spent by employees of business organizations trying to develop satisfactory answers to the question: What sort of an organization is this? The person's

[3] D. J. Levinson and E. B. Gallagher, *Patienthood in the Mental Hospital,* 1964.

work on this role-task is crucial in determining the productiveness of the bond between the man and the organization. It is not part of the task assigned to members of purposive organizations, nor is it part of their personalities. The role-task arises from the meeting of the organization structure and the individual personality in the apperceptions and evaluations of the individual.

THE NATURE OF THE EXECUTIVES' ROLE-TASKS

SEVERAL ISSUES became apparent in the executives' personal transactions with their administrative object worlds. We distinguished seven issues that can be examined somewhat separately from each other. The issues in themselves, however, were very much interrelated. The executives' role-tasks comprised the continual assessment of these seven issues, the posing and answering of the questions they involved, and the integration of the several answers in a person-position orientation, or "stance," that was satisfactory to the individual and productive to the organization.

The components of the executives' role-tasks were as follows:

1. It was incumbent upon the executives to develop an over-all conception of the organization of which they were senior members, to delineate general lines along which it might advance, and to formulate basic guidelines for the achievement of that advance. Put simply, the questions addressed to this issue were: *What sort of an organization is this?* Where is it likely to go in the foreseeable future? How will it get there?

This component of the executives' role-task often occupied a central position in their thinking. The expectation that they would hold a well-articulated image of the organization was both explicit and frequently encountered in other members of the hospital. The executives were assumed to have a *conception of the organization,* toward the realization of which they would systematically work. Other members were continually interpreting each executive's actions in the light of an imputed executive conception of the hospital and where it was "headed." Considerable sentiment, pro and con, was aroused by these actual and implied executive conceptions of the hospital and its goals. It was observed, however, that those instances in which a *lack* of over-all conception was implied were generally *less* acceptable than those situations in which one *disagreed* with the goals that the executives were apparently trying to achieve. Any direction was better than none. At the very least, it gave others something upon which to focus their complaints.

The executives themselves were highly invested in evolving and implementing an over-all conception of the hospital and its future. It was apparent that they had done considerable "homework" in developing the conceptions of the hospital that they held. These conceptions embodied many of their personal and professional hopes. They were the product of individual vision and motivation, and they in turn sustained and enhanced the visions and motivations. These ideas helped to carry the men through tense, difficult, and unrewarding periods of their work within the hospital. The ideas had another function, of course. They attracted and motivated many people who were past, present, or prospective members of the organization.

2. Given an over-all program for the hospital and its "future," the executives found it necessary to decide what position they were to have in this program. The question was, in essence: *Where do I fit into this organization?* The executives had evolved, around this issue, the elaborate scheme of No. 1's and No. 2's that is the subject of this book. It should be noted that this issue is different from the issue: What *role* will I play in this organization? Or, how will I fill my position? This is addressed in the next category.

One of the interesting features of the concept of role-task

is that it permits the reintroduction of *position* into analyses of men in organization. Certainly, in this study the subjects' executive positions had powerful symbolic meanings for themselves and others, and thereby influenced the flow of behavioral events highlighted in our *role* analyses. From the observational point of view, role behavior was the pacemaker of the study. From the executives' points of view, their experiential response to their *positions* was the starting point of executive behavior.

3. The executives had also worked out their ideas about what role each was playing, or was to play, within the organization. This differentiation of roles was only a sometimes explicit entity. This was a shifting phenomenon, requiring the executives continually to expend at least a minimal amount of energy re-evaluating their stances on role issues, such as: Who is going to be boss around here? Who is going to be the tough guy? Who is going to crack the whip? Who is going to be the nice guy? Who is going to cleanse the wounds? Who is going to control? Who is going to clarify and explain? Who is going to motivate and support our subordinates?

As with the issue of relative position, so the above issue of diagnosing one's role in the executive hierarchy was also a relative one. It involved the appraisal of who was already holding down what roles, as well as what positions. It involved ascertaining who had appropriated what roles unto himself, and to what extent he would struggle to maintain these roles.

4. The executives could not properly diagnose or decide the above issues without addressing the more personal one: *What sort of a person am I?* What do I want out of life? What do I want to give, to receive, in my work here? Despite the customary norms about personal privacy, modesty, and administrative impersonality, the executives provided considerable information concerning their engagement on this issue.

Certainly, enough information was provided to be able to say that this issue was constantly being addressed—usually in an almost subliminal way—even by these mature persons who were generally perceived within the organization as having answered such questions once and for all, as having "put them to bed," so to speak, in eminently successful ways.

5. Events in the hospital repeatedly posed this issue for the executives: *To what extent am I a part of this organization?* This statement of the issue is not intended to imply that they were not integrated into the organization at the time of the study, or that they were on the verge of leaving it. It serves to highlight those situations in which it became evident that their conception of the organization would not be realized, because of forces beyond their control. They were then faced with the decision whether to give up on certain goals, or to continue investing their time, energy, and aspirations pushing for their attainment.

6. A corollary issue faced the executives in situations where they had to choose whether they would act as independent professionals or as agents of the organization. Essentially, the issue was as follows: *How much shall I allow the organization to become a part of me?* How much shall I accept those designations of my person that exist within the organization? Each executive was aware of a modal characterization that had been built up in the organization around himself and around each of his other two colleagues. He tended to feel both pleased and displeased with the reified image of himself, and to feel somewhat derisive but also somewhat envious about certain aspects of the reification of his colleagues. The executives fostered these images, but at the same time they sought to avoid them. They appeared to shift from acting as an agent of the hospital toward acting as an individual in situations in which the reification they felt was being assigned to them was unacceptable to them. They were more ready to act as agents of the hospital when the organizationally assigned

image of their persons was acceptable and in conjunction with their self-image.

The last two role-task issues were the ones most easily overlooked. This was due to the conceptual scheme with which these men approached their work. As psychiatrists their orientation toward, and ability to think about, the important issues of personality and the proper management of oneself was developed to an extent uncommon among administrators. As executives, their orientation toward and ability to think about organization and the proper management of the hospital was more than conventionally well developed. However, the executives were less explicit and fluent in their thinking about issues 5 and 6. It may seem odd that highly effective top executives were still facing the issues of how much to enter into the life of the organization, and how much to let the organization permeate their own lives. However, these remained problematic for all these men and, we imagine, for many other executives as well.

7. The final role-task issue is the one that usually receives the greatest attention in research on executive roles. This has been termed: *Getting on with the business of administration.* The norms governing executive positions and roles are such that the incumbent-actor is expected not to use his work as a vehicle for introspection and contemplation. He is expected to work on his identity crises off the job. His major effort is devoted, in the official view of things, to getting his work done, work that is useful to the organization. Accordingly, the executives were under some constraint not to exhibit their working through of the previous role-tasks (1 through 6) in public. They evidently felt free to do so to some extent, in certain instances, and before selected audiences. This not infrequently took place in the older-man-shares-wisdom-of-experience-with-young-aspirant context of the sometimes guild-like atmosphere of the residency training program. But it was always done deftly, discreetly, in such

a way that the thrust of a statement was frequently quite implicit, to be understood, overlooked, or misconstrued according to the motivation and empathic ability of the listener.

THE COMPONENTS OF ROLE-TASK WORK

ROLE-TASK WORK consists of intrapsychic acts, or decisions, and the correlative unconscious and preconscious activities that link the individual with the flow of organizational life around him, or dissociate him from it. This synthesis or antithesis is influenced by the individual's conception of the object world surrounding him in the organization, his conception of himself, his assessment of the congruence or disparity between his personality characteristics and the properties of his object world, and his judgment as to the developmental potential for himself. The productive outcome for the organization and the developmental outcome for the individual depend greatly on the quantity and quality of mental work done by the individual on his role-tasks.

Discovering and Creating the Organization as an Object World

Around every executive in every organization there exists a gallery of figures with whom the individual carries on an inner dialogue about life and hard times in the organization. The external objective referents for these figures are the other people in the organization and some outside reference persons. They include his immediate superordinates whom he must deal with every day and his distant superordinates whose actions are often only to be inferred, whose influence upon his own life in the organization is significant but largely impalpable. They include, as well, his immediate subordinates, and his distant subordinates whose actual behavior is largely undeterminable but crucial in determining his success as an executive. Despite the importance of this vast social network, it extends beyond the horizon of his vision in whichever direction he looks. The network is thus a reality and a mystery into which the individual often projects the inner figures whose dialogue legislates the constitution of his personality.

In an important sense, then, the persons around an individual are only the outer referents for the figures they come to represent in his mind. It is accurate to refer to such individuals as *objects* in the individual's life space in the organization. They are, of course, autonomous individuals with object worlds of their own, of which our individual represents but one figure. However, in the psycho-economics of the individual's transactions in the organization, he invests them with value and meaning as he chooses. This process is open to continuing validation and correction by "information" from the outside world. However, there is always some degree of selectivity here. Moreover, if the confrontation of objective fact and subjectively assigned meaning becomes too difficult or threatening, the individual often prefers to terminate his relation with the refractory person, rather than to modify the meanings or values of the figure he has created.

The process whereby one's organizational milieu is translated into an object world is known as *symbolization*. Chapter 3 has presented the structure of role relations that is basic to symbolization generally. It is not surprising that the structure is *familistic*. It is the family into which the individual is born, and in which he learns his first, most profound, and all-encompassing lessons about object relations. Thereafter, in all group situations, the individual experiences at varying depths of awareness the functioning of power and equality, of task specialization and emotional expressivity, as it existed in his own family. Unconsciously or preconsciously, he invests the new group with the remembered dynamics of his family. He associates contemporary individuals with roles played by particular members of his family. His past relations with family figures are, to some extent, transferred to new figures in the nonfamily group. Thus, in his adult situation of subordinacy in a purposive organization, he becomes reacquainted with issues of powerlessness and dependency that he first confronted as a child within his own family. Again, as he grows up in the organization, he is also growing up in his adult family of procreation. The lessons in superordinacy he is slowly learning as a father have their functional equivalent in his position of superordinacy as a developing manager. The sociopsychological equivalence of these role relations is as real, at some level of his experiencing, as the substantial differences between family and work organization.

Evolving a Concept of Himself as a Person

The individual's conception of himself is never complete. Not only is it incomplete, it is always to some extent inaccurate. In growing up, the individual grasps at a fragmented series of cues as to the total reality that he is. Certain statements by members of his family, certain reflections by his friends and acquaintances, certain preconscious indications all prompt him to think of himself first in one way, then in another. As indicated in Chapter 2, the process of growing up involves a series of experiments in identification and self-conception. The individual gathers together an increasing number of ideas about the sort of person he is and would like to become. At the same time, he begins to select and reject among them, to establish a hierarchialized conception of what he is really like, somewhat like, not very much like, and not at all like. A relatively stable hierarchy of this nature provides the essential structure of his identity. It permits certain transpositions and substitutions of concepts, but a stable identity implies a stability in the over-all hierarchy of selected motives and traits.

This psychological structure requires continuing effort in its maintenance and enhancement. It is never complete, in that psychological limitations preclude the conscious encompassing of all biological and societal forces impinging upon oneself. Its accuracy is always subject to the test of experienced anxiety, which gets aroused as inner drives and societal imperatives engage one another in the conscious workings of the individual's ego. Expanding the scope and correcting the content of his self-conception is a continuing task for the maturing individual. In the organizational setting, it is still another phase of his role-task.

Managing the "Fit" Between Personal Values and Group Demands

In Chapter 2 we presented Parsons' notion of the link between the individual and the surrounding society as being composed of values which are simultaneously internalized in the individual and institutionalized in the society. The more of a society's values the individual internalizes, the more fully he becomes a member of that society. The more an individual's values are represented in a society, the more hospitable that society appears to him. Hierarchies of values are involved in this linking process. It is the importance of values to the individual and their predominance in the society that determine the link between the two systems, rather than the absolute numbers of values involved. Disparity of primary values renders the link problematic, despite commonality of secondary values. Commonality of primary values lays the groundwork for a meaningful affiliation, with considerable freedom permitted for disparity in secondary values.

In the organizational setting, congruence in values is an important condition for productive membership: it facilitates growth on the part of the individual and innovation by individuals within the organization. The individual has a system of values when he enters the organization. The organization has an established value orientation. As he gets transactively linked up with the organization, he may come to internalize some of its values that are new to him, and he may introduce certain values previously unrepresented in the organizational system, or modify existing ones. Both commonality and disparity in values are focal points in the man-in-organization equation around which developmental and contributive potentials become realized. The individual must discover these commonalities and disparities, and activate them in his dealings with the organization. It is part of his role-task to do so.

Developmental and Contributive Aspects of Organization Membership

The "fit" between individual and organization rarely approximates complete disparity or complete congruity. Either extreme would be ruinous for the individual and for the organization. As in the issues presented in Chapter 2, balance is once again essential. The optimal range of congruity and disparity is what is crucial. What degree of congruity provides the most effective stimulus for the individual? What amount of diversity among members renders the organization most adaptable to its environment? The second question is one of policy, to be decided by management in its selection of persons for employment and promotion. The first question is a personal question which only the individual can address. It is the culmination of his role-task. How he resolves this issue will establish what he makes of himself, and of what use he is to the organization.

The individual's course in the organization and the various choices he makes in his role-task work are influenced by many factors in the organization and the wider social environment. However, the choices themselves, the necessary decisions of personal management, get made nowhere else but inside the individual, and by no other agent in the system than the individual himself. Working on these decisions, making them, acting on them, living with the consequences, and making further decisions; that is the substance of role-task work.

PART III. EXECUTIVE SUCCESSION AND THE EMERGENCE OF A ROLE CONSTELLATION
The Coming Together of a Top Management Team

WE TURN NOW from our description of individual roles to an analysis of the relations that existed among roles. That is, we move from the individual executives to the executive group conceived of as a psychosocial system, a constellation having various social and psychological properties. In Part III, we present the historical events and the psychological processes that culminated in the executive role constellation we observed in operation. This particular group structure, like many others, was formed as a result of a succession in the No. 1—the superordinate—position. The psychological and interpersonal points of origin, in a succession such as this, are crucial in understanding the subsequent development of the constellation. In order to understand this development, we now step back several years in time from the point at which the observations of Part II were made. We go back to the period in the Institute's history immediately before and after Dr. Suprin's entry into the organization as its superintendent. We start there, showing how in the initial course of the succession the executives, and other members of the organization, engaged in the role-task work that laid a basis of interpersonal accommodation upon which the constellation was built.

The departure of the previous superintendent, and the

entry of an outsider to the vacated position, caused some disturbance in the ongoing social system of the Institute. This is true in all situations involving a succession in leadership. In the present case, the newcomer had a markedly different personality and administrative style from that of his predecessor. His entry required adjustments in established work routines and realignments of interpersonal relations, particularly in the upper levels of the organzation. It required those around him to reassess whatever aspirations they may have held toward the No. 1 position, and to re-evaluate their probable future situation in the organization. This was a major psychosocial task for all those in management positions who remained in the M.P.I. after the succession, and who thereby had to evolve a personal-professional relationship with their new superordinate.

This task was a particularly important one for the assistant superintendent and the clinical director, who were the most senior "holdovers" from the previous administration. As we shall see, the process of working through led these men, each in his own way, to become reacquainted with their previously stabilized conceptions of themselves and their organizational roles.

CHAPTER 8

A New Superintendent Enters the Organization

WE DEAL in this chapter with the response to the new superintendent that occurred throughout the organization generally. We focus more specifically in the next chapter on responses within what was to become the executive role constellation. Our attempt here is not to get into detailed accounts of individual reactions, but to give a broad and approximate outline of how a whole organization reoriented itself in relation to a new superordinate. We show how members responded not simply to the new man as such, but to the predecessor-successor *pair*. The data, provided to us through the generous cooperation of Dr. Myron Sharaf, who was gathering data in the organization at the time of the succession, indicate that members' feelings and conceptions regarding the predecessor were of great significance in determining their response to the successor. This indicates that there were at least two figures, not just one, integrally involved in members' role-task work regarding the newcomer.

The constellation that existed at the time of our study came into being as a result of Dr. Suprin's succession to Dr. Sherman as superintendent. This event occurred approximately two and a half years before the beginning of our study. The succession was accomplished smoothly, despite the potentially divisive frustrations that underlay the process. The event could have proved disastrous. Dr. Suprin himself realized this. He made several joking references to the possibility of having an organization but nobody to operate it, had the succession led to the departure of Drs. Asche and Cadman and other senior staff members. The smoothness of the succession, from the organizational point of view, was largely a credit to the personal maturity of all involved, to their sensitivity to their own demands, the expectations of others, and the requirements of the organization. Dr. Sherman played a large part in bringing Dr. Suprin into the hospital as his own successor. Suprin was his choice. Sherman was thereby instrumental in bringing the "Suprin, Asche, & Cadman agency," as Suprin called it, into being. This study was conducted two and a half years after Suprin replaced Sherman, but Sherman was still a great influence on the immediate social relations among our three subjects. We found that none of the three top executives could talk for long about their present situations without making reference to Dr. Sherman, and how things had been for him during his administration. The executives' assessment of Dr. Sherman was still an important factor in their retrospective assessments of their own roles and the development of their roles in the hospital. Dr. Sherman was, so to speak, an invisible but important fourth man in the executive triad.

This being so, it was important to find out something about the processes that had been initiated when Suprin had replaced Sherman. Retrospective data were useful, but were subject to all the usual and well-known motivational distortions of memory. The three executives were unusually skilled at seeing themselves honestly, but their involvement in the succession process had been so great that it appeared useful to check their recollections against data gathered on the spot by Dr. Sharaf at the time the succession had actually taken place. Our theoretical approach to the analysis of these data is as follows.

Psychosocial Aspects of Management Succession

THE PROCESS of management succession involves the removal of one figure from the ongoing management system and the replacement of that figure by another. We refer to the individuals most closely involved as "figures" in order to highlight the fact that the succession process is as much influenced by the meanings and values assigned to these individuals by others in the system as it is by the actual characteristics of the predecessor and his successor.

Prior to a succession, the antecedent manager is a stable figure in the object world of those working around him. He is the focus of object cathexis by these others. The network of such cathexes provides many of the dynamic forces of the management system. When that individual is removed from the system, much of the subsequent disruption arises from the detachment of object cathexes from the departed figure. Each of the remaining individuals experiences a disturbance in relation to his organizational environment. He experiences object loss.

It seems to us that there are two main types of response to the loss of a significant object and to the replacing figure. From the data obtained in the M.P.I. by Dr. Sharaf, it would appear that both types can coexist, with cyclical variations in the predominance of one over the other. The first type of response involves the idealization of the departing figure and the focusing of inappropriate hate or aggression upon the successor. Feelings of grief and abandonment by the predecessor are accompanied by expectations of oppression, deprivation, and failure in the face of the newcomer.

The second type of response involves the devaluation of the departing figure and the focusing of inappropriate love or regard upon the newcomer. The idealization of the successor, accompanied by elated hopes for the future and excessive anticipations of positive change, are as unrealistic as the denigration of the predecessor, and are therefore eventually followed by disillusionment, despair, and the feeling of having been "sold out."

Given the first type of response, the individuals who experience object loss, and who are faced with the task of realigning themselves with a changed environment, focus their anger over these unpleasantries, or their hopes for a better world, upon the newcomer. He is unconsciously experienced as the cause of the succession, and of the others' *experience* of that succession. If the departing figure becomes idealized as the personification of everything good, the aggression that formerly was focused upon him is displaced upon his successor.[1] Given the second type of response, the departing figure becomes, in the minds of his formerly equable subordinates, the personification of everything bad, and the affection formerly focused upon him also gets displaced upon his successor.[2]

It is these displacements of affect that contribute to the mythogenic property of management successions. The oversimplified conceptions of the individual predecessor and successor find their expression in mythical stories that portray the individuals in the roles cast for them by the dynamics of the succession process. Usually the myth of the predecessor is the more clearly articulated, since he has departed from the scene, and the reality of his personality no longer stands in the way of the wish-fulfilling myth. Myths about the successor also get built up, however, and help others in the organizational system to form new attachments, aversions, and conceptions. We will see both sorts of myth in operation in Dr. Suprin's succession of Dr. Sherman.

[1] See A. W. Gouldner, *Patterns of Industrial Bureaucracy,* 1954.

[2] See R. H. Guest, *Organizational Change: The Effect of Successful Leadership,* 1962.

THE WORKING-THROUGH OF A MANAGEMENT
SUCCESSION

THE PROCESS of Dr. Suprin's accession to the superintendency was filled with emotion. Dr. Sherman had established himself deeply in the affections and thoughts of the many who had worked under his auspices. His departure necessitated a realignment of the relations that people had built up with him and required the reallocation of the sentiments and the identifications of which he had become the object. It appears that there was a considerable amount of temporarily unattached, free-floating affect in the hospital during that period.

"I can't imagine this place without Sherman," said one of his staff. "And it's only a month away when he'll be leaving. I was practically in tears this morning, talking about Sherman's leaving."

Dr. Sherman had earned the love and respect of hospital personnel. Although it was much more difficult to detect, he had also engendered some antipathy and disrespect either for his administrative style or for his professional views. The vituperative strength of some of the remarks made about Dr. Suprin, who at that time was scarcely more than an unknown to most of the staff at the hospital, indicated that some of this negative affect was, for a time, displaced from Sherman to Suprin. Feeling mad about Dr. Suprin was less painful than facing the imminent loss of Dr. Sherman.

"I am just crazy about Sherman," said one resident. "I had a fifteen-minute appointment with him today, and I hated to end it. Right after it, I made another appointment with his secretary.[3] He's such a wonderful man. What I like about him especially is his ability to say no and make you love it. You never

---

[3] The reader has already seen, by comparison, how different Dr. Suprin was in terms of his accessibility to his junior staff during those periods when he was in his office.

feel any hostility in it. I think that's why you can take it from him, whereas you couldn't take it from others. It's pure.

". . . He talks a lot with me about his own feelings,[4] and I wonder: Why is he talking with me about it? Who am I anyway that he should talk with me?

"I'm so happy I came here while Sherman was still here. I love working under him. . . ."

Observer: "How do you feel about Suprin?"

"I think he's a sneaky, no-good bastard, and I think I'm going to have trouble with him."

Observer: "Any acquaintance with him?"

"No. I've just seen him once or twice, but I don't like him. He's sneaky and sarcastic. I don't like talking [about it]. . . ."

Dr. Sherman was not an easy man to succeed. His benign air seemed to make people uncomfortable saying nasty things about him, and Suprin provided a target that evidently proved irresistible to a number of people with aggressive feelings to vent.

"I think he is a jerk," said one. "Tactless, ignorant, blowhard. A jerk! It's all very well for Cadman to say he [Suprin] is new and that is his way of getting to know people. I don't give a damn! If somebody spills soup on you, that may be his way of getting to know you but you don't have to like it. One staff, I'm going to get up in the middle of it and say: 'The emperor is naked.' "

Even though such expressions as this indicated as much about the respondent as about the object of response, they cannot be viewed completely as displacements. The reality of Dr. Suprin's behavior was such that statements of this nature—usually more controlled than the above—did possess certain points of descriptive reference. Suprin spoke and interacted in such a way that reactions of anger and hostility were the first that many people experienced until they got

---

[4] This was to be another dimension along which Suprin differed considerably from Sherman in dealing with subordinates.

to know him better, and until they began to view him less in immediate juxtaposition with the grandfatherly image that Dr. Sherman began to represent in the succession process.

Dr. Suprin appears to have been aware of this latent positioning of himself and Dr. Sherman in the role-expectations of the hospital personnel. He is reported to have viewed it, in part, as "the transition from the kindly old father to the aggressive young bastard."

Dr. Suprin had an objective appreciation of the accomplishments of the hospital under Dr. Sherman's administration. However, he actively avoided any personal deference to his predecessor, at least in the presence of groups comprising his future subordinates. His rejection of humility—his "cockiness"—in the face of the great man was one element of his performance to which his audience appears to have been sensitive.

There were other ways in which Dr. Suprin rejected the sentimentality of the succession process. He evidently was more comfortable with the hostilities that were focused on him than with any but the most distant expressions of sympathy and support that might have been his had he encouraged them.

"You have my sympathies," Suprin was told by a staff member after the eulogies about Dr. Sherman at a dinner in his honor.

"Thanks, I need them."

Staff member: "It must be tough coming into such a situation." (This person, in reporting this event, added: "and then I went too far.")

Suprin (stiffening) : "I'll manage."

Staff member (with an arm around Suprin's shoulder) : "I'm sure you will."

In other words, Dr. Suprin chose to keep pretty much to himself, except for a hierarchializing form of jocularity that was never greatly removed from his task orientation. Thus,

for all his outspokenness, a certain sense of mystery surrounded the man—"I don't know where his primary commitment is"—as well as an aura of aggressive administrative
effectiveness. Said one staff member:

"Take this guy Suprin. He's out for what he wants. No personal
consideration. He'll say: 'Why waste money with these people in
the back wards? Help the people you can help, who are costing
the state more money. You can feed the others for three and a
half dollars a day. Work where you can accomplish something.'
There's a lot to what he says. He's not held back by any personal
considerations for friends or anything like that. . . . And since
mental health is involved in everything—recreation, prisons, education—that's where Frank is: everywhere. And he's so effective
that he can rise very quickly."

Not even the simplest of personal habits or administrative
actions were exempted from microscopic examination, and
interpretations that were palpably apprehensive and critical.

Dr. Ross was quite annoyed with Dr. Suprin. Suprin had
started a meeting with him by saying: "Shoot."
Ross thought: What a hell of a way to start a meeting.

. . .

A staff doctor reported: "I can tell you one anecdote. I don't
know what it means. I went to Suprin's office one day to see him,
and found him going over a lot of figures from the accountant's
office. Adding them up. Sort of checking up on them."

However, this doctor proceeded in his remarks to strike a
balance in his evaluation of the new superintendent that was
tentatively optimistic.

"He won't put up with things Sherman put up with. But I
think the direction he'll move in will be a good one. I don't
believe that it will reach the point of oppressive authoritarianism."

It is difficult to represent the complexity of this process of
"shaking down" to the new superintendent. Responses to

Suprin were not all negative at the start; there were also favorable responses to the man and his actions.

"He did a good thing," said one doctor about Suprin's introductory address to the hospital. "He emphasized how good the place was *before* he came, rather than saying as did the man who took over at —— [another hospital] how great he was going to make it."

"But," that same doctor went on to speculate, "There's something about him I don't like. . . ."

It was reportedly said of Dr. Suprin by one of his colleagues outside the hospital that, "You have to learn to hate Frank before you can learn to love him." This was a myth that was picked up several times during field work. Many of those who worked under Dr. Suprin gave evidence of passing through such a transition with varying results. The shift was still detectably in operation during our period of observation in the hospital. But the transition was not a simple, unidirectional phenomenon. Some gave evidence of never having made it at all. More interesting, however, were those who oscillated between both attitudes toward the superintendent, apparently having some difficulty forming stable conceptions of the man and his role.

"I don't think he is too hot clinically," said a resident. "He's a little guy. I'd say about 5'8"." He smiled. "I've noticed I'm afraid of him. I find myself talking too much. . . .

"He has a nice smile. You can be worried about how things are going, whether he is understanding a report, and then you look over at him, and you see that smile which says, everything is O.K.

". . . I've heard this guy works weekends and never takes a holiday. Also that he's got ulcers. I'm glad of that." The resident smiled again. "Doesn't he just exude the picture of success?"

Ten days later, the same resident said the following about Dr. Suprin.

"I like him, I think he is great. He's a relief after the old, fuzzy, befuddled everything-will-be-all-right guys. I've spoken to him several times. You go in, ask him for what you want, and he does what he can. He's great. Direct, down-to-earth, straight-forward. I think he is hard to. . . .

"I must be an 'as if' person. I used to walk like Sherman, and now I find myself walking like Suprin. . . ."

As the assessment of Suprin's personality and new role achieved greater perspective, as the attitudes toward him became more favorable, Sherman and his role seemed to be re-evaluated in the opposite direction. It appears that this process took place most readily among those who had worked closely with Dr. Sherman, and would do likewise with Dr. Suprin. Those who were hierarchically removed from the position of superintendent—the residents—had, as a group, a more difficult time working through this process.

"He's become much more benign, even to me!" said one of the hospital's medical executives about Dr. Sherman, just prior to the latter's departure. "Used to be, I'd be a minute late and he'd yell at me. Now he lets me be late. . . . He's mellowed a lot lately."

One of the staff doctors mid-level in the medical chain of command was struck by the *similarities* between Sherman and Suprin.

"In many ways I think he [Suprin] is like Sherman," said the doctor. "After all, you usually like people who are like you, and Sherman does like him. . . . I talked with a friend who knows him [Suprin] down at the [other hospital at which Dr. Suprin was superintendent], and my friend said that while he has to one-up you until he gets to know you well, and while he can stir up a big fuss and talk very sarcastically and hostilely, usually it doesn't go beyond that. If anything, he's criticized for not being tougher. . . . Yes, before the recent benignness, Sherman was a man who wasn't given to very much warmth, who could be very sarcastic but who in the end didn't go beyond that."

Another doctor reported that Dr. Sherman, the kindly gentleman of the hospital, was rumored to be a tough boss in his new position.

"Where he is now [after leaving the Institute], they are all saying: this guy Sherman is tough. He won't understand us. He keeps looking over your shoulder."

As Suprin worked his way into his new position, the staff began to get a working knowledge of the man, and a more informed appreciation of him came to be expressed more frequently. "Suprin is a man who likes to have things clear and definite," said one resident. This was hardly a novel observation. What was novel, but became less so, was that the resident then went on to back up his observation with a firsthand experience he had had with the new superintendent.

"I was substituting for Simms as chief [resident]," he said, "and Suprin called me up one day and said, 'Ralph, is so-and-so psychotic? I've got to know right away. I've got to write a letter.' I said yes. Suprin said 'Thanks,' and hung up. I like this crisp, clear way. I think Suprin is a person you could depend on if you needed something."

The formation of a reified image of the new superintendent was facilitated by the departing superintendent. He was reported by the residents as trying to relieve their concern about Suprin, telling them that he was really a good fellow.

". . . when a new man comes in," said Sherman, "there are some realistic grounds for fear. There is usually the idea of housecleaning. There is some truth to that. Another thing is that the top men hand in their resignations when the new super comes. And that is in effect what they did. [A number of the staff] went to see Suprin. He was quite amused by it.[5] He has the fondest

---

[5] Suprin evidently experienced it somewhat differently. During the period of observation, Suprin laughingly remarked in an executive committee meeting that these overtures had frightened him considerably. "They scared the hell out of me," he said. "I saw myself with a hospital to run, and nobody there to run it."

feeling for all of them. . . . He is a sarcastic person. . . . I was about the same when I was his age. But he leaves them alone more than I believe I do. He is just interested in the finished product. And he is a very brilliant, competent person. He works 16 hours a day. He reads very fast. I think people will find him very good. The highest compliment is that his secretary is all upset about his leaving."

The composite picture of the new superintendent was, it can be seen, a study of contradictions: that he was tough to the point of ruthlessness, and that he was not really tough enough; that he was opportunistically involved in his personal career, and that he was dedicated to the advancement of larger professional and humanitarian objectives; that he was all show, and that there was more to him than met the eye. Many of the more "mature" remarks seemed to fall somewhere between these poles, although it is perhaps more accurate to say that they incorporated elements of both extremes.

"When he [Suprin] first came to meetings," said one resident, "the atmosphere was so thick you could cut it. It's better now. . . . I like him. I think he's good."
"But you know," said another, "actually I've never heard one mean incident that Suprin was involved in; one actual mean incident. The worst I've heard is that at a meeting of superintendents with [two other superintendents] present, Suprin spoke of what he wanted 'my gang' to do. That's callow but you have to extrapolate quite a bit from there to meanness or ruthlessness."
"But lately," said a third, "through my work at the prison, I've been hearing more about the other side, about all Suprin has done to build up mental hospitals and mental care in this state. I've learned that he hasn't built his reputation on nothing."

The following themes emerged with some clarity from these data:
(1) Dr. Suprin was perceived as active, intelligent, aggres-

sive, outspoken, sarcastic, decisive, domineering, orderly, competent, directive, trustworthy, and hard-working. It appeared that in a variety of organizational settings, particularly in amorphous ones, Suprin's basic interpersonal response was a hierarchializing one. His intent was to establish himself as the dominant figure—"one up"—before relaxing that dominance and getting on with the business at hand. Suprin seemed to prefer and to operate more effectively in relationships that were predominantly counter-personal, rather than in those that tended to be in any way over-personal. To accept Suprin, and his dominance, was often to act in a dependent, affectionate way toward him, which made him feel uncomfortable and which he rejected. The resultant feeling of insult on the part of the subordinate would then jeopardize his acceptance of Suprin. The "trick" was to find out when, where, and how to act dependent, and when, where, and how to act independent under the new superintendent. Taken on an organization-wide basis, the resolution of this issue comprised the hospital's major task in assimilating its new No. 1 man.

(2) Dr. Suprin was expected to establish a tighter, more orderly, and more authoritarian regime in the hospital. "He is a more orderly man than I am," said Dr. Sherman. "He likes to have things click right along."

"He's not going to be another Father Sherman," said a secretary. "He will be very energetic, decisive, and that's what we need."

Such expectations prompted their own fulfillment.

"It's self-tightening," said a secretary. "It's going on already [prior to Suprin's arrival]. People are laying low. . . ."

A resident reported that he noticed himself tidying up his office more than had been his custom.

". . . they think he is going to crack the whip," said a ward worker. "But that's what they want. It's funny, but that's the way they feel."

(3) It was expected that Dr. Suprin would leave people alone, that he would interact less frequently and less warmly with hospital pesonnel than had his predecessor. He would thereby provide a degree of personal freedom greater than that under Dr. Sherman. There were mixed feelings about this.

"I say, 'Hello, Doctor,' and he hardly says, 'Hello,' back," said a nonmedical hospital employee. "He wants everybody to do their job. Sherman used to be involved in everybody's business."

(4) One of the new freedoms consisted of a change in the emotional climate of the new administrative organization. People expected to be able to admit or express more aggression and less affection toward the superintendent than they could toward his predecessor. "I think I'll have an easier time getting angry at Suprin than I did at Sherman," said one of the doctors who reported directly to both superintendents.

"I've changed my thinking about Suprin," reported a resident after Suprin had been in his new position for a short while. "I still think he is rude and tasteless, but I'm not sure that's so bad. If he can be rude, then I can be rude. And one thing I don't like is that you're not supposed to get angry, not supposed to be direct [around the hospital]. That's one thing nobody can stand around here.

". . . During the discussion, he [Suprin] said that it was interesting that the case went better after I, on his suggestion, started to go into the patient's transference to me. I said that I had my own perception of what happened, and went on to tell it. He said nothing. If Sherman had been there, I wouldn't have said it, but with Suprin there I felt free to."

(5) Finally, it was expected that everyone who did his work properly, who fulfilled his responsibilities in the organization, would have nothing to worry about from Dr. Suprin. This seems to have been expressed most directly by nonpro-

fessional hospital personnel; that is, by people who could with less apprehension than more highly placed individuals come to grips with the advent of a man who gave signs that he was ready, willing, and able to fulfill his new role as the No. 1 authority figure in the hospital.

The simplest, most concise description of the whole succession process was given by one of the women of the hospital's housekeeping group.

"He's a *very* brilliant man," she said of Suprin. "He's fair if you do your work."

Observer: "How do you know about him?"

"I knew his lab technician who worked with him for three years. His hobby was working in the lab. And he told me about him. He said he could be very brusque. If he asked you something, he wanted a straight answer. He's quick on the draw. We'll never have another Sherman again. He let you alone. He hardly ever bothered you. And you could go right up and speak to him real easy. Always a smile. He didn't get mad often, and when he did!!! That's the way that type is. This man [Suprin] is more brusque. He's a more brilliant type, more an organizer. Sherman was a teacher. If you do your work, he [Suprin] won't bother you."

We have seen the manner in which the organization coped with Dr. Sherman's departure and with the advent of Dr. Suprin as the new superintendent. We examined the mythical representations that were built up around the two men in the initial stages of the succession process. We demonstrated the highly emotional character of these myths and pointed to the gradual diminution of affect displacement as the organization settled into the realities of working with its new superintendent.

CHAPTER 9

The Formation of an Executive Role Constellation

THE SUCCESSION of superintendents was more than a change of incumbents. It was a qualitative change in the upper management system of the hospital. The selection of a new superintendent from outside the hospital brought about a major realignment of internal organizational forces. We are here concerned mostly with the realignment that took place at the top executive level in the organization. With the advent of the new No. 1 man, a complex accommodation had to take place among the top three executives; the assistant superintendent, the clinical director, and, of course, the new superintendent. Each of these three had role-task work to do in coming to grips with the new interpersonal situation in which the affairs of the hospital, and their own lives in it, would be directed and administered. This was a great deal more than a redefinition—under new management, so to speak—of the duties of each executive, or a new division of the workaday job-tasks one might find listed in the formal description of each man's position. The more basic process was a more profoundly personal, and a more intimately interpersonal, one than this. It involved a reworking of a previously existing division of psychosocial functions, a recasting of organizational characters into roles requiring different manifestations of personality, or a manifestation of different aspects of personality than had existed before. To a significant extent, this called for a reassessment of one's personality;

never an easy or painless undertaking. It called for a re-appraisal of one's personal, professional, and organizational goals in the light of the new situation obtaining within the executive group. It resulted in a gradual move toward an integration of consensually accepted, specialized personal styles and a pattern of emotional exchange among the three top executives, and between them and their subordinates. This was the basis and the initial substance of the executive role constellation.

It is difficult to study and report the processes of such a change, due to the resistances engendered by the painfulness of transition, and by the sense of indiscretion often surround-ing the exposition of this process within an organization. Nevertheless, such a reallocation of internal resources was more than hinted at in the behavior of the hospital execu-tives at that time.

"Is the transition painless?" a resident asked Dr. Cadman.

Cadman: "Such things are never painless. Some people are just better at covering it up than others."

One dimension of readjustment was delineated by the out-going superintendent just prior to his departure from the hospital. In talking of the forthcoming succession, he said:

". . . Another factor that makes for complications is that there were two men here who were perfectly qualified for the job, and there may be some feeling about that."

An examination of the data gathered in the hospital at that time made it clear that there were other people in the hospital who thought or felt the same way. In fact, attentions were turned to the assistant superintendent and the clinical di-rector. The behavior of these two was the focus of consider-able scrutiny and interpretation, as other "holdovers" in the organization sought for clues as to how the succession was pro-

ceeding, how the two executives in question were responding, and how they themselves might legitimately feel about
the whole process. In this highly mythogenic situation there
was much casting about for acts or persons upon which to at-
tach realistically the feelings and impressions experienced at
the time. The senior figures were all fair game for the psy-
chologizing that was then going on, and to which the reader
has already been partly introduced. To what extent the characterizations of the top figures were then valid cannot now be
clearly established. However, the fact that reifications did
exist in the hospital at the time must in itself have presented
problems to the central actors. As one of their immediate
subordinates speculated:

> "I think Cadman and Asche were both disappointed that they
> didn't get the appointment. I don't think they ever gave up the
> fantasy that they might get it."

To what extent did these executives possess the feelings attributed to them? To what extent were these feelings, both
ascribed and actual, related to the redefinitions of role precipitated by Dr. Suprin's accession to the superintendency?
Data gathered directly from these executives both during and
after the succession give evidence of strong feelings and efforts at reassessment. The data indicate that each executive
reflected intensively on what was involved for him in relating himself to his subtly redefined position and role, and to
the others within the new top management system. This reflective work was the instrumentality by which the role constellation gradually emerged. Chapters 4–7 have already indicated where and in what way this work was *still going on*
in the role-transitions within the constellation.

The issues the executives faced were most visible in the
group setting in which they and the staff were required to
interact together. One such issue is nicely illustrated by the
statement of a resident who, when participating in such situa-

tions, felt as though his allegiance to each of these top figures was being contested among the three.

Observer: "How do you find Suprin?"

Resident: "I think he's great. He's my type. I can understand him. I find he agrees with my ideas. I throw out ideas, and he says, 'Good,' and picks them up.

"The only trouble I have is with the other senior figures. When they are there and I am there, it's a problem. I feel uneasy. I sense that they are uncomfortable with Suprin, that there is some jockeying going on. If I throw out ideas critical of the way things are going, I feel I am criticizing them. I know Suprin will agree with me."

Observer: "Is it a question of loyalty?"

Resident: "Yes, that's exactly it. It's a very uncomfortable feeling."

Having stated the general situation following the succession of Dr. Suprin to the position of superintendent of the M.P.I., let us now consider the adaptive efforts each executive made toward the formation of a functioning executive team.

ADAPTATION THROUGH THE REINTEGRATION
OF AN EARLIER IDENTITY

DR. CADMAN'S RESPONSE to such situations was to remain silent. He held his participation in such meetings down almost to his mere presence, and in so doing was conspicuous by his silence. This was especially apparent in the larger meetings in which both Dr. Cadman and Dr. Suprin were present. Dr. Cadman was also reported to have been silent in meetings in which Dr. Sherman had been present. Suprin was initially perceived by some as attempting to stimulate Cadman into more active participation in such events. "He won't let Cadman just be folksy," it was said. However, Cadman persisted in this pattern. There was some annoyance among residents that Cadman did not speak up more for himself, for them, and for the way things had been before Suprin had become involved. Those who wished he would assert himself more vigorously expressed strong feelings about his being weak.

"He's pathetic. I can't admire him," said a resident [who several years later gave evidence of admiring Cadman considerably]. "He's not a *man*. All he is is a teacher."

However, the wish remained unfulfilled that Cadman vigorously expound the professional beliefs and persuasions subordinates had learned from his teaching. Cadman persisted in not actively shaping the changing management situation according to the way his students thought he should. That was not his way. He thereby fell heir to resentments, some of which had little to do with what *he* did or did not do. Sometimes the anger that was directed to him was appropriate to the tasks of the hospital.

"It got me so sore," said one resident about Cadman's silence in a general meeting. "He didn't say a word. Here we were, talking about what patients feel, trying to figure it out. And here he was silent, with all his experience."

Other remarks made at that time appear to have been less appropriate. They seemed to say one thing but mean another. For instance, the concern was expressed that Cadman, through his outward passivity, was allowing himself to be victimized by the dynamic new superintendent. The possibility that he might have been *realizing* most of his own preferences or objectives in the way he thought best for himself seemed to have been overlookd. Also, feeling sorry for Dr. Cadman was in some instances carried to such an extreme that anger was perhaps a more important determinant than genuine sympathy for whatever difficulties Cadman might have been experiencing. Cadman represented a type of condition shared by many of the younger doctors under him in the hospital. He demonstrated by his behavior the condition of being *more acted upon than acting*. Yet he was in a formal position in the hospital where he was seen as being able to do something about changing that condition. It appeared to others that he *chose* not to do so. Apperceptions of him tended to reflect the feelings aroused by the image of dependency accepted.

"Cadman is very nervous. It's really a pity to see him sitting there, taking notes like a little boy while Suprin talks. I think Suprin's using him the wrong way. . . ."

"Cadman is very anxious. He's poking his nose into a lot more of the details than he used to. He doesn't like it. Suprin will lose him if he keeps it up. Cadman made it very clear that he didn't want to be bothered with administrative matters when he took this job. Now he has to find out whether the trays are hot, and he's very anxious about it. He used to leave all such jobs to the chiefs, and we'd act as buffers for him. When he took this job, he said he didn't want to hear about anything unless it went wrong. That was great with me. You could be dependent or independent. . . . Now he wants reports every day. . . . He'll push Cadman out if he keeps this up. Cadman wants time to think and pursue his own interests. He shouldn't be involved in petty administrative things.[1]

"I wouldn't want to be chief [resident] here if it were going to be this kind of setup. The old way allowed plenty of room for you to fit it to your own personality. Each echelon acted as a buffer for the one above it. You could go your own way." [2]

---

[1] Cadman could easily elicit the feeling and perception that he was absolutely desolate and helpless in the face of the powerful newcomer. His magnification of the tragedy and pathos of life reinforced such impressions, as in the following:

Cadman: "Wait till you're 45 and have to give up all your fantasies."
Respondent: "I'd die if I had to give up all my fantasies."
Cadman: "A lot of people do."

[2] Several years later other chief residents were talking in almost identical terms about the increasing hierarchialization and authoritarianism, and the decreasing individual professional freedom, that they perceived were latent in a number of executive actions of that year. They, too, decided that they would not have wanted to be chief resident under the newly authoritarian regime they knew was going to be instituted in the following academic year.

Cadman would talk freely about how, "when you reach a certain stage, you have to evaluate your life and you realize you may not have made of it what you wanted." To some extent, Dr. Cadman appears to have been using himself as an instrument for teaching his residents about some of the issues that would form the texture of their future professional careers and practices. This is not to say that he was wholly detached from what he said and did in the hospital at that time. Reactions such as the following probably told something about Cadman as well as telling a great deal about what was going on in his organizational audience at the time.

"Such concern with status!" exclaimed a resident who went on to say he found such behavior on Cadman's part to be distressing and a little distasteful. "He goes around talking about it all the time."

The data gathered in the hospital during this period of succession do indicate that Dr. Cadman was experiencing difficulty in adjusting to his position in the new administration. He was apperceived by some as having "put all his eggs in one basket, and lost."

His comments later on indicated that he, too, considered this partly to be the case. He stated it to the observer in the following way:

Cadman: "I made this decision a long time ago, of course, in 1939." (He lifted his fingers in the Churchillian "V" sign.)

Observer: "What's that?"

Cadman: "That some day I would be top clinical man, but that I would never be top administrative man. They had things set up in that way in those days too, where all the top jobs were held by administrative men. So I knew where I was headed when I made that decision: That I'd never be head of an organization."

Thus, Dr. Cadman's basic pattern of career aspirations existed prior to the succession and facilitated his adaptation to the new superintendent. The advent of Dr. Suprin required Dr. Cadman to reacquaint himself with his decision of 1939, but it did not require him to build a *new* career plan, or to rebuild one that had been thwarted in its essentials. Despite his disappointment, Cadman saw himself as very well suited for the role related to the No. 2 position in the hospital.

Despite his realization of his own interests and capabilities as a "top clinical man," Cadman could not deny experiencing disappointment in not being chosen as the new superintendent.

Cadman: "I ran this place for two years from my office. Did you know that? After Sherman retired. . . . I knew I wouldn't get the appointment."
Observer: "How did you know that?"
Cadman: "Everybody knew." He laughed. "Everybody knows I am not interested in administrative detail. That's part of the decision I made in the 1930's. Did I tell you about that? About choosing the clinical [route]? I knew then that I would never be No. 1, because all the No. 1 jobs are administrative. I'm not cathected to administration."

This characteristic of the man—not being cathected to administration—was the essential operational basis for the close working relationship that Cadman and Suprin established. This is illustrated by the ease and rapidity with which Cadman's thinking moved from his disinterest in administration to his working relations with Suprin.

Cadman: "Most of my administrative work is done between teaching, supervision, and consultations—I guess because I don't get too much gratification from it.
". . . Dr. Suprin is very tolerant of the little administration I do.[3] He does a lot of it that I would have to do otherwise. In

[3] We were impressed by how much administrative work the clinical director *did* do. Younger doctors, either on the staff or among the residents, who felt close to Dr. Cadman occasionally commented that Cadman was being "buried under a mountain of administration." As one might have come to ex-

other hospitals, the clinical director in a position like this never leaves his desk, never sees a patient, because he has so much administration to do. When Suprin came in [as superintendent], he knew the type of schedule I liked to follow. I went over to see him the moment I heard he was going to become the superintendent of this hospital and offered my resignation. I believe the top man should have the right to choose the man he wants to run the show. So in this sense, he hired me, although from the Institute's point of view, I continued right on from before he became superintendent."

Observer: "So he knew the type of workday you were interested in living before he ever came to this place?"

Cadman: "Oh, yes. Absolutely."

The observer did not understand what Cadman actually meant about offering his resignation to Suprin. Did he actually hand in his resignation, or was he using the phrase figuratively? In following up on this query, a great deal more was learned about the basis of the observed relationship between the two men.

Observer: "You told me that Suprin 'hired' you. You went over to see him. Did you actually hand him your resignation?"

Cadman: "I can tell you the exact place I saw him. . . . I said to him I would be happy to resign if he wanted someone else to work with. Nothing changed hands in the way of paper, but we discussed it and came to an agreement that we could work together. I believe firmly that a man who takes on responsibility for running a show should have the right to pick his own men, to

---

pect, much of the initiative for this burial was seen to reside in Dr. Suprin, whom one doctor saw as "trying to steal Cadman's charisma." The point here is not how much was "much" administration. Obviously, different standards were being applied for different reasons. The importance here is that Cadman's manifest view of himself as *liberated* from administration by Dr. Suprin contributed greatly to the warmth and appreciation that he brought to his working relations with the latter. For the sake of accuracy, it must be noted that his above statement does not denote any simple, objective truth about his work situation. His coexistent complaints about being "America's No. 1 scut boy" supported this.

pick men he can work with, and not be loaded down with hangers-on. . . ."

Observer: "What was the agreement that you and Dr. Suprin reached?"

Cadman: "I've known Frank for 20 years, and he knew what sort of a person I was. . . . I went to him with this project that is now getting under way as part of the [research] program. He was also a friend of [a professional colleague], and we both knew each other through [a professional association]. And I knew him out West. . . . I heard all about Frank then. And then I got interested in research and, of course, Frank had written something on it. So I got to know him there, too. Then after the war, he asked me if I were interested in coming to work in [his hospital]. And then, he's from Missouri, and so I knew what he was like. I know people from Missouri. I was like that myself. . . .

"When the trustees were interviewing about the appointment, they interviewed me to find out what I felt about Frank and whether I could work with him. I said I could. . . . You know, both Howard [Asche] and I were considered for the job at least at the discussing stage. We both sort of wanted the job, despite our better judgments. If I had been offered the job, I would have taken it, although I know that administration isn't my strong point, my long suit.

"But the trustees are very good at finding out that sort of thing. But I decided that Frank and I had common interests, a mutuality of purpose, that could allow me to work with him, and not always be trying to work against him, show him up, and trying to take over his job rather than *helping* him with it. I decided there was a personal compatibility between Frank and me as persons that was strong enough to let us work together. I think that the most important thing between two people in this type of situation is a personal compatibility. Otherwise they wouldn't be able to work together."

In other words, the basis for the relationship between Cadman and Suprin existed long before Dr. Suprin's actual appointment as superintendent of the Institute. This comprised (1) a history of acquaintance, (2) a mutuality of purpose,

(3) a personal compatibility, and (4) a constructive attitude on Dr. Cadman's part toward the authority of the superordinate, similar to that delineated by Henry in his analysis of the psychodynamics of the executive role.[4] For Dr. Cadman, these were the role-requisites for a person in a subordinate position—a No. 2 man—and Cadman saw himself as possessing them. It appears that they facilitated his decision to work with Suprin, which in turn aided him in his resolution of subordinacy to a new No. 1.

Fulfilling the role requirements as he saw them was a process that required much giving on Cadman's part—ostensibly more giving than getting, which annoyed some of his subordinates who wished that he would stand up and demand more—but he also received less visible rewards that meant a great deal to him. For instance, he found that under Dr. Suprin he could work in a management system that encouraged him in his efforts as a teacher and therapist. He also found himself in an administrative climate that was direct and precise, that felt "clean" to him, and that allowed him to preoccupy himself with problems other than the delineation of administrative responsibilities and the enforcement of regulations. These he could more or less leave to the superintendent.

"Suprin and Sherman have very different administrative styles," said Cadman. "But they also have much in common. Both left no doubt as to who had the responsibility. They kept things separate. There was no ping-pong going back and forth around here, you know?" Cadman described the decision-making process in several mental hospitals in the vicinity. In reference to one in particular, he said: "Nobody knew where in the world he was in that place. The ping-pong ball was going back and forth all over the place. I couldn't work in that atmosphere again, where no one ever knows where they are. You need somebody to make the

4 W. E. Henry, "The Psychodynamics of the Executive Role," in W. L. Warner and N. H. Martin (eds.), *Industrial Man*, 1959.

decisions. It's a funny thing, but even if you disagree with it [a decision], it gives you something to work with. If I disagree with Dr. Suprin, I tell him so, and hope he will change his mind. If he doesn't, I go along with what he says. That doesn't mean I stop collecting data, and giving it to him, and hope he will change his mind. But I work with it until he does. It's clean that way, you know?"

Business as Usual: An Attempt at Role Constancy

THE INITIAL ADJUSTMENT to his position in the new administration was less stressful for Dr. Asche than for Dr. Cadman. This may have been due in part to Asche's greater powers of denial, to his tendency to emphasize the more cheerful aspects of problematic situations, and to his practice of keeping quiet about the things that were bothering him. In any case, for him the transition was manifestly more matter of fact. "Just a couple of guys doing a job together" was the way he put it at the time. He perceived Dr. Suprin as reaching out in an effort to establish working relations with his new subordinates.

"He's treating me with respect," said Asche. "Cadman too. Cadman was terribly scared in the beginning, but now I think he feels better. *Suprin sort of regards us as a triumvirate.*" [The emphasis has been added. It appears that the three executives were not long in recognizing their own role complementarity.] "He goes out of his way to back up what I say."

Asche's apperceptions of the superintendent were not completely devoid of a sense of threat, but this threat had a more external and less personalistic referent than people seemed to detect in Cadman's responses to the situation.

"The trouble is, he's very interested in research," said Asche of Suprin, "and it will be a question of whether you can have two people [Asche and Suprin] so involved in research."

This was the closest that Asche came to expressing his unsettled feelings about the new superintendent. Also, Asche evidently experienced a greater potential freedom of retaliation against any aggressions that might be directed at him— "I feel like asking him sometime if his lab is justifying the money it's costing"—and even if no concrete action was taken, it rendered Asche's initial transactions with the new superintendent somewhat less agonizing and more equalitarian.

"Look, I'm not afraid of this guy," said Asche at the time of the succession. "I'm willing to tell him . . . but let's wait a while, and see what happens. . . . I don't really know him very well. I'm going to cultivate his friendship. We've had several talks together . . . I put the cards on the table. . . . I've told him about things here—table of organization, things like that. I'm teaching him. (Smiles) He'll learn fast."

Asche also saw Suprin's administrative style as being more definite, open, and precise than Dr. Sherman's had been. "He's neat," Asche said of Suprin. "His fingernails are neat. His desk is neat. Everything is up to date." But it was more difficult to determine how this *affected* Dr. Asche than was the case for Dr. Cadman.

"Frank's decision structure is like a pyramid," said Asche. He outlined the shape of a pyramid with his fingers. "Dick Sherman's was more like a snake, always changing shape." Asche drew several convolutions in the air. "Frank's decision structure is a lot easier, clearer, and more concise than was Sherman's. Dick's was like the hub of a wheel with spokes of different lengths. Not everybody can get in to see Frank. Only the heads of departments are the men he really welcomes, and he delegates a lot of authority to them. With Sherman, though, every little man could find the way into his office if he wanted, and if there was a gripe in any part of the organization, Dick was sure to find out about it."

The new superintendent did, however, pose certain problems for Dr. Asche; or as he saw it, to the hospital staff in general.

"He's an excellent man," said Asche when the observer pressed him about his personal responses to Dr. Suprin. "He's really fast, and he makes sound decisions. He's a precise, clean thinker. . . . However, Frank's actions tend to be traumatic in three ways, I think. First, he tends to blow up. He doesn't do this too often, but when he does, he does a good job at it, and it has its effect around the hospital. Second is this business about 'I'm telling you.' (Asche demonstrated, jabbing his forefinger at the observer's chest.) He gets a lot of people's feelings hurt that way. Third, he tends to brag a lot about himself, in a straightforward sort of way, which is just the sort of person Frank is. I've gotten to know Frank, and I find this bragging about himself doesn't really mean too much. The same thing goes for his blowing up. But when people are new here, they don't know about this. I've had a lot of people come into my office straight from Frank's office, feeling hurt. I've tried to explain to them this business about its not meaning too much. They usually end up going back to see Frank in a couple of weeks, and he sometimes even apologizes for the way he behaved before. But I want to make it clear that I think he is a wonderful guy."

Just as Dr. Cadman experienced benefit in the "clean" style of delegation of authority, so Dr. Asche found Dr. Suprin's assertiveness to be dependable and worthy of trust. For instance, in referring to a medical faculty meeting that he would not be able to attend, Asche told a colleague:

"We got Frank there. He'll put in a plug for his boys. He takes his time, but every now and then he will say, 'Look, we've got to do something about this department.' He'll get somewhere for his boys to go. We've got a good man there. As Watchamadink said—you know, —— [a name] —— 'You've got to learn to hate Frank before you can learn to love him.' "

Colleague: "I found that when I stopped trying to get love from him, I got more of it."

Other Elements of Change That Contributed to Role Constancy

THERE WERE OTHER advantages as well in the role behavior of the newcomer. It was generally believed that Suprin tended to specialize in moving people—patients, trainees, and staff—*out* of the hospital, whereas other executives tended to let them stay *in*. The observer did not obtain direct information on the workings of such a specialized subsystem, but the belief that it existed was widespread in the organization. This was largely due to the fact that the superintendent himself was fond of describing this setup to the various audiences he addressed in the hospital.

"I think the residents come to me," he told the observer, "when they want someone to tell them to get a patient out of the hospital, to move him along to some other institution, or to lay down the law to him. They go to Cadman if they want someone to tell them to keep a patient, and keep working with him, although they are sometimes surprised. Sometimes Cadman will fire a patient out of the hospital before the resident has hardly opened his mouth. But this doesn't happen too often. Mostly they'll come to me if they want to get rid of a patient."

This point of view became widespread throughout the organization. A group of residents at lunch described the same set of relationships.

Richards: "Once a resident has made up his mind about a patient, he takes matters concerning that patient to the doctor he knows will agree with him. How does he know who will agree with him? That is the sort of thing the residents talk about among themselves. It is part of the mythology of the hospital. The residents pick up the general orientation of the staff from watching them perform on ward rounds, staff conferences, and in supervision."

Rizzo: "For instance, you go to Suprin if you want to move a patient out, and you go to Cadman if you want to keep a patient in the hospital."

Ralenitis: "Cadman likes to get patients out of the hospital, too. At least, this is what he says to the chief residents. But he may say to a resident, 'Oh, let him stay another year.' "

As mentioned, this uniformity was not confined to moving patients out of the hospital. Dr. Suprin had a list of staff people he quite openly said he would like to see leave the hospital. The residents also were not exempted from this pattern of influence.

These skills and preferences of their new superordinate permitted Dr. Cadman and Dr. Asche to carry on in their customary patterns of supportiveness and friendliness, without having to add extra elements of enforcement and control to their role performances. This would not have been the case if a predominantly nondirective, friendly, and supportive individual had taken over the superintendency.

THE NEW SUPERINTENDENT BUILDS HIS TEAM

THE RELATIONSHIP between Drs. Cadman and Asche tended to be somewhat distant. Their comments about each other were infrequent, and much more guarded than their statements about their relations with Dr. Suprin. This reflected many things. For one, the reality of their work situations was such that the relation of each to the other was much less important to them, and to the hospital, than was the relation of each to the superintendent. Their observed interactions were highly infrequent, and around relatively trivial matters, except when both were interacting together in the company of Dr. Suprin. Also, their professional views about psychiatric treatment and research manifested the not uncommon differences in attitude and approach separating clinicians and researchers. They felt no organizational pressures to gloss over these differences. In fact quite the contrary seems to have been true, since both they and Dr. Suprin considered the presence of a variety of psychiatric modalities to be a good thing in a training hospital.

At the same time, neither of these two men was inclined to exploit their separateness, and they chose to say little about each other, either to their subordinates or to the observer. People were left to form their own judgments as to the relations between these two men, and the presence of an active, outspoken superintendent influenced these judgments. Without subscribing to the several projective generalizations— such as "sibling rivalry"—that existed in the organization around this topic, we shall simply report the relative disengagement of these two men in comparison with the greater engagement of each with Dr. Suprin. The absence of relationships was as much a factor as their presence in the structure and functioning of the executive role constellation.

The interrelated system of conceptions of self and other would not be complete without a description of Dr. Suprin's apperceptions and judgments of his two immediate subordinates. The reader has already been presented, in previous chapters, with some of Dr. Suprin's impressions of Dr. Cadman and Dr. Asche. His impressions of these two men tended not to be elaborate, complicated, or reserved. He had a knack for putting the essentials of his judgment into mordant and laconic phrases. These he tended to express quite often, in a variety of organizational settings, so that they became factors to be reckoned with in the internal workings of the staff.

Dr. Suprin viewed Dr. Cadman as a top-rate clinician and therapist, full of love for people in general and patients in particular. The one difficulty that Dr. Suprin professed to have with Dr. Cadman was the latter's disinclination to take the initiative on administrative problems, to decide what to do, and then to take steps to have it done.

Dr. Suprin was impressed by Dr. Asche's hard work and was appreciative of the results produced therefrom. But just as there was a certain distance in Asche's remarks about Suprin, so there was in Suprin's remarks about Asche. (It should be remembered that these statements were being made in comparison with the remarkably personal remarks that Cadman and Suprin made about each other.) The Cadman-Suprin relationship gave evidence of being a closer, more complementary one than that between Suprin and Asche. Suprin often referred to all three as a tightly knit team—the "triumvirate" or the "Suprin, Asche, Cadman agency"—but he related himself more often to Cadman than to Asche. "Take Paul and me," he told a staff group. "Our theory is almost the same, but . . . our styles are different. . . . Paul and I," he told residents, "believe in firm control." Just as a midwestern rural background served as a linkage between Suprin and Cadman, so the dissimilarity of this background with that of a northeastern urban boyhood conveyed the lesser proximity of Suprin and Asche.

"What did you think of Asche's little talk yesterday?" Dr. Suprin asked the observer. (Dr. Asche had addressed a group of residents on the career development of researchers. He had used the pattern of his own development as an example.)

Observer: "It interested me. What about you, Doctor?"

Suprin: "I enjoyed it. You can't help but enjoy the sort of picture he presented—sort of the poor struggling boy, striving for success. He certainly has achieved a lot. For me, it is more a case of, 'How the hell could you miss.' " [5]

[5] Dr. Asche had been very open with his audience, telling the residents a lot about his personal history, prefaced by the remark that he had never been psychoanalyzed. Dr. Suprin sat next to Dr. Asche during the talk. One implication that was raised was that Suprin would do likewise in a future meeting. This seemed quite out of character with Suprin's tendency to maintain distance between himself and others, particularly subordinates.

"Will you give a talk like that?" asked the observer.

Suprin: "Well, hell. I hate to disappoint some of those enthusiastic young boys. I'll have to think it over. I don't know, though. (Smiling) Maybe I'll have my analyst come over and talk to them."

The differential closeness and distance between these three men were reflected in Suprin's description of the following incident. Dr. Suprin was once more telling the observer of the similarities between himself and Dr. Cadman, and that both he and Cadman had come from midwestern rural stock. Suprin liked to talk on such matters. As a man who prided himself on the high caliber of people he could interest in working with him, the interpersonal relations that Suprin maintained with these people were very important to him. These comprised a series of topics that he thought and spoke about often, and in which his involvement was easily tapped. He derived a noticeable amount of pleasure in perusing the "team" he had built up around him in the hospital, and his relations with members of the medical executive committee were something that he did not take lightly, even though he usually spoke of these people in that manner.

"We behave quite differently, he and I," Dr. Suprin continued, remarking on his relations with Dr. Cadman. "As different as two peas in a pod can be. But we see things very frequently in the same way. Asche is sort of a different person again. He often sees things differently from me. For instance, on this application for the [research] grant, Cadman and I both saw us as applying for funds to study the [biosocial aspects of psychosis]. Howie, from the very same application, thought we were applying for a continuation of the physiological work [presently being carried on in the hospital]. And he worked on the application with me!

"I called him [Asche] up and asked him to get in a proposal in time for this fall. He didn't think it could be done in time. He was talking in terms of next year, or even longer. Howie's a gem. He can always find time for the important things. He got right to work and wrote up the application. I'd say he is the best damn writer of research applications in the country. I took it and polished it up a little, and we both read it over and sent it in. And then we found out that we both thought we were applying for different things! That's our strength. We can see things differently, but we work well together."

DIFFERENTIATING ONESELF FROM ONE'S PREDECESSOR

DR. SUPRIN said many times that, when he took the hospital over from Dr. Sherman, he intended to run it differently. The professional and managerial substance of these differences was harder to detect than was the personal and interpersonal texture thereof. Dr. Suprin himself would preface his most articulate, and apparently most meaningful, remarks with statements such as, "Well after all, Dr. Sherman and I are two very different people, so naturally we would be expected to run the hospital differently." He would then proceed to describe the differences between his administration and Dr. Sherman's, largely in terms of personality and interpersonal style. He responded almost monosyllabically to questions about the professional substance of these differences. The locus of difference that he experienced as most important was personal-interpersonal rather than professional-managerial. The management succession was perceived by hospital personnel, as well, in personalistic, not in professional, terms. A few relatively neutral remarks were recorded about alleged differences of professional opinion between Drs. Suprin and Sherman. However, the salient responses to the succession were not of this nature.

The following was characteristic of Dr. Suprin's responses when he was pressed about the nature of the differences in his and Sherman's programs for the hospital.

Suprin: "Of course I would run it differently. Sherman and I are very different people. Dick believed that if people wanted to keep the corridors clean, they would do it, and if they didn't want to do it, they wouldn't. Either way was O.K. with him. If he came in in the morning and found a lot of litter on the steps, he wouldn't raise a fuss with anybody. He'd just wait until somebody cleaned it up of their own accord. So, there were a lot of things he didn't get done around here that I like to see done. But he didn't have some of the problems that I have, either. If I came in in the morning and found the front steps in a mess, I'd raise holy hell until someone cleaned them, pronto!"

There is no intent to show here that the personalistic is more or less important than the professional in delineating the uniqueness of Dr. Suprin's administration. However, the above quote indicates how one such characteristic—cleanliness—permeated the psychological climate of administration and became one important dimension of the other executives' role adaptations to Dr. Suprin.

Succession and the Development of a Role Constellation

In the last two chapters, we have outlined the historical events and the sociopsychological processes that brought the executive role constellation into being. We examined the realignment of organizational forces and personal cathexes brought about by Dr. Suprin's accession to the top executive position of the M.P.I. In examining the intermeshing of personalities in the changed management situation, we highlighted the redefinitions of roles that took place among the Institute's senior administrators. This role-task work involved all three of the central executive triad. The superintendent was faced with the necessity to mitigate certain administrative and interpersonal predispositions, because of the potential threat of having no experienced staff personnel to help him fulfill his new responsibility for operating the Institute. The clinical director was faced with the necessity of reviving an antedating role definition, of becoming recathected upon a professional and personal identity that existed prior to the succession. The assistant superintendent initially resisted the role-task work necessitated by the succession, but he moved gradually into it. As he did so, he worked through to a conception of himself and to a definition of professional and organizational role that were factors contributing to the eventual dissolution of the executive role constellation.

As we have stated, and as the data themselves indicate, these processes were in no way superficial to the individuals concerned. The thinking and reflection that went on during the formation of the executive role constellation impinged more closely upon intense personal materials than is routinely considered when the topics of organization and administration are researched or discussed. Certainly, the processes we have delineated are not reported with any frequency or forcefulness in the literature on management succession or organizational behavior. Perhaps this is because the nature of role-task work, as we have outlined it, is too personal for many managers to have the desire or the skill to talk much about it. Thus it is not gathered as data, and therefore not reported in studies designed to portray the world of the manager. Our subjects, professionally trained in self-awareness and interpersonal sensitivity, and committed to the development of knowledge about people in and out of organizations, afforded us a glimpse of an entire subcontinent usually excluded from the investigations of most researchers of organizational behavior.

What we found has been termed, for the purpose of analysis and presentation, an executive role constellation. We consider that such constellations will be found to be the vital latent substructures of all effective groups, contributing to their effectiveness in two ways: (1) by stimulating the constructive expression of the unconscious and deeply personal forces of members in the context of administration, and (2) by facilitating the harnessing of these forces of the individual to the furthering of collective, organizational goals. Without such a substructure, we hypothesize that such forces (1) are largely repressed by the individual, thus not available for furthering the work of the organization, and also leaving the individual with less energy for work due to that allocated to the maintenance of repressions, or (2) are expressed in a multitude of covert and not-so-covert attacks against the surrounding organization, destroying the interpersonal relations through which administration is conducted and obstructing the achievement of the organization's objectives.

In referring to role constellations as latent substructures, we must be clear on the meaning of the term, "latent." As we have seen, the executive role constellation of this study was not latent in the sense that it could not be observed in operation, if one took the time and trouble to look for it. It was latent only in the sense that it was not usually talked about, certainly not in any direct or explicit manner. Even in the M.P.I.—and much more so in other organizations, we believe—such an entity tends to be thought of as outside the boundaries of any proper—that is, impersonal—consideration of management and managers. Yet this book makes it obvious that we disagree. We take the view, as of yet largely undocumented, that the top executives of any organization—except one that is being pulled apart—form a close-knit group that is of key importance to all aspects of that organization's operations. Such executive groups, we think, usually consist of two or three (rarely more) central individuals, although some others may be peripherally involved, as were the other members of the M.P.I.'s executive committee, for instance. We have used the term "constellation" rather than "group" to emphasize the significance of the personal relations among members, the emotional climate of the group, and the psychological properties of the interactions that define the group.

Constellations, as we view them, involve (1) role specialization of executive members, (2) differentiation among individual roles, and (3) complementary relations among them. This would indicate that little in the way of group development could occur among individuals who had, for personal or tactical reasons, not specialized their organizational roles either instrumentally or expressively. In other words, the promise of a constellation emerging among a collectivity of managerial "generalists" would not be great. Also, if all members specialized along the same dimensions—that is, were undifferentiated—a constellation could not be formed, and vital executive functions would be left unfulfilled. Further, if role differentiation had occurred between members, a constellation in our sense of the term could only form if a sense of trust permitted complementarity to exist among roles. That is, individuals would be willing to live and work constructively with sometimes quite wide differences of managerial interest or administrative style existing among them. In such a situation, cooperation would exist among executives inside the organization, while competition would tend to be directed outside the organization, toward legitimate objects of competition in the environment. However, where complementarity did not exist because of mistrust or the inappropriately great desire to "upstage" fellow executives, conflict would be the customary rule of procedure, and competition would be turned inward, toward fellow executives and away from more constructive objects in the organization's environment.

Hopefully, future research will more fully document, develop, and modify our present conception of the fully functioning executive group. Perhaps in this process we may be able to contribute something to a greater and more explicit understanding of this wellspring of executive drive, creativity, and effectiveness. Andrew Carnegie is supposed to have stated that, if all else but his organization were taken from him, he could have rebuilt all he had in a very short period of time. Without that organization, he would have lost all he had in an equally short period. Carnegie spoke with a profound knowledge-of-acquaintance of the relationships he valued so highly. Modern managerial sciences have hardly begun to specify and explicate the nature of such productive organizational relationships. We consider the concept of executive role constellation, and its analytic application to managerial situations, to be a step in that direction.

PART IV. THE DYNAMICS OF THE EXECUTIVE ROLE CONSTELLATION

The Interpersonal Transactions of the Executives Within the Organization

IN PART IV we describe and analyze the dynamics of transaction among the members of the executive role constellation. The focus is on interaction between self-systems; that is, on the minute-to-minute flow of feelings, cognitions, and actions between two or more interacting individuals within and around the role constellation. The dynamics of the constellation had an inertia of their own. This inertia was based on the personal dynamics of the participants, but it was also somewhat independent of each individual's participation. Each member of the system could, in part, impose his own personality on the system, but there was a limit to the extent of any one individual's control over the system. Even if all *three* executive members acted in concert, they were sometimes faced with those dynamics of their role constellation that were rooted in the apperceptions, identifications, and vested interests of their subordinates. Attempts to move the constellation in some direction were often met with some sort of reaction within or outside the triad. We shall examine these processes inside the constellation, and the role-tasks they posed for the executives.

The transactional approach taken in this section requires that we present, as simultaneously as possible, two or more dissimilar and related points of view, frames of reference, sets of experience, conceptions of self and other, *et cetera,* as these were brought into dynamic interaction in the course of administering the Institute. The basis of this approach in the work of Leary and Goffman has been reviewed in Chapter 2. A similar approach is to be found in A. Strauss, *Mirrors and Masks,* 1959. Our own development of this approach to interpersonal transactions lies in the greater integration of interactional phenomena with the dynamics of the personalities involved.[1]

We proceed to examine how the executives enacted—technically, how they interacted out—their self-concepts and role-definitions; how they initiated the chain of interactions comprising the social transmission of the story of themselves throughout the hospital; how in this process a modal "persona" and a modal set of role-expectations was created within the larger social system of the hospital; and how these resultant abstractions—or myths—were behaviorally reflected back upon each actor-referent.

Some of these circular interpersonal processes have already been presented. They provide a necessary ground to the more sharply figured interpersonal analyses about to be attempted. Chapters 10 through 13 demonstrate how the executives behaved when face-to-face with each other, and when they were together in the company of others in the hospital. The strategy of these chapters is to capture the essence of each man's administrative role performance, and the complementarity among the three roles, as these phenomena became manifest in ever-widening circles of interaction within the hospital. First to be presented is the behavior of these men in predominantly noninteractive settings: that is, when they are "alone," interacting with themselves, with as few interruptions as was possible within the hospital setting. Then, the interpersonal behavior of the two subordinate officers and the superintend-

---

[1] See D. J. Levinson and E. B. Gallagher, *Patienthood in the Mental Hospital,* 1964, and A. Zaleznik and D. Moment, *The Dynamics of Interpersonal Behavior,* 1964.

ent is presented, as each of the former interacted singly with his immediate superordinate. Finally, a description of the behavior of all three interacting together. In this way, the reader will be able to see the manner in which the executive role constellation was staged, and the way it came across to the audience of peers and subordinates in the hospital.

Finally, we present in Chapter 14 a theoretical model of the processes involved. A brief preview of the concepts that make up the model will assist the reader through the data chapters that follow immediately. First, our view of role performance is that, in addition to being a patterned sequence of behaviors of the individual in some organizational setting, resulting both from the role-expectations of others and from the individual's personal role-demands, that performance is also a preconscious and unconscious self-dramatization on the part of the individual before the audience of those around him in the organization. All the world may or may not be a stage, but in our view, the organization frequently functions as one on which the individual communicates impressions, both intended and unintended, of his character to friendly, neutral, or hostile audiences.

Second, the manner in which an audience responds, what interpretation they place on an observed role performance, and what their consequent behavior is, contributes greatly to the success or failure of the individual as a communicator and change agent in the organization; that is, to his success as an administrator. Yet the interpretations and responses of an audience are largely out of the control of the performer. All he can control are certain aspects of his performance, which is the input to the audience response. The output is influenced by intervening factors such as the motivations, prejudices, preferences, and interests of each member of the audience. Given certain information about a performer, his audience puts it together with their own intrapsychic tendencies, to produce a conception of the character of that individual. The audience's conception of the other—that is, the performer—varies in its accuracy. Yet, regardless of a great deal of inaccuracy concerning the "real" character of the performer—which remains a mystery to most of his audience—that concept-of-other is acted on as though it were the real thing. It is in this sense that we refer to the concept-of-other as a reification.

People in organizations act toward one another on the basis of their reification of the other person. That is, their behavior toward that person is a reflection of what they think of him. This he may find rewarding, if the reflection is congruent with his ideal self-concept, or extremely punishing if it is incongruent with that concept on significant dimensions. The individual's responses to the reflections of others upon him always involve the working through of painful reflections toward more rewarding ones. Two different ways of going about this involve the individual either in working over his self-concept to bring it more into line with the way others see him, or working on others through intensified self-dramatization in role performance, to bring others more into line with his self-concept. Most individuals are involved in both processes, but some individuals seem to specialize in attempting to bring themselves into line with others, while some apparently specialize in attempting to bring others into line with themselves.

It is through these complex transactional processes that the executive role constellation in the M.P.I. came to be established, maintained, and modified. As we have seen, and shall see again, each executive was constantly performing a distinctly specialized self-dramatization in his organizational role. These specialized performances were perceived by organization members, including the executives, as being differentiated from each other. These differentiations were reflected back upon the executives by their subordinates, and by each other. These reflections represented, initially at least, a corroboration of important dimensions of each executive's self-concept and of his organizational role-demands. Because of the preponderance of rewards over punishments in these reflections of differentiation, the executives were able to come together in a complementary, cooperative, and not antagonistic set of working relations. In this way, the major prerequisites of a role constellation came into being.

The following chapters will attempt to trace through these processes as they were observed at the time of our study.

CHAPTER 10

The Staging of Alone-Time: Its Personal Meaning and Organizational Consequences

WE BEGIN our analysis of the constellation's dynamics at the point of most limited interaction—when each executive was "alone" in his office—and then work through the ever-widening circles of interaction of the executive role constellation. We follow the sequence beginning with each man's self-dramatizing role performance. Then we consider the reifications that tended to get built up in the organizing around each executive's performance, the manner in which they were reflected back upon the individual, and his response to those reflections.

WHEN EACH MAN WAS "ALONE"

THE LOGICAL and psychological point at which to start the presentation of the executives' role performances in inter-active settings is in the description of each executive's be-havior when he was alone—with himself—in the hospital. The executives' aloneness was in no way discontinuous with their interactions among increasingly large groups of others. Insofar as its impact on them individually and on the organi-zation was concerned, the difference between their aloneness and their interactions was one of quantity rather than of kind.

We shall see that, individually, each man's "off-stage" and "on-stage" performances were interrelated. Each man was, even when alone, still in the presence of himself. He was still seeking to realize his own role definition and satisfy situa-tional role-expectations that were personally and professionally important to him. There was no "off-stage" soldiering, goldbricking, or otherwise laying aside of significant portions of his more public role performances, as has frequently been found in blue-collar and white-collar jobs, where the relationship between self and position is often experienced as personally degrading.

The executives' positions were enhancing to them as persons. The men experienced them as such. It was no accident that they did. They demanded of themselves, and of the organizations that might employ them, jobs that were challenging, intriguing, engrossing: that is, positions that were self-enhancing. They had planned and developed their careers by choosing a series of such positions, and by leaving others when they ceased to be as self-enhancing as the ones they were being offered. If for some reason a position ceased to become self-enhancing, they thought in terms of moving on. As professionals, the alternative always existed for them of going out on their own, of "hanging up a shingle." Although only a small amount of time was spent dwelling on this possibility, it *was* mentioned, and it *did* always exist as a latent force in the continual "on the fly" reassessments by these men of the balance of costs and gains existing for them in their positions. During the time of this study, each executive professed a general satisfaction with the profit accruing to him in his organizational position. This satisfaction is seen as related to the observed consistency of the executives' "off-stage" and "on-stage" performances.[1]

---

1 Here the researchers are, of course, caught up in the nature of their research method. There is no such thing as observing the executives "off-stage." Except for fleeting instances of forgetfulness, they were always "on-stage" to the observer whenever he was in their presence. Their tolerance of this presence was a precondition of the study. The unusual experience of being "on-stage" for significant periods of time before a not unreceptive outsider seemed to have facilitated the flow of data more often than it inhibited it. However, this limitation on observed aloneness should not be ignored in considering the above text.

Organizationally, there was also no real aloneness for these men. If they were alone in one part of the hospital, often they were noticeable in their absence in some other part of the hospital. This was particularly the case when an executive had to cancel his engagement at a teaching round, usually at short notice, because of some work he had to do. Then too, subordinates had merely to walk by the open door of an executive's office and take a quick but thorough look at what was going on inside, to obtain ample grist for the mill of reification concerning "that man's" putative personality and behavior patterns.

In the following analysis of the executives' alone-time, the concept of aloneness has been used in its symbolic sense as well as in the more concretely interactionist sense of people not meeting people. In other words, aloneness has been treated as a state of mind as well as a sociometric condition. Of course these two levels of social psychological reality were very much related, as will be seen; but they were also somewhat separate. It was this separation that made it difficult for the researchers, whose observational position was in the *interactive* milieu inside the hospital, to capture the content of *non-interactive* events, even though the latter had an important bearing on psychosocial conditions and administrative events in the executive realm.

Dr. Asche: Marginal, Problematic Aloneness

Of the three executives, Dr. Asche seemed to be found at an idiosyncratic disadvantage by aloneness within the organizational context. This characteristic appeared not only by comparisons between the executives, but by comparison of Dr. Asche-in-interaction with Dr. Asche-alone. In interaction, his considerable energies were clearly manifest in his frequent expansiveness of physical movement and in the enthusiasm with which he "did business" with others. Alone, his quietness appeared, by comparison, to be something different from thoughtfulness and relaxation, however genuinely these two processes were involved. His solitary quietness, when it occurred, had the quality of an hiatus, of energy run out; a sense of dejection emanated from Dr. Asche under these conditions. There was evidence that this emanation was perceived by some of those who came into contact with him on such occasions; was reified by them according to their own feelings about aloneness or dejection; and reflected back upon him, usually in a way that helped him over these occasional "rough spots," but occasionally in ways that seemed designed to intensify or prolong whatever difficulties were involved.

In addition to these personal and interpersonal comparisons, there was another set of factors of a more structural nature that contributed to the different sense of aloneness that surrounded Dr. Asche. He was responsible for, and highly involved in, a variety of research projects. In this capacity, his removal from the main stream of events up and down the medical hierarchy was threefold. His involvement in the *content* of research made him, despite the existence of considerable good will, somewhat foreign to those of his professional colleagues who were immersed in clinical practice and clinical teaching, and who thereby were or felt themselves to be unable to assess how much of a contribution was represented in a given piece of research, or by research in general. Asche's involvement in the *ideology* of research made him the target of occasional aggressions from those who wondered why all the research was necessary. The feeling was easily elicited in such people that the efficacy of their clinical methods was being challenged, not only by the findings of certain research, but also by the mere assumption that further research was necessary, especially when it was directed toward the methods they were settling into and hoped to use for the rest of their professional lives. Dr. Asche's involvement with *researchers* often linked him with groups of low visibility and little attractiveness within the medical chain of command, partly because a number of the projects that Asche considered important took place outside the M.P.I., and partly because they involved nonmedical personnel from whom the medical doctors not infrequently felt they had little to learn.

Dr. Asche recognized this structural state of affairs and some of its consequences for him. However, he chose to maintain his commitments to what he felt were worthwhile undertakings, regardless of their marginality or centrality in a given organizational context. Further, he chose actively to represent in the hospital a number of professional points of view that he felt were inadequately represented at that time. In other words, he more than passively accepted the psychosocial condition of marginality that his research interests, professional opinions, and personal values made him heir to. He actively carried this marginality with him into the organization. Therefore, he occupied a position of some peripherality in regard to the medical hierarchy—in which as assistant superintendent, he might have played a tightly integral part—and sustained the costs that arose therefrom. The costs, as well as the rewards, seemed to resonate with certain psychological predispositions of the man.

Performance

Dr. Asche's times alone did not occur regularly. They were often dictated more by the contingencies of people's comings and goings than by his own planned wish to be alone. When he did set aside time to be alone at the hospital, it was for the reading or writing associated with the meeting of a research deadline. Sometimes, when an unscheduled block of free time occurred, Asche experienced some difficulty deciding how to fill it. Sometimes he would stand scratching his head while he looked at the pocket-sized index card on which his secretary had typed his activities for the day. "What shall I do now?" he once or twice mused aloud in the presence of the observer, apparently expecting no reply. Then he would usually go into his secretary's office and consult with her on matters such as phone messages, correspondence, and newly made appointments.

The frequency of Dr. Asche's scheduled interactions was high, making him a difficult man to see except according to the terms of his schedule. This ran counter to his own philosophy of how to run a psychiatric hospital, and his ir- regular "tours" through the hospital functioned partly to cor- rect this situation. We shall get to these tours presently. Com- plaints were regularly being heard about how busy Dr. Asche was, and how difficult it was becoming to see him. Many of these comments were directed face-to-face to Dr. Asche by people who resented figuratively standing in line with other contenders for his time. (Similar feelings existed with regard to Dr. Suprin, but these were expressed less often, and were never observed to be directed toward him by the plaintiff in any face-to-face situation.) Sometimes these comments were made affectionately, prompting brief nostalgic reveries among the interactors about the good old days of the Insti- tute, when life was simpler and more cohesive. Dr. Asche en- joyed these infrequent reminiscences and went about his work with added relish after such an incident had occurred. Sometimes, however, comments by another person about Asche's busy schedule and heightened inaccessibility were underscored by feelings of hostility and rejection. This made Asche uncomfortable. It was a paradox to observe a range of people trying to link up with Dr. Asche by expressing to him their annoyance about him, thereby sharpening his aware- ness of his marginality in the minds of many he interacted with, and his own sense of being alone even at the center of a veritable cloud of such marginal interactions.

Incidents in which this was an issue were difficult for Dr. Asche, and it not unusually took several minutes for him to collect himself again before pressing on with the schedule of events. On such occasions, when the others had left his office, Dr. Asche would sometimes sit quietly in his chair for a short while, wordlessly rubbing the bridge of his nose under his glasses. Then he would often get up and go into his secretary's office, as he did after one particularly unpleasant session with one of his staff.

> After a researcher left, Dr. Asche got up and walked into his secretary's office.
> "What will I do now?" he asked her.
> "Take a deep breath," she replied with a smile.

After such occasions Asche would sometimes take a tour through parts of the hospital. These tours served several functions. Dr. Asche used them as a way of relaxing and as a way of gathering information about events and situations in the hospital. He considered it important to keep track of the general level of morale in the hospital since "mood sweeps" were particularly important in the functioning of psychiatric wards, and Asche used corridor contacts to assess the mood of the organization. At the same time, he made himself available for casual, nonhierarchical interactions with those who saw him going by and had something to ask or tell him. This they might not have done had they been required to submit to the discipline and the time lag involved in making an appointment to see Dr. Asche. Asche was at his best in this setting: relaxed, articulate, and effective.

This method of Dr. Asche's had been more common under Dr. Sherman's administration than it was under Dr. Suprin's. Indeed, it was part of Sherman's style. Asche's perseverance in this method was noticed and appreciated by some of the longer-tenure employees of the hospital, who had been around long enough to recognize what Asche was doing. But to others, this casual sauntering "alone" through the corridors had no meaning, except perhaps that it seemed somewhat out of keeping for a senior executive figure in an otherwise bustling, tightly scheduled organization.

Late on the afternoon of the above-mentioned incident, after Dr. Asche had been gently prompted to relax for a while, he took "one of my walks," as he phrased it. First he visited the business officer, and the two of them discussed a matter of budgetary concern regarding two ongoing research projects. Then Asche strolled out into the main lobby of the hospital where he sat quietly for about five minutes, slouched nearly horizontally in a soft, red-leather upholstered chair. Several residents and a service consultant passed singly by, glancing down at Asche sprawled out in the chair, as they wordlessly went about their business. Then, looking up at the wall clock, Dr. Asche said "I've had my rest." Getting up, he walked back to his office.

We are considering performance while alone, performance that was at the same time perceivable by others in the organization, as in the above situation, and then reified in such a way that its reflection back upon the actor would influence his situation in the organization. As always, these matters were mostly comparative. Certainly, one did not often see Dr. Cadman "on tour" except to a ward conference or an occasional visit to the cafeteria, not sprawling casually in a chair in the hospital lobby. When Dr. Suprin toured the hospital, he did not saunter along, making it easy for people to initiate interaction with him. He set a fast and jaunty pace that forbade casual conversation with subordinates. His "little trips" were sometimes a cause of alarm, since he would appear rapidly and unexpectedly in almost any part of the hospital. Then, unless he stopped to investigate something "wrong," he disappeared just as rapidly and mysteriously, snapping his fingers at his sides as he went.

Reification and Reflection

The impression that Dr. Asche's role performance made upon those who worked closely with him was of a kindly, considerate, possibly "soft" administrator, who was not suited for the tough organizational politics of the kind that Dr. Suprin so obviously appeared to relish. The *juxtaposition* in the staff's perceptual world of these two senior administrators was perhaps more important in determining their judgments than were the impressions received *separately* from each. Few of the staff could talk about one of the executives without basing the bulk of his judgmental and evaluational thinking on comparisons with one or more of the others. This was the case even for impressions about the most intimate characteristics of these men, deriving from chance observations of even the smallest bits of executive behavior, such as facial expressions or bodily postures and movements observed in passing the open door of an office, or of entering unexpected and unannounced, before the executive could compose his official self. Asche's behavior in such nonceremonial moments contributed to the following evaluation of him by a staff doctor who was in a position to know him quite well. The reader will see that, further to the point of judgment through comparisons, this judgment was as much one of Suprin as it was of Asche. The possibility of projecting one's own feelings and preoccupations into the putative relations between two superordinates can be seen to have been immense. The Machiavellian tone that permeated the following statement triggers the uninvolved listener to that very possibility.

"He [Asche] is losing his place in the hospital."
Observer: "His place?"
"Yes. His position. His *power*. He's losing his power in the organization. He's starting to slip. . . . Suprin knows he [Asche] is the sort of guy he can push around. Asche has shown him that by now. So now he's starting to push him around."

The speaker would not specify the ways in which Suprin was pushing Asche around—"Oh, in many small ways"—but the impression nonetheless remained.

On this occasion the observer felt that the above informant was primarily indulging in wishes and fantasies that were typical of him. "Hard" facts were secondary in his remarks. However, the observer was not about to get into any sort of dispute with this informant about the information that he was helpfully and openly rendering. And, what was more important, the above data themselves were symptomatic of a new reification that was coming to be placed with increasing frequency on the organizational realities of the hospital. This demonstrated that "soft" facts had their own subjective reality, and also the tendency to induce corresponding "hard" facts in the world of objective reality. The presence of staff personnel who saw top management relations in terms of someone "pushing around" somebody else, and who oriented themselves to these senior figures as either "winner" or "loser" of some putative "power struggle," created conditions that over time tended to validate these symbolic interpretations.

The characterization of Dr. Asche, the reification of his "persona" within the medical chain of command of the Institute, was not as clearly developed as were those of Dr. Suprin and Dr. Cadman. One reason for this is that Dr. Asche's personal style was more conventional, more at the "balanced mean," and less easy to categorize than were the more specialized performances of the other two men. Thus, the difficulty in "coming to grips with" the "real" Dr. Asche would probably have been greater than was the case of the other two men, even if each were being perceived and evaluated separately. However, each stood in some relation to the others within the organizational context, and each was to some extent perceived and evaluated according to these relations.

There was a second reason for the relative lack of clarity

of Asche's reified persona and role-expectations. Asche was presented to the hospital as a member of the central executive triad. This was done in a variety of ways, but most effectively by Dr. Suprin's repeated public statements linking Cadman, Asche, and himself together as the group that really operated the hospital. But in comparison to the other two members of this triad, Asche was sometimes rather unknown as a person, in his own right, to many of the Institute personnel. Again, as Dr. Suprin put it, Asche was sort of "in between" himself and Cadman.

Certain problems occurred around Dr. Suprin and Dr. Cadman that were directly related to the *discrepancy* between a given performance and the highly specialized reification that others strongly held about them. However, Dr. Asche was faced with problems stemming from the difficulty other people had in *coming to grips* with what sort of a person he was. Dr. Cadman had trouble, both from himself and others, when he tried to "get tough" in the organization. It was "obvious" that such a person as he could never "really" be tough, and such apparently became the case. Dr. Suprin got into the same sort of trouble, but in his case it arose when he feinted in the opposite direction, moving from his accustomed "tough" instrumental mode of behavior toward a more "soft" expressive mode. Dr. Asche was faced with difficulties other people had in consensually fixing him at *any* coordinate in the biaxial space of power and role specialization, from which point he could be judged *and* misjudged, and from which he could see himself as others saw him. Dr. Asche had some difficulty getting across his interpersonal bids for others' recognition and support of role-demands or substantive points about administrative or professional matters.

There were many clear, stable, productive, and satisfying elements in the observed reflections upon Dr. Asche; for instance, Dr. Suprin's reflections on Asche's great abilities as a researcher and research administrator, and the reflections of

a number of people who knew about his being kind, generous, hard-working, and productive. Within the limits of the
Institute, however, many people tended to develop a neutral
conception of Dr. Asche. He could be friendly or argumenta-
tive, but most of all he was "in between." Thus, insofar as
the respect for Dr. Asche was fearful, the fear was experienced much more directly in relation to Dr. Suprin (or to a
clinical supervisor, or a patient). Insofar as the affection for
Dr. Asche contained love, the love was experienced much
more directly in relation to Dr. Cadman (or to a clinical
supervisor, or a patient). Thus, less identification was reflected upon Dr. Asche from the members of the Institute
than was the case for the other two executives in the triad.
We shall examine Dr. Asche's responses to the ambiguities
of his organizational role.

Response to Reification and Reflection

One of Dr. Asche's responses was to go outside the hospital
for his rewards. Why did he do so much outside work? "For
kicks," he replied. "Because it's interesting work with interesting people, and it needs to be done." Dr. Asche was his
most forceful, eloquent, and persuasive self when talking to
interested undergraduate students about mental illness, mental patients, and working with mental patients. There was
much in the open, youthful, and unsophisticated behavior of
the students that Asche found rewarding, that he missed in
the more reserved, haughty, and worldly wise performances
of many of the psychiatrists in training at the Institute.

Another of Dr. Asche's responses to the reification-reflec-
tion-performance situation facing him was along the lines of,
"nobody knows what I do around here." Here again was an
instance of symbolic, though not interactional, aloneness. It
appeared that Dr. Asche himself was not overly cognizant of
what he did—how much he did, and for whom—in the hospital, but he did manifest the feeling that, whatever he did,

other people were not aware of it, which left him a little short of recognition and reward. (Again, we are not referring to such things as titles and salary, but to little, fleeting reflections such as, "Gee, that's great," or, "You've certainly helped me a lot.") During the early stages of observation, Dr. Asche would be asked about what he had done on the previous evening. Dr. Asche would occasionally ask the same question of the observer. In so doing, Asche found out that the observer had been spending three hours in the evening dictating or writing his daily observations of Dr. Asche. Asche was surprised, impressed, and pleased. During the day in which he found out this information, and for several days thereafter, Asche took the occasion to jokingly inform some of the people he was friendly with in the hospital:

> "You see this young fella here? If you want to find out all that I do around here, you just ask him. He can tell you. He's got the picture. Why, it takes him three hours just to write down what I do in a day. Imagine that! I didn't realize I did that much, did you? It's a real pleasure to have someone around who really appreciates how much I do in this place."

The incident has already been presented in which some typing was requested of Dr. Asche's staff by Dr. Cadman through Cadman's secretary. The feeling that permeated the interaction between Dr. Asche and his secretary around this matter was that of feeling misunderstood and unappreciated. This was based on their judgment that others salient in the organization were ignorant of the nature and amount of their work. It was Asche's secretary who gave voice to these sentiments. In so doing she expressed one of the consequences of sharing Dr. Asche's relative positioning in the structure of the larger organization. Asche himself remained quiet on the matter, which was consonant with his observed reticence in other situations about putting across what it was like for him in the organization.

One could describe Dr. Asche's organizational role performance, both in initiating and in responding to reifications and reflections of others' role-expectations, as having a muted quality to it. He consistently underplayed his own ideas, interests, beliefs, opinions, views of himself, and role-demands. In keeping with his equalitarian style, he often underplayed himself to help others to enhance themselves. Sympathetic others were provided with ample cues that permitted them to come to the realization that "something was going on" inside Asche. Then, if they wanted, they could easily find out what they wanted to know. Often, it was simply a question of asking. Dr. Asche wanted people to want something before he gave it to them. Rather than forcing something of his own on others, he let them come to him. However, many people found they were—or chose to be—too busy for that. The result was something of a stalemate. Many clinical and research persons saw him rarely or never. Nonmedical clinical groups were almost equally unrelated to him on an interactive basis. The head of one such group saw Dr. Asche as "withdrawing from us," and "going off in another direction," which that person presumed to be toward more research. Most people did not think much about it. Each had problems pressing more actively in upon him and people making more active demands on him. In such a situation it was difficult to think for long about the *absence* of something. When they did think about Dr. Asche, people in the clinical services tended to speculate in many diverse ways about the enigmatic figure who was assistant superintendent.

"It's his own fault," Dr. Suprin was quoted as saying after an incident in which Dr. Asche had underplayed his presentation of himself and his hard work. "He should have spoken louder," the superintendent concluded. There were other people who sometimes felt that Dr. Asche should have spoken louder for himself in the organization and in life. But the fact remains that he did not. In this, his performance was consonant with his concept of himself as a hard-working, quiet, patient, and constructive individual whose leadership was most effective when others did not realize they were being led. This did not permit Dr. Asche as much freedom in stressing his role-definition as Dr. Suprin was observed to possess. Also, Dr. Asche's role-definition was changing from that of a researcher-research administrator to that of an administrator—No. 1 figure. He was probably less eloquent in presenting his demands because he was less clear about them. Then, too, there was no place for a second No. 1 within the boundaries of the Institute.

Dr. Cadman: Infrequent, Unwelcomed Aloneness

We now turn to an analysis of Dr. Cadman's behavior in minimally interactive situations. The same analytic framework will be employed.

Performance

Of the three central executives, Dr. Cadman was observed to be alone the least. Work with patients, ward rounds, supervision of residents, meetings with the medical staff, total staff conferences, executive committee meetings, planning or administrative meetings with special project groups and with residents or other clinical personnel; all these kept Dr. Cadman within a flow of interactions that was of a higher and more sustained frequency than was the case for Dr. Suprin or Dr. Asche. At one point during the period of observation, Dr. Cadman appointed a group of his clinical subordinates to form a committee to study committees. The rapid proliferation of meetings was disturbing to all, and it greatly reduced the flexibility of administering the residency training program and the wards. Often the most difficult and frustrating part of a meeting would be that period of time devoted to arranging the next meeting. Everyone present, including Dr. Cadman, would get out his pocket calendar and riffle through it, calling out times that would be suitable for him. Most suggestions were unsuitable to others, because of previously arranged engagements, and these others would respond with equally unsuitable counterproposals. Unless a meeting was regular and weekly, it would usually end up by being set by fiat (or, when Dr. Cadman did not assert his authority, by those who shouted the loudest). It was unusual that everyone then present could attend a meeting thus set up.

The profusion of interactions around Dr. Cadman was such that, when the observer initially attempted to contact Dr. Cadman about doing field work, he found Dr. Cadman's secretary keeping *two* lists of appointments. The first list enumerated the people who wanted to see Dr. Cadman, and why they wanted to see him. Dr. Cadman's secretary explained that he was so pressed for time that he looked over this list first, to decide which ones he wanted to see. The chosen individuals then graduated to his second appointments list, and there they made arrangements to see him in the customary fashion.

Despite his occasional protestations to the contrary, Dr. Cadman usually enjoyed the matrix of interactions in which he was imbedded. It was during group meetings with the psychiatrists, the residents, and other trainees in the hospital training program that Dr. Cadman came into his own, that he was at his most "Cadmanian" best, talking in quietly peremptory tones, with intricate simplicity and hard-headed empathy, about the life forces governing the fleeting but all-pervasive states of human health and sickness, happiness and despair, productivity and stultification. In such didactic situations he was his most charismatic self. Both he and his listeners enjoyed and felt somewhat exalted thereby; he speaking with charming forthrightness and dignifying eloquence, in a way that his subordinates sometimes wished he would also use in his administrative handling of their common interests in the hospital; and the audience listening with heightened attentiveness to the ruminations and controlled self-revelations of the gifted [2] man who both was and was not their leader. Dr. Cadman sometimes seemed to experience something akin to a sense of letdown when such a group disbanded and he was left temporarily alone before entering into his next engagement.

Nonetheless, the pressure of events in general, or of a particularly fretful problem, sometimes got the better of Dr. Cadman. Then he would begin to expostulate quietly to himself as he worked away at the piles of paperwork before him on his desk. "America's No. 1 scut boy" was the phrase he used to characterize his perception of himself at such moments as these. His secretary would often get caught up in this mood, and the resultant prodding back and forth between the two was such that the harder Dr. Cadman pressed into his work, the less he seemed to get done. On such occasions, Cadman would sometimes get up from his desk and, without a word, walk out of his office. He would "just disappear," as his secretary put it, sometimes for minutes at a time. Anyone who called on him during those periods would find him out. They would inquire of his secretary as to his whereabouts. The visitor and secretary would stand in the doorway of the latter's office, looking up and down the corridor, remarking on Cadman's absence and waiting for his return. Cadman would then return to his office without explanations and resume his work.

Such behavior reinforced the "absent-minded professor" image that those close to Dr. Cadman were fond of attributing to him. Weight was thereby added to the general notion of Cadman as befuddled and as administratively disoriented in the sense of being attuned to the inner realities of life to the virtual exclusion of other sets of more external reality.

[2] Charisma, *n.* (Gr.: gift). *Webster's New Collegiate Dictionary*, 1956, p. 140.

More people were favorably disposed toward Dr. Cadman for his intraceptive-empathic skills than were unfavorably disposed toward him for his administrative-managerial disorientation. The hospital was, after all, in the business of therapy, not in the business of business. Dr. Cadman was, therefore, in a setting appropriate to his skills and inclinations— he had planned it that way—and the reifications of "persona" and role-expectations reflected upon him were predominantly positive.

In the group of first-year residents coming into the hospital at the beginning of this study, the admiration of Dr. Cadman was a palpable phenomenon. Many of the residents had already become acquainted with Dr. Cadman during their medical studies, and he was perhaps a main force in their decision to enter psychiatry. At least, he was often talked of in the hospital as having that influence.

The manner in which the appreciation of medical personnel was created is illustrated by Cadman's opening performance before a group of incoming residents in psychiatry. On their first work day in the hospital, Dr. Cadman took the new residents aside after they had first been addressed by Dr. Suprin. Suprin's "address" had been scheduled, Cadman's "little talk" had not, so the relative bureaucratization of the two executives was immediately made apparent to those among the residents who responded to such matters. Other dimensions of differentiation and specialization between the two men rapidly presented themselves. Suprin's address was on the legal and official regulations governing the operation of the hospital. Suprin delivered his address with energy, verve, and humor more than sufficient to quell the few groans and exchanged glances that had occurred at the back of the room when Suprin announced his topic. Suprin's remarks were made to the residents in his own office, where they had assembled.

After this address, Cadman gathered the group in the library adjoining Suprin's office. When he was "alone" with the residents, he sat down and talked to them about their forthcoming work with patients. Starting quietly and ploddingly with the hospital's diagnostic forms, Cadman's presentation became more forceful, more simple, more personalistic, and more persuasive as he moved away from talking about organizational requirements toward describing what it would be like for a young psychiatrist to be face-to-face with his patient.

"Here you have this guy," said Cadman, "with a lifetime of some form of behavior [i.e., the case outline having been completed, the psychiatrist now finds himself face-to-face with another human being]. Perhaps it is that he has been making believe all his life. However, he *is* moving along in *some* manner, in *some* way. Then something happens, and it happens to *him* (striking his chest) —you know?—and he starts to take a detour. He starts to take a detour from life. We all know what that is. You know what I'm talking about? Where it's easier to go *around?* Because what's there is just *too,* hey?" (Pause)

The group became progressively quieter and more focused on Cadman.

"What happened to make the jitney break down that way? Or, what happened to make the Cadillac break down that way? For it is the same with Cadillacs as it is with jitneys. What is it that stopped this guy from being able to limp along as best he could to actually taking a big detour from life?"

Restlessness and laughter at the simplicity of Cadman's remarks ceased.

". . . Where can I put my foot into this situation to get things moving? Where can I get started? *Not,* how can I cure this person?"

The intensity of the speaker, combined with the anxiety of the audience,[3] and with the dark wood and the tiered volumes of the library setting, imparted an almost sepulchral tone to words that imprinted themselves in the memories of Cadman's audience. Repeated references were made by residents to these remarks throughout the year that followed.

"I do not expect you to cure *anybody*," Cadman continued with a smile. "At least, not in your first year. All I expect you to do is to investigate, investigate, investigate. When in doubt, investigate, investigate. (Pause) Learn, learn, learn. (Pause) You should be learning about your patients (pause), about yourselves (pause), and about your relations between these two, all at the same time. Your principal concern should be, 'How can I help them to do things themselves?' The proper role of a therapist is to help his patients become the masters of their destinies. That is the only thing you can do to help patients. That is, help them to do the work themselves. (Pause)

"The only analogy that comes to my mind is that it is easier to give a child a nickel than it is to teach him how to earn money. This analogy is probably somewhat inaccurate," he smiled, "but I think you residents will get the spirit of the analogy." (Smiles throughout the audience)

". . . You are not doctors any more. (Pause—Silence) Did you know that? As of July the first you have become psychiatrists," he smiled, "and you have thereby given up the life-long ambition of doctors to tell people what to do." (Smiles throughout the audience)

"If I had a stomachache, I'd go to a medical specialist I know and ask him, 'Bill, what should I do?' Bill would diagnose the situation and say, 'Paul, this is what you should do, or you will not get better.' As far as you residents are concerned, these ways are gone forever." (Speaker and audience exchange smiles) "If I could transfer this little story into the psychiatric world, the

3 Composed largely of the negative anticipations experienced by many neophyte psychiatrists about to come into intensive interpersonal contact with mental patients for the first time, with the necessity of fulfilling professional standards in their conduct of these cases.

doctor would ideally say to his patient, 'It's your bellyache. It's up to you to do something about it. How can I help you?'

". . . We sure are an opinionated bunch, aren't we?" (Laughter) "Remember, I don't expect you to cure anyone. You don't have to cure anybody here. All you are expected to do is to investigate, investigate, investigate. If you don't know what is going on with a patient, wait awhile and it will come clear."

Reification and Reflection

Throughout the year residents would cite (and recite) this speech verbatim to Dr. Cadman. Mostly this would take place in the context of a resident reporting his mastery of a difficult clinical and therapeutic situation, and how much he had learned from Dr. Cadman, and how clearly Cadman's words had come back to him in his period of difficulty. "I remember your telling us that we didn't have to cure anybody, at least in our first year. I remember your saying that what we were supposed to do was to investigate, investigate, investigate. So I decided I didn't know enough about her [the patient] after all." [4] Dr. Cadman would smile, obviously pleased. The reader will recall how rewarding this kind of reflection was to Dr. Cadman. Teaching residents—"looking after my posterity"—was what Dr. Cadman experienced as the most important reason for him to continue working in the hospital, and not, for instance, to go into private practice when things got "hot" for him as chief administrator of the hospital's residency training program.

Some residents gave evidence of some decathexis of Dr. Cadman as they advanced in their psychiatric training. To these, the man and his thoughts became somewhat "old hat." Simultaneously, these residents were transferring some of their positive professional identifications to other clinical

---

[4] This statement was made to Dr. Cadman during the period of observation by a second-year resident. This indicated that Cadman's address to incoming residents was probably the same each year, and that the impression it made on the minds of some of them lasted longer than one year.

staff members who were less salient than Dr. Cadman in the organization of the hospital, but whom the residents got to know as their training progressed. But some residents—perhaps many—always maintained "a special place in their hearts" for Dr. Cadman.[5]

This pattern of relationship had its "pinches" as well as its pleasures. Among the midlevel staff group, the feeling for Dr. Cadman was exceptional since most of that group had also been members of the smaller, closer, and more cohesive groups of residents studying under Dr. Cadman in the "good old days" of the Institute. Even among these people, the predominance of Cadman's personal and professional charisma not infrequently waned, and his administrative passiveness became the focus (and the cause) of some of their own administrative frustration and aggression.

"If only you could just . . . ," remonstrated one of Cadman's subordinates, wishing Cadman would more actively uphold the rights of the in-patient staff against certain claims and charges being laid against them from elsewhere in the hospital. But the staff member did not even bother to com-

---

[5] This sentiment was sometimes reflected back to Dr. Cadman in excruciatingly embarrassing ways. Once, an ex-resident of the hospital returned to visit. He looked to be a man in his late thirties, and he had distinguished himself professionally in some way since leaving the hospital's residency training program. Dr. Cadman invited him to attend the regular weekly meeting of the Institute's medical staff in Cadman's office. During that meeting, the group discussed the constituents of "good clinical teaching" in psychiatry. It was decided that the only logical point to start such a discussion was by defining what was meant by a "good clinical teacher."

At this point, Dr. Cadman turned to the visitor and asked, "Do you have any thoughts on this?"

The visitor replied with a manifestation of intensity and sincerity that approached the melodramatic. He leaned forward from his seat, looked Cadman full in the face, and said slowly and softly, "The only definition that I know of a good clinical teacher is spelled C,A,D,M,E,N." [*Sic*]

Cadman looked away, coughed, and shuffled some papers around on his desk. "I didn't ask for a testimonial," he said. After a pause, others in the group stopped smiling and picked up the discussion.

plete his sentence. Cadman smiled. "Oh, I know. I know,"
replied the subordinate. "I'm asking you to do something
you just can't do."

It was at times like these, when administration was the
focus of attention and issues of diagnosis, classification, and
psychotherapy were temporarily secondary, that Dr. Cadman
began to complain about his "saddle sores."

Response to Reification and Reflection

Accomplished therapist, eloquent teacher, inefficient administrator: the reader already knows that this reification was
very close to Cadman's own conception of himself and his
role-definition in the organization. Having established a psychosocial situation around himself that was so close to his
own desires, Cadman's response thereto could well afford to
be "passive." Receiving much of the kind of reward that
meant most to him, Cadman's response was to *enjoy* it.
(Hardly an active mode of behavior) Cadman did, however,
act in his own way to maintain this predominantly positive
state of affairs. In his "passive Cadmanian way" he continued
to communicate his personal and professional charisma down
through the ranks of the medical chain-of-command, appealing to all in their capacities as doctors working directly with
patients; not as technicians, not as administrators, but as
therapists face-to-face with persons needing help. The reader
has seen how successful Cadman was at this, despite the increasing size and tempo of the hospital and the resultant
"bureaucratic depersonalization" that increased Cadman's distance and decreased his charisma among successive generations of incoming residents.

Cadman also responded to the "lousy administrator" aspect of the role-expectations reflected upon him. Although he
said that this was the way he was—the way he saw himself—
there was a part of him that disagreed. This became apparent
in the heat of problematic events: fully involved and rela-

tively unselfconscious, Dr. Cadman became angry, and stayed angry for considerable periods of time, when he found himself in situations wherein many of those present were taking it for granted that he was a lousy administrator, that he didn't know what he was talking about, and that any mistakes or oversights obviously were or would be Cadman's fault. Cadman's attempts at self-defense on such occasions tended to be relatively monosyllabic and relatively ineffectual. Usually, when he remained self-composed, Cadman refrained from such attempts. Instead, he preferred to respond in his "passive Cadmanian way," incorporating the painfulness of being misunderstood, the insult of being laughed at, and the uneasiness of being less than a man's man; working it through and *performing* this working-through with humor and insight before the rapt audience of his clinical subordinates; and thereby exchanging the costs of ascribed ineffectiveness in the "tough politics" of administration for the added rewards of greater personal and professional charisma. In so doing, Cadman reinforced all three facets of the tripartite imagery that revolved around him in the performance-reification-reflection-response network, binding him and the organization together.

DR. SUPRIN: PLANNED, SOUGHT-AFTER ALONENESS

WE TURN NOW to an analysis of Dr. Suprin's behavior, employing the same framework as before.

Performance

Characteristically, Dr. Suprin actively structured the events of his day so that he would be alone in his office for significant periods of time. During these periods he transacted important quantities of extra-organizational work that he had to do. Much as he was interested in the progression of events within the hospital, he also enjoyed his period of detachment from it. Not infrequently he would enter his office, coming from a conference he had greatly enjoyed—"There, what do you think of my boys? They're a wonderful bunch, aren't they?"—to turn himself away from it completely—"Ah, now for a moment to myself"—toward matters of importance to him outside the hospital. He resisted attempts to break down his commitment of his time to matters outside the hospital. He thought of himself as having set up his staff "team" in such a way that he could disengage himself from routine matters of hospital administration. He took pleasure in the competence of his staff to carry on mostly on their own, although he was fond of recounting that in situations in which there was "real big trouble" people would come directly to him, even in the middle of the night. But under normal operational conditions—that is, when the chaos was controllable without the intervention of the superintendent—the organization that Dr. Suprin had built up allowed him a great deal of freedom. When any unscheduled interaction initiated by a subordinate did occur, Suprin tended to perceive it as an interruption. He also saw it as an attempt on the part of a doctor to evade the unavoidable necessity of making his own professional decisions, which was something Dr. Suprin disapproved of strongly. Such incidents were noticeably disturbing to him, and he acted vigorously to dissuade their repetition. They worried him more than their frequency and duration might otherwise have indicated, since he tended to see them as symptoms of a possible breakdown in the operation of his "team": that is, an increasing inability on the part of his staff to handle the administration of the hospital, thereby passing up to him an accumulation of problems that would hinder him from accomplishing the work he wanted to do. He also saw it as a breakdown of the training in self-reliance that his organization was designed to provide to its younger doctors.

Reification and Reflection

The resultant image of Dr. Suprin, which he himself perceived and to some extent shared, was that of a loner, an independent individualist, much like the stereotypical cowboy of the old West, working hard, traveling light, and always ready to "mosey" along. This early Western motif was reinforced by many small things: by the horsiness of many of his jokes and remarks to residents about some of the patients they were treating, by his reminiscences about earlier experiences in the midwest, and by the paintings that hung in his office, a dominant theme of which was horses and a big Colt revolver. This aura of transience—"Maybe I'll go into surgery next"—was to some extent an outward rejection of the relations of interdependence that surrounded or enmeshed Dr. Suprin as superintendent. As such, it rendered him liable to easily elicited charges that he didn't really care about the hospital, that his position there was more or less a stopping point in the longer-term trip to Washington that figured in his putative career plans. Also, many of the mid-level and junior staff would like to have had more frequent and more regular contact with Dr. Suprin. Why? Because they wanted to learn from him. But in other contexts, many of the *same* people often rejected much of Suprin's ability to teach them anything, even along the several dimensions of his professional and administrative expertise. It became apparent that these people simply wanted to have more opportunity to sit next to the source of power that they experienced as guiding much of their behavior in the hospital.

Response to Reification and Reflection

These points were not lost on Dr. Suprin. He tended, however, to reject them. He did this in two ways. "They're big boys now," he said more than once about senior residents and junior staff. "It's time they grew up." Further to this point, he considered that several of these people were standing in the way of their own professional progress by staying on at the hospital in positions of dependency that were unworthy of them. He made no secret of these convictions, openly stating them in a variety of ways in the hospital. The other way he rejected these dependency bids was by continuing to work hard in his pattern of wide but infrequent interactions, many of them outside the hospital. When he was alone in the hospital—that is, when he might have interacted more with subordinates in this "free" time—he tended not to let go of his independent program of activities, as the other two executives were observed to do more readily. He usually ate his lunch at his desk, often carrying on with the work at hand. No consistent pattern of interactive relaxation was observed during such periods. When the going got tough, Suprin would "work little tricks" on himself, switching from dictating to writing by hand, or vice versa, as he pressed on with his writing of speeches, his formulation of plans, his schedule of engagements, and his travel arrangements.

SUMMARY

THIS CHAPTER has outlined the cyclical nature of each executive's role performance, the reifications and reflections of others to those performances, and the executives' responses to these reflections of themselves as others apperceived them. This chapter has described these self-other transactions in their simplest form, when the executives were essentially "alone," either by themselves or before large audiences, but not involved in the intricate dynamics of interaction that made up the specific nature of the executive role constellation. It is to these intricacies that we turn our analysis in the following chapters.

CHAPTER 11

The Transactions of the Clinical Director Within the Executive Role Constellation

THE CLOSEST WORKING DIAD—indicated by highest interaction, most specialization, and complementarity of roles—was comprised of Drs. Suprin and Cadman.[1] We shall examine what happened between two top executives who behaved so differently in the hospital, yet who perceived themselves as working closely with each other.

Both executives were in a social situation that reinforced the complementarity of their roles. Although this complementarity of behavior corresponded with genuine components of each executive's personality, there were personality characteristics common to both executives that were not overtly expressed in the constellation. These latent similarities were repeatedly hinted at, as in (1) Cadman's statement that he had been more like Suprin in the past, but that he had learned to change in order to get what he wanted out of life and out of the organization, (2) the stories one could hear now and then about Cadman's being tough—"a regular Napoleon"—during his professional service in other hospitals, and in other times but the present, and (3) Suprin's sense of

---

[1] This statement is limited to the medical executive committee. According to the above three criteria, each of these three men had closer working relations with someone *outside* the medical executive committee; for instance, with their secretaries. These nonexecutive relations were not as significant from the point of view of the total organization nor did they seem to occupy as much of the executives' thinking time as did their relations with their own peer-colleagues.

umbrage at what proved to be the writers' initial overestimation of his image as a "tough administrator" and the concomitant underestimation of him as a "kindly teacher."

Thus, the similarities and differences between the two executives were often expressed in situations in which the manifest behavior of each addressed underlying personality issues of the other. The reader will notice the functioning of this dynamic in the interpersonal transactions reported below. In these transactions, the interactor's attention frequently became diverted from the manifest agenda of interaction. Manifest items were often unresolved. Or, if the executives each felt that a manifest issue had been resolved, the dissimilarity of their apperceptions about the resolution indicated that it did not, in reality, exist. In many of the executives' interactions, important thoughts were left unspoken. Many important interpersonal issues were left untested. There were many items for consideration that each executive preferred to take away with him from an interaction, to work on alone rather than in conversation. This left detectable gaps in the substance of not a few interactions between the executives.

ROLE PERFORMANCE AS A SUBORDINATE

As HAS ALREADY been shown, Dr. Suprin was given to acting in a confident, positivistic manner. His style of administration was "neat." It was "clean." Confusion and uncertainty were anathema to him. He had considerable skill in reducing chaos to disorder, both in the administrative realm and in supervising residents' work with their patients. However, matters that were inherently confusing or uncertain—such as the informal, "running" diagnosis of a co-worker's personality—tended to get short shrift from him. In "offstage" moments he would readily admit that his conception of a given object might be faulty, but in the press of everyday events he talked and acted as though his thoughts on a given matter, or person, were definitive. This was the case for his conception of Dr. Cadman's personality and role in the organization. For instance, he regularly spoke of Dr. Cadman's discomfort with administrative initiative and executive decision making. Cadman acted in such a way as to provide much substantiation of these views. But Suprin also interacted with Cadman in ways that often left Cadman with few other behavioral alternatives short of discord, which he preferred to avoid. One result was that he behaved as he was expected to, and Suprin's conception of him was thereby reinforced.

The following incident is hard to present as cogently as it occurred. It illustrates the operation of this process.

Drs. Suprin and Cadman met in Suprin's office to decide which of the residency applicants they would select for the next academic year. Each had already compiled his own list of approved candidates. (There was approximately 85% consensus between these two lists, which was something that both doctors were unsurprised by, since they had come to expect it of each other, based on past performances.) The procedure was to work from the top of each list—most acceptable—to the bottom. The cutoff point was determined primarily by the number of vacant pay blocks made available by the departure of present residents. Suprin and Cadman began to estimate how many of the existing residents would be staying, and how many would be leaving.

Cadman began to explain to Suprin, by a *method of subtraction* (the reason for the emphasis will shortly become plain), what that number would be.

Suprin (impatiently): "What are you *doing?*"

Cadman explained what he was doing.

Suprin (interrupting): "Do you know what you're doing?"

Cadman began to explain, slowly and in a quiet voice, what he was attempting to do. Suprin shifted in his chair for several seconds, then interrupted.

"*That's* not the way to do it," he said sharply. "You don't know what you are doing. We'll do it *this* way." He then proceeded to explain an *additive method* for reaching the figure re-

quired. To do this, Cadman began to call off the names on a list
he brought with him into the office. Suprin copied them down
and added them up.

Suprin again explained what they were doing. "O.K.?" he
asked. Cadman nodded, and read off some more names. Suprin
copied them down.

Whether or not Cadman's subtractive method would have
worked cannot be determined. Regardless of the potential
utility of this method, however, it is clear that both Cadman
and Suprin reinforced their preexisting positions on the
active-passive issue of their relationship. Their conceptions
of each other were thereby reinforced.

Coping with Superordinate Assertiveness

Fleeting incidents like this occurred frequently, usually
before work and after it. (Often, the most useful time for
the observation of group meetings occurred in that five minutes before the meeting "began" and in the five minutes after
it had "ended.") This can be illustrated by the events that
occurred after Suprin and Cadman had decided how many
residents they would accept for the following academic year,
and which of the applicants they would accept.

At the conclusion of the meeting between Suprin and Cadman,
during which they had selected from among the residency applicants those whom they would accept in the next year's residency
training program, the number was tentatively set at 10 or 11,
pending further clarification.

At this point, the reader should recall that Suprin and Cadman had been through this selection procedure several times
before, ever since Suprin had become superintendent. Also,
Cadman had been through it several times *more* than had
Suprin, since he had been clinical director before Suprin
came into the hospital as superintendent. Suprin's behavior in
the following incident should be considered in this light. Ex-

actly how necessary it was for him to take Cadman step-by-step through the acceptance procedure cannot be determined. However, one might not unreasonably assume that another person would let a man with Cadman's experience in the matter do it more on his own, and that under such conditions Cadman would have managed the task adequately.

Suprin then suggested that Cadman send out letters to the people definitely accepted, and to those definitely rejected, but to hold off on the intermediaries a little longer. Next, he proceeded to dictate the wording of an acceptance letter, which Cadman copied down.

Suprin: "We have made the selection . . . are offering you a position. . . . Although an affirmative answer is not required until October 15, if this is your first choice, we would appreciate your letting us know. . . ."

Cadman finished writing what Suprin had dictated, then asked, "Will you be in on Monday?"

Suprin: "Yes."

Cadman: "Would you like to sign the letters then?"

Here again we see how Cadman's performance substantiated Suprin's notions of his lacking initiative and independence. Cadman also held a certain conception of Suprin, and was acting on the basis of this as much as on the basis of his own needs in the situation. He based his behavior on his conception of Suprin as a man needing to control others and needing to make decisions. Cadman thought of himself as a person who, more than most, could afford to let other people act out their needs in their behavior toward him. He was "nibblable." That is, he could afford to let people "nibble" on his rights, prerogatives, kindness, gullibility, and so on. He could afford to let Suprin boss him around. He saw Suprin as a person who enjoyed doing so, who needed to do it, and himself as a person who could withstand being bossed around. Occasionally he could not withstand it. He became annoyed, but since there was little he could do to control

Suprin's behavior, and nothing he could do to control Suprin's perceptions, there were only three alternatives open to
him: (1) aggress uselessly against the uncontrollable; (2) re-
treat from the field, that is, leave the hospital; or (3) acqui-
esce to some of the inevitable consequences of continued participation in the executive role constellation. Considering the
rewarding nature of his position in the constellation and the
hospital, Cadman was not likely to leave that position because of relatively infrequent painful exchanges with a fellow executive. Cadman valued the operation of the hospital
too highly to start or support any sort of internecine warfare
among the medical executives. He said so himself. Therefore,
he tended to let such matters slide, and Suprin's opinion of
him as passive and dependent again became "right."

Cadman considered it good for Suprin, good for himself,
and good for the hospital generally that Suprin's predisposition toward decisive, directive behavior be facilitated, or at
least unopposed. He regularly provided Suprin with unobtrusive—Cadman believed they had to be unobtrusive to be
effective—gambits for decisive action. We see below that
Suprin's immediate response to Cadman's question, "Would
you like to sign the letters then?" was to seize the action offered to him. He immediately agreed to sign the letters. Only
upon reflection did he relinquish the action, and then only
half-heartedly. Cadman could take action, ". . . if you like."
Cadman's conception of Suprin was thereby proven "right"
once more. Suprin "really" wanted to sign the letters himself.
Cadman then knew what action on his part would be appropriate. He let Suprin sign the letters.

Cadman: "Would you like to sign the letters then?"
Suprin: "O.K. (Pause) I don't have to sign them. You can sign
them, if you like." Cadman did not respond. Suprin continued.
"You better send 'No's' to everybody below —— [a name]."
Cadman: "I'd like to hold the 'No's' for another week, if that's
all right with you."

Suprin: "If you want to, but I like them to know where they stand."

Cadman left Suprin's office and returned to his own.

Now we shall see Dr. Cadman turning to his previous experience in selecting residents, and combining it with the possibly new requirements from Dr. Suprin.

Mrs. O'Toole followed Dr. Cadman into his office. Cadman handed her a sheet of paper.

"This is your list of residency selections," he said to her. "We'll be sending letters to all of them. Do we have a copy of last year's letter?"

Mrs. O'Toole: "Yes."

Cadman: "Well, you better bring it to me. There may be some changes of wording from last year."

Exit Mrs. O'Toole.

The observer later received information that indicated it was Dr. Suprin, not Dr. Cadman, who signed those letters. This indicates two points: (1) that Dr. Cadman voluntarily surrendered his option to sign the letters—it was hardly a coveted task, after all—and (2) that Dr. Suprin readily reappropriated that activity. Again, the disparity between the administrative initiative of the two men reappeared, supported by both.

Living with the Superordinate's Reification of Oneself

In such a diad, it can be seen how readily each person would form a definite judgment about his colleague. Several incidents were observed in which these judgments proved to be "inaccurate." That is, each executive was often wrong as to the other's conscious decision or conclusion on a specific manifest problem. At the level of latent interpersonal issues, however, each executive often surmised correctly the "guts" of the other's position in a given interaction. The level of confidence with which each perceived the other's latent stance was such that this inaccuracy about conscious decisions tended not to come to the attention of either man involved. In one incident, the focal point of interaction was around a resident who was violating the attendance regulations of a required weekly seminar. Cadman brought the matter up one day, while he was in Suprin's office. The two men discussed it.

Cadman: "He's a second-year resident, and I think he should live like one."

Cadman stated his position with noticeable forcefulness, the intended inference perhaps being that he planned to handle the matter as he saw fit. Maybe Suprin was resisting such assertiveness from the passive-dependent member of the diad. He responded as he often did when he felt needlessly bothered by some person or issue.

Suprin: "What are you bringing it to me for?"
Cadman: "I'm perfectly willing to handle it. . . ."

Cadman seemed to know what the hidden agenda was. The empathic therapist was responding to latent issues.

Cadman: ". . . but I'm sure it will come to you, so I wanted to let you know."

But Suprin was not having any of this independence, it appeared.

Suprin: "But why are you bringing it to *me?*"

Suprin pressed this point, not satisfied that Cadman's stated intentions and manifest determination were congruent with Cadman's having broached the issue with him at all.

Cadman: "Because he'll probably come in to see you after I've finished with him."
Suprin: "Well, I'll send him back to *you.*" He smiled as he placed great emphasis on the last word.

Suprin did not accept Cadman's communication, or his performance, at face value. The observer spoke with Dr. Suprin shortly after the above interaction. Suprin's dominant conception of Cadman as a lovable and dependent "softy" predisposed him to disbelieve Cadman's manifestly assertive communication of independence in favor of viewing the inter-action as another attempt on Cadman's part to "lean on" the No. 1 power figure in the hospital, namely Suprin himself.

Observer: "When Dr. Cadman came to see about Dr. Randolph [the resident in question] on Thursday, what was he doing?"

Suprin laughed. "Paul was about to spank one of his children," he replied, "and he wanted to let me know, so that if Randolph came crying to me, I would not let him off."

Observer: "So he wanted to get your stories straight before he went ahead and did anything."

Suprin: "Yes."

Observer: "Was that why he was talking to you?"

Suprin: "It was a question of administering punishment, and Paul doesn't like that sort of thing. I have to push him to take the responsibility. What he would really like me to have said was, 'That's sort of a messy business. Why not let me handle it for you?' He would really have liked me to take it off his hands for him. That's what he wanted."

Suprin's last statement illustrates why he kept inquiring of Cadman as to the reason he was bringing up the matter of the resident *at all.* He perceived Cadman as trying to get Suprin to take over an onerous punitive duty, but he could not get Cadman to admit to that latent intent.

Cadman's response to that same interaction was different from Suprin's. His statements were self-explanatory.

Observer: "When you spoke to Dr. Suprin last Thursday about Randolph's misunderstanding with [the seminar leader], he said to you twice, 'What are you bringing it to me for? What are you bringing it to me for?' I'd like to know what was going on there from your point of view."

Cadman: "Dr. Suprin has vested interests in [that resident]. So when I spoke to him, I wanted to get the full benefit of the boss's feelings on the matter. You know, when you are No. 2 in an organization, it's in your benefit to find out what No. 1 feels about something, before you go ahead and act."

Observer: "So you wanted to find out what Dr. Suprin felt on the matter before you took any action."

Cadman: "That's right."

Observer: "And how did he feel on the matter?"

(Pause)

Cadman: "He felt it was time we did something to help [the resident] get straightened out."

The reader will recognize that this point was not contained in the substance of the interaction being discussed. Considering Dr. Cadman's hesitation over this statement, and the immediate introduction by Dr. Cadman of a new direction of conversation, the observer felt that Cadman was trying to avoid a topic that was painful to him. This turned out to be the case. As will be seen immediately below, Dr. Cadman had more immediate impressions about what Dr. Suprin thought about Cadman's actions, his organizational role, and his personality. Cadman possessed some carefully controlled bitterness about what he termed his "old lady" role in the executive structure of the hospital. This affect was communicated when he began to speak about what he thought Suprin thought about him. The self-denigration was muted, however, in that Cadman was able to ascribe much of what went on between Suprin and himself to the way *Suprin* was. That is, the incongruence between Cadman's concepts of self and role, and the socially defined self and role Cadman perceived being ascribed to him, was rendered less distressing to him because he felt that a person such as himself was needed to be an effective No. 2 man to the kind of No. 1 man that Suprin was.

Cadman continued: "Were you here when I discussed it with [the seminar leader] on the phone?"

Observer: "No."

Cadman: "We talked about whether it [the seminar] was required or elective." (Pause)

Observer: "What did he think?"

Cadman: "He thought it was an elective. But he said he [the resident] couldn't have it both ways." (Pause)

Dr. Cadman was apparently ready to carry the conversation along at this level indefinitely.

Observer: "I felt, when you spoke to Dr. Suprin, that he thought you were trying to get him to take over, trying to push the decision off on him. Was there any of that?"

Cadman grimaced: "I *know* that's what Suprin thought! I know from the way he responds that that's the way he often sees people."

Observer: "But you were ready to take all the necessary steps?"

Cadman: "Oh, sure. But you see, that's the way it is with a person who has a certain amount of authoritarianism to him. Suprin's a little more authoritarian than Sherman was, and he expects his people to be a bit authoritarian, too."

Observer: "You make more decisions now than when you worked for Dr. Sherman?"

Cadman: "When I worked for Dr. Sherman, I had to pick up the pieces. With Dr. Suprin, I pick up the pieces *and* make decisions too." [2]

Observer: "And your talking to him about [the resident] was not an attempt to get out of making decisions yourself?"

Cadman: "I knew he had an interest in the situation, and I was letting him know. I was also finding out what way the wind was blowing. But you know the old saying about throwing crap into a fan. Well?"

As stated, Cadman tended to "go along" with the expectations placed upon him. He did not strive to revise or eradi-

[2] How does this relate to Cadman's perception of being freed from administrative burden by Dr. Suprin? The nonsimilarity between Cadman's statements about his freedom from administration and the actuality of his day-to-day situation has already been discussed. The above is as close as Cadman got to putting this discrepancy into words.

cate them, even when they caused him difficulty. His conception of authority, of the role of No. 2, his genuine interest in
getting the work of the hospital done with the minimum of
friction, his affection and respect for Dr. Suprin, his conception of where his rewards came from and what he must put
up with in order to get these rewards; all these contributed to
his unwillingness or inability to dispute these mythical representations of himself. It would not be too inaccurate to say
that a main element in his conception of himself was that of
a person capable of living with the inevitable misunderstandings of himself by the people comprising the social world
around him.

Therefore, in his "passive Cadmanian way," he avoided interpersonal conflicts. He was thereby faced with the necessity
of living with more intrapersonal conflict than might otherwise have been the case. He demonstrated great skill in doing so, and this in turn greatly contributed to his professional
charisma in the hospital.

(Dr. Suprin, on the other hand, seemed more adept at living with interpersonal than with intrapersonal conflict, and
his behavior could be viewed as a programmed—i.e., consistent over time—series of attempts to minimize the latter at
the expense of the former.)

Proactive Contributions to Being Misunderstood

If there is any residual notion in the mind of the reader
that Dr. Cadman's being misunderstood in the above-cited
interaction was entirely the "fault" of Dr. Suprin, the following incident will show the substantive positions of Suprin
and Cadman *reversed*. In the above incident, Suprin saw
Cadman as not wanting to "take charge" and Cadman saw
himself as ready to do so. In the following incident, Suprin
saw Cadman as ready to "take charge" but Cadman saw himself absolved of the necessity of doing so.

12:10 P.M. Dr. Cadman left a cup of tea in his office and walked down the corridor to the desk of Suprin's secretary. "Is your boss around?" he asked.

The secretary, pointing to the corner of the filing cabinets: "He's over there. In the corner. I've got him standing in the corner."

Cadman to Suprin: "Are you free? Can I talk to you for a minute?"

Suprin: "Sure. My office is busy. Why don't we take yours."

They turned to Cadman's office. Cadman took his seat behind his desk. Suprin sat in the chair next to him. In several minutes Suprin's secretary brought in a cup of coffee for him, and several minutes after that, a hamburger. Cadman and Suprin sat and sipped and chatted. Cadman spoke to Suprin in a low voice, leaning back in his swivel chair with his arms folded in front of him, his chin on his chest. Suprin tipped his chair back casually. Their initial remarks were interspersed with "comfortable" silences. Suprin munched on his hamburger, while Cadman looked at him closely.

Cadman informed Suprin of a resident's stated intention to leave the program.

Suprin: "Good. That's one more space available."

Cadman: "Say, I'm a little mixed up on this clinical research business. (In a slightly querulous tone) I'm not too sure what you have in mind for me. At one time I thought I had over-all clinical responsibility for the unit—like with the other study—to make sure that nothing goes wrong. On the other hand, do you want me to be one of the staff? Do you want me to be on the project as a worker? At one point, I got the impression it was you and I on the project, but then I got the impression it was you and somebody else."

Suprin: "Oh, no. It's you and I that are in charge of the project."

Cadman: "That's the impression I had, but when you asked me for a list of therapists at the meeting, I was surprised. I mean, I don't want to get involved in it administratively, like that."

Suprin: "Oh, no. It's your project. It was your idea in the first place. I just helped you with it. Remember?" (Suprin then gave a history of the project.)

Cadman: "Then on the clinical business, it's you and I?"

Suprin: "It's *your* project, Paul. I just have the habit of running things. You know that. I'm redesigning Howie's half of the project, too."

Cadman: "I'm just one of the workers on the project, then?"

Suprin: "Don't you want the project?"

Cadman: "Oh, yes. (Smiles) I've wanted it for a long time."

(Pause) Then Dr. Cadman started to list the names of several people he thought would be suitable on the project. The discussion then turned to personal matters, after which Suprin left Cadman's office.

Cadman turned to the observer: "I've got that settled."

Observer: "What agreement did you reach?"

Cadman: "That I'm part of the project, but not head of it. Just one of the workers."

Observer: "Did last Thursday's meeting confuse you about this?"

Cadman: "You remember when Suprin turned to me and said, 'You prepare a list of people for the project.' I don't want to take the administrative responsibility for it like that. But the meeting was not the place to make an issue of it."

This, however, was not the way Dr. Suprin construed the same interaction. That same afternoon the observer had the opportunity to talk briefly with Dr. Suprin in his office.

Observer: "What understanding did you reach with Dr. Cadman about the research you discussed?"

Suprin: "What do you mean?"

Observer: "Is he the head of the project, or just one of the staff?"

Suprin: "No. That is his project. It was his idea, and I helped him with it when I was [elsewhere]." Suprin then went into a complete history of the project, the formulation of the research proposal, to what agencies it had been submitted, with what outcome, and the committees that had sat in relation to the project. Suprin gave the impression that everything was perfectly clear and completely understood.

Observer: "Was there some misunderstanding on this matter?"

Suprin: "He knew it was his project. There was never any doubt in his mind about that. But for some reason, Paul has the attitude toward me something like a little boy saying, 'Mommy, am I your little boy?' He wanted to be reassured."

Observer: "So he is *more* than just one of a number of the staff on the project."

Suprin: "Certainly. It is his project."

Observer: "Will he prepare a list of therapists for the project?"

Suprin: "He'll recommend some. His recommendations will carry more weight than others, but the project is run by a committee, and they will make the nominations." Suprin then went on to describe the membership of the committee.

The observer experienced some difficulty in understanding what was going on. One resolution was that Cadman was freed from any implied or inferred responsibility to select the staff for the project by himself. Beyond that, the clearest themes that emerged were the reflection one or more times that (1) Suprin perceived Cadman as being dependent upon him—"like a little boy"—and needing to be reassured by him, and (2) Cadman's disengagement from administrative responsibilities. Yet, in this instance, Suprin made it plain that he saw Cadman as "head" of the project, but Cadman saw himself as just "part" of the project. That is, in one instance where Suprin apparently set Cadman up in a hierarchically ascendent position, Cadman's response was to descend to a peer-like position in relation to his future co-workers.

In terms of our present analysis, it appears that the reification of the symbolic content of Dr. Cadman's behavior in the hospital had produced a social definition of his person, and a set of role-expectations that did him justice and were rewarding, and also did him some injustice and were frustrating. As measured by Cadman's conception of himself, the "persona" and role ascribed to him were predominantly accurate, and the net of the rewards and costs of his sociopsychological situation in the organization produced a profit for him. The injustice or inaccuracy of the reification of him arose from a consistent distortion in the direction of over-emphasized kindliness, benevolence, empathy, altruism, passivity, and dependence. This distortion occasionally caused situations that gave Dr. Cadman considerable pain. However, when faced with the opportunity to modify or break down the image—distortion included—Dr. Cadman acted in such a way as to reinforce it in its totality.

INTERPERSONAL REFLEXES IN MULTIPLE-ROLE SITUATIONS

WE HAVE SEEN several examples of the way Dr. Cadman interacted with Dr. Suprin. We have seen the relationship between this style of interaction and (1) Cadman's self-concept and role definition, and (2) his conception of the sort of person Suprin was, and the way Suprin liked to behave. We have seen Suprin's conception of Cadman as a man, a therapist, and an administrator. We have seen the way that Suprin acted on that conception, the way that he reflected it back in the form of role-expectations upon Cadman. We have also seen the ambivalence of Cadman's response to these reflections upon himself.

Data have also been presented showing the almost rhapsodic response to Cadman's therapeutic skills that was not untypical of incoming residents at the time of the study. What about the personnel *in between* the superintendent and the residents? It was with the midlevel staff that Dr. Cadman had the bulk of his administrative-clinical interactions. What was his performance in their presence? What was their conception of him, and how did they behave toward him? There are sufficient data to carry the answers to these questions into Part V, on the consequences of the executive role constellation. Several highly selected "vignettes" will be presented here to demonstrate (1) Cadman's specialized role performance in wider interactional settings that included peers and subordinates, (2) the equally specialized role performance these others adopted in interacting with Cadman, the person around whom such a specialized "persona" and set of role-expectations had been built, and (3) the complementarity of this reciprocating specialization around Dr. Cadman, existing juxtaposed to the different patterned relations around Drs. Suprin and Asche.

Supportiveness Toward Superordinate and Subordinate

In the following incident we shall see Dr. Cadman as he interacted in an "unexpected" meeting with Dr. Suprin, Dr. Asche, and two younger professionals on the staff of the hospital. It will be important to note:

(1) Cadman's behavior in relation to Suprin: Dr. Cadman carried forward his habitual deference to the expectations placed on him by Dr. Suprin. Cadman did this in a way that facilitated Suprin's task leadership and preferred style of expressive behavior. In this outwardly self-effacing way, Dr. Cadman was behaving consistently with certain beliefs he held about the proper role of No. 2, and the proper relation between the No. 2 and the No. 1 figures in an organization. These ideas he presented to the observer at the close of the following incident.

(2) The behavior of Drs. Cadman and Asche in relation to one another: this was a relationship characterized by some uneasiness, by a certain amount of competition and closing of the ears to one another, as witnessed by the frequent interruptions, and by the tendency to return to one's previous statements despite intervening remarks by the other.

(3) The behavior of Dr. Cadman in relation to the midlevel psychiatrist in the meeting: Dr. Ginsberg, the midlevel psychiatrist in question, was formerly one of Dr. Cadman's subordinates. Interestingly, the reader will see Dr. Ginsberg

turn repeatedly for support and understanding to Dr. Cadman—and get it—when faced with criticism and teasing from
Suprin and Asche. Having trained under Dr. Cadman, Ginsberg still perceived Cadman as having "a place in his heart"
for junior personnel to an extent that differentiated him
from Suprin and Asche.

(4) The impact of Suprin's demands upon Cadman's relations with other people in the hospital: Cadman decided
to forego other previously arranged engagements to fulfill
the requirements unexpectedly placed on him by his superordinate.

9:00 A.M. Dr. Cadman picked up the morning reports, which
he reviewed. "Let's go," he said, and we left his office, walked
down the corridor and into Dr. Suprin's office. There, Cadman
reported on the admission of four patients to the hospital. He
and Suprin discussed one patient who was a readmission. Then
Suprin queried Cadman as to the disposition of another patient.
The information that Cadman was able to provide satisfied
Suprin.

Meanwhile, Dr. Ginsberg had entered the office and taken a
seat. Cadman finished his morning report in less than five minutes. (Only rarely were these interactions longer than five minutes. If they were, it was usually because of trouble that had
arisen.) As he got up to go, Suprin mentioned that there was
about to be a research meeting in his office. There was a brief
pause.

"Would you like me to stay?" asked Cadman.

"Yes, I would," Suprin replied.

Cadman settled back into his chair and lit a cigarette.

Either Dr. Cadman had not been aware that the meeting
in question, concerning the Institute's research, was to take
place that morning, or else he had not realized that his
presence was expected. In either case, he had not planned to
attend that meeting. The first he knew of it was when Suprin
mentioned it to him, immediately above. It was only a matter

of seconds between Cadman's being apprised of the meeting (and Suprin's expectation that he attend), and his decision to forego his other planned activities in order to attend the meeting. Cadman had a direct interest in the clinical part of the research in question, as has already been presented earlier in this chapter. Suprin later pointed this out to the observer, giving it as the reason for Cadman's rapid decision to change his plans and attend the meeting. Cadman reported that his decision to attend was based on Suprin's need for his presence at the meeting. Cadman's decision was probably related to both his vested interests in the research *and* his acquiescent support of Dr. Suprin in face-to-face situations. It was as characteristic of Cadman that he should view his decision as based on Suprin's *needs,* as it was characteristic of Suprin to view Cadman's decision as based on Cadman's *interests.*

The reader should bear in mind that as the meeting approached and passed 10:00 A.M., Dr. Cadman had another engagement scheduled in his office for that time and teaching rounds later on in the morning, plus work of his own to be accomplished in between.

Dr. Asche and Dr. Pomantzeff entered Suprin's office, and the meeting began. It was now shortly after 9 A.M. There was some joking about Dr. Ginsberg's article in a then current issue of a popular magazine, and then a discussion of some psychoanalytic literature.

9:10 A.M. "Well, now. The research," said Suprin, summoning the meeting to order. Asche and Ginsberg took the initiative in presenting the personnel arrangements they had made to date for the project. Asche then turned to Suprin for a brief query, and reply, as to how to present certain financial requests to officials in Washington.

Meanwhile, Dr. Cadman remained silent, and smoked. (He had contributed nothing substantively to the meeting so far. The reason and necessity for his presence was, therefore, not yet clear to the observer.)

The discussion reverted to personnel matters. Ginsberg, Asche, and Suprin were the discussants.

Dr. Asche then raised the question of the development of a measuring device for tapping into the ego strength of patients: an "ego scale," he called it. Ginsberg presented an idea about the measurement of ego strength. Suprin and Asche then directed a number of remarks about this to Ginsberg. These remarks were not manifestly critical but they did prompt a re-examination of Ginsberg's initial idea. After this had gone on for several minutes, Ginsberg turned to Cadman, who was sitting beside him, and asked, "What would *you* say about it, Dr. Cadman?"

Cadman was about to reply when Asche added several more of his thoughts on the measurement of ego strength. Cadman interrupted Asche. Addressing his remarks to Ginsberg, he talked briefly about testing for ego strength by clinical methods.

Asche and Suprin then talked to each other about going to Washington for additional grant money. Asche was asking Suprin, "How do you do it?" Suprin was replying why, and in what ways, "It's easy." Asche concluded with a laugh, "Jeez, I could never do that."

Suprin joked about Ginsberg's hiring people for the project before he had money to pay them, and then "clearing out to the South Pole" (another reference to Ginsberg's magazine article). Cadman continued the joke, saying, "We have to establish the reliability of Dr. Ginsberg" (a pun on the previous discussion about establishing the reliability of a psychometric instrument, also emphasizing Cadman's already known preference for working with people rather than with tests and other "instruments").

9:30 A.M. Suprin, Asche, Ginsberg, and Pomantzeff embarked on a lengthy discussion of the research design of the over-all project that was to comprise the work for which the Institute was seeking funds. Cadman did not engage in this conversation. Instead, he sat back and lit up another cigarette.

Suprin directed a question to Cadman about giving therapy to half of the patients in the experiment, or to the whole group of patients. Cadman replied, indicating his preference for giving psychotherapy to the whole group, and using the patients as their own controls. Dr. Pomantzeff disagreed and talked about the necessity of distinguishing between psychotherapy and normal psychological functioning (spontaneous recovery?) over time. Cadman did not press the matter.

10:05 A.M. The general discussion of research design continued. 10:12 A.M. Cadman lit up another cigarette. 10:17 A.M. He glanced conspicuously around at the clock behind him on the office wall.

Ginsberg told Cadman of his idea to have those patients who were not seeing therapists, see clergymen. This way, everybody would be seeing somebody. Ginsberg presented this idea as having already been objected to by Suprin and Asche.

Ginsberg directly to Cadman: "I already know what the others think, but what do *you* think about this idea? If we have five patients in psychotherapy," Ginsberg continued, "and five non-psychotherapy patients, what if the second group were to see clergymen for two hours a week, so that at least they would be seeing somebody?"

The content of Cadman's professional beliefs often became fused with the sort of person people thought him to be, when they were interacting with him primarily on the basis of their own needs. Dr. Cadman regularly stated his clinical opinion, in training situations, that "everybody needs somebody, and some people will even settle for a therapist for a while." His style as a therapist, again manifested in training situations, prompted those in his audience to see how this opinion was the basis of much of his interpersonal behavior toward the patient in a given interviewing situation. Cadman did not distinguish sharply, in his public statements and behavior, between his roles as therapist, teacher, administrator, and human being. Indeed, one of his tenets was that they were "all one ball of wax." This tempted some subordinates to seek to place themselves in what was essentially a supportive-therapeutic relation to Dr. Cadman, despite the fact that the situations surrounding such attempts were structurally nontherapeutic. Not only were most of such situations devoted to nontherapeutic objectives—as for instance the one being presently considered, which was devoted to the planning and administration of research—but the people who wittingly or unwittingly were seeking therapeutic support from Cadman would probably have resisted any explicit reflection upon them of the role-expectations of patienthood. Dr. Cadman sometimes permitted himself the luxury of responding briefly and informally to these bids. In fact, this comprised much of the especially affectionate nature of the relations between Cadman and some of his younger colleagues.

Dr. Ginsberg turned to Cadman for interpersonal support and for professional corroboration of a point substantively close to Cadman's everybody-needs-somebody opinion. Ginsberg's several overtures to Cadman during and after this meeting indicate that he also felt the need of "somebody" for the understanding and support he perhaps did not experience himself as getting from Asche or Suprin. He turned to Cadman, and Cadman replied as expected.

Asche immediately interrupted with a rhetorical question— "What is psychotherapy?"—and then proceeded to reply to this question by analyzing his reasons for rejecting Ginsberg's ideas. Suprin added, "I agree."

Ginsberg turned to Cadman again. "What did you think?" It began to appear that, for whatever reasons, Ginsberg was beginning to play the role of "agent provocateur"; playing the three executives off against each other on points of disagreement, or different frames of reference that were widely "known," that is, widely represented in the staff's accurate-and-inaccurate reification of the role constellation of the "big three."

Cadman replied that he thought a close watch would have to be kept on exactly what it was the clergymen were doing with the patients.

Asche entered in with his thoughts of holding the therapy variable constant—giving therapy to all experimental patients—

and manipulating the drug variable—giving half the patients drugs and the other half placebos.

After Asche had finished, Cadman turned and continued his remarks to Ginsberg, saying that it would make an interesting experiment to record the content of confessionals, and then analyze them in terms of the communications involved.

This was not a particularly tense meeting, but whatever tension there was seemed to peak at this point. Asche sat back in his chair with a hand over his mouth, as he did on other occasions when he wanted to keep his personal reactions to himself. (If the researchers' understanding of the sort of research Asche liked is correct, then Cadman's proposal for research was not the kind that Asche would go for.) Suprin appeared to be reading something on his desk.

Ginsberg again raised a point of publicly recognized difference between the executives, one that Suprin often talked about to residents.

Ginsberg raised the question of having a researcher-administrator split on the experimental ward quite similar to the therapist-administrator split used on the other wards of the hospital.

Cadman: "Dr. Suprin [3] wouldn't agree to that. . . ."

Raising the isssue of the therapist-administrator "split" called explicit attention to a point of professional and administrative dissension in the executive ranks of the Institute. (The dissension focused on whether or not hospitalized mental patients should be looked after administratively and treated therapeutically by the same doctor or by different doctors.) At this, Cadman acted to elucidate a point of contention that seemed to be passing by uncontended. He consolidated the executive subgroup by prompting the explicit statement—by Dr. Suprin—of the differences between them,

[3] When talking with medical personnel and staff groups, Suprin usually referred to Cadman as "Paul." Cadman usually referred to Suprin as "Dr. Suprin," even in medical executive committee meetings.

which meant that future planning would have to take account of these differences rather than subvert them. This was Cadman's point of major contribution in the meeting, and it represented almost the ideal act according to his conception of the proper role of the No. 2 man.

Suprin appeared not to have been attending.

". . . *would you?*" Cadman persisted.

Suprin: "What? No. The therapist-administrator split interferes, I believe, with the treatment of schizophrenics. Paul doesn't agree with me on this, but I know I'm right. (Smiling at Cadman) I think I've been winning him over."

Cadman smiled, but did not otherwise reply.

Ginsberg to Suprin: "Oh. Then it would have to be settled, wouldn't it?"

Suprin to Ginsberg: "Yes, it would."

10:40 A.M. Asche said that he felt considerably clarified at this point. Suprin replied that he thought they were ready to go down to see "brother Jonas" in Washington. With that, the meeting adjourned.

Helping Others Through the Supportive Role Specialization

Dr. Cadman later told the observer that he stayed at the meeting because Suprin "needed" him at the meeting. If Suprin had not needed him, he would not have asked him to stay. This statement is presented out of its order of occurrence because it sheds greater light on a fleeting interaction that occurred between Cadman and Suprin as the above meeting was breaking up. As the others were walking out of the office, Cadman approached Suprin's desk.

Cadman: "I didn't know there was a meeting today."

Suprin leaned back in his swivel chair and lifted his hands in the air. "Neither did I," he said. "It just happened."

Cadman: "Do you want me to attend next time?"

Suprin (somewhat petulantly, it seemed to the observer) : "You are supposed to be *helping* me on this."

Cadman: "Will it be a regular meeting at this time?"

Suprin: "Yes." They both made notations in their little black pocket calendars. Exit Cadman.

On the way back to his office, Dr. Cadman had the following interaction with Dr. Ginsberg. Ginsberg had been waiting in the corridor between Suprin's and Cadman's offices to speak to Cadman.

Ginsberg: "I just wanted you to hear me out on this." He went over his idea again about having clergymen see the nonpsychotherapy experimental patients. He continued, saying that he thought this to be an important social issue, with which people like clergymen were in an ideal position to cope; namely, working with people before they became sick, and providing treatment not as costly as that provided by psychiatrists.

Cadman listened smilingly. "This is an important issue," he replied. "I think there are two kinds of ministers; the peasant type, who have seen death and accepted it; and those that overreact against death. The first type have great empathic abilities, and the second are more skittish, constantly invoking God. There are probably two types of psychiatrists too, and the second type is constantly invoking theory instead of God."

Ginsberg: "I realize that the others [at this meeting] had good reason for not liking the idea, but I wanted to tell it to you. (He laughed.) I thought they would kick me out when I came out with it."

Ginsberg stepped back to break off the interaction. Cadman smiled at him, and called after him down the corridor, "Nobody would kick you out. Nobody wants to see you go to South America." Smiling and shaking his head, Cadman returned to his office.

The reflection-response-performance reification of Dr. Cadman, the supportive specialist, had spun through another reciprocally reinforcing cycle.

The Burden of Supportive Role Specialization

It was 10:50 A.M. when Dr. Cadman returned to his office. Two students had been waiting for him for 50 minutes. Here we see the cost of alternatives, since for these two people, the event was potentially the initiation of a "disorganized administrator" cycle of reification and reflection upon Cadman, based on his performance of being "late."

Cadman chatted casually with these people for five minutes, until they had to leave. (He did not explain his lateness, and they did not inquire.) After they left, Cadman turned to the observer.

Cadman: "Did you see that? That is the problem of the second man." He went on to explain that, when Suprin asked him to stay for the research conference, he had made the decision to stay despite his previous engagement.

Observer: "Why?"

Cadman: "When Dr. Suprin asked me to stay, he needed me there and my job is to help him. He is in a demanding position. The top man is like a tower in the sea, you know? You know what the waves can do to it? They can topple it over. It can be buffeted down. The top man, like the tower, starts where we leave off."

Observer: "How long did you think the meeting would last?"

Cadman: "Over an hour."

Observer: "Would you have foregone ward rounds as well?"

Cadman: "Yes. I would have got my No. 2 man to go."

Observer: "Who is that?"

Cadman: "Dr. Ackroyd. I would have had Mrs. O'Toole contact him if the meeting had gone on much longer."

Observer: "Did Dr. Suprin know of your appointment with [the students]?"

Cadman: "No."

Observer: "What would have happened if you had raised this with him?"

Cadman: "We would have got into an argument about which is more important. He would have got mad, and then he would not have been able to concentrate on the task at hand. The second man must make peace with himself on this, or he will get torn to pieces in an organization."

Observer: "Does this happen often to you?"

Cadman: "Too often."

Observer: "What do you get in exchange for it all?"

Cadman: "What I get in exchange is that I don't have to take all the responsibility on my shoulders, as the top man has to. You can call this weakness if you like. Or you can call it strength, in that I have to make my own decisions to do what I want to do. Instead of doing what I would have to do as a boss. It also makes me a member of an organization that is moving ahead, that is doing something."

Observer: "That is, accomplishing something you are interested in."

Cadman: "Yes. A cog in the wheel that fits. Have you ever seen a gear that's a little out of cog with the other wheels? What happens to it? Well?"

Observer: "It gets ripped to pieces."

Cadman: "Right. That's right. That's what happens to it. (Pause) I made this decision a long time ago, of course. In 1939, to be exact." He lifted his fingers in a Churchillian "V" sign.

Observer: "What's that?"

Cadman: "That someday I would be top clinical man, but that I would never be top administrative man. They had things set up that way in those days too, where all the top jobs were held by administrative men. So I knew where I was headed when I made that decision; that I'd never be head of an organization."

Summary

WE HAVE TRACED through some of the dynamics of Dr. Cadman's participation in and contribution to the functioning of the executive role constellation. The analysis started with the simpler interactive settings in which Dr. Cadman was observed, and moved toward more complicated settings in which Cadman was enacting more than one role relationship simultaneously. We have examined the way those around him in the management hierarchy acted toward him, and how he responded. We have examined the manner in which his own interpersonal reflexes and role definition set up the manner in which others behaved toward him. We have briefly outlined the contributions of Dr. Cadman's role performance to others, as well as some of the rewards and the problematic issues this specialization provided for Dr. Cadman himself. We turn next, in the same vein, to Dr. Asche.

CHAPTER 12

The Transactions of the Assistant Superintendent Within the Executive Role Constellation

IT WOULD BE EASY, and not entirely inaccurate, to state that there was "less" in the working relations between Asche and Suprin than existed between Cadman and Suprin. The data of the Asche-Suprin diad did not present themselves with as much forcefulness and clarity as did those of the Cadman-Suprin diad. The complementarity of the juxtaposed roles was not as great. The interlocking of instrumental and expressive modes of executive behavior was not as extensive. Teamwork there was, but it was more along conventional masculine-equalitarian lines of "buddies" sharing the same work, and rather less the teamwork of opposites forwarding dissimilar phases of a larger operation. Both men were related to each other through joint involvement in their work.

DIFFERENTIAL COMPLEMENTARITY OF ROLE RELATIONS

THE ASCHE-SUPRIN diad lacked the articulate expressiveness that Cadman infused into his working relations with Suprin. Cadman's success was not achieved by the popular method of placing as much hierarchical distance as possible between one's self and "the mass," the people embroiled in the "crap of life," as Cadman put it. Instead, Cadman had made the opposite work for him. His success was based on sustained, intensive and well-dramatized work *with* "the crap of life," both directly as a therapist and indirectly as a teacher of therapists. His success remained intact and meaningful, and was in fact enhanced by Cadman's not being No. 1 in the organization that provided the setting for most of the rewards he received for his eloquent, therapeutically useful stand against the capitulation of one's self to the societal pressures of "success."

Dr. Asche had different terms of success. He did not embrace as readily, nor use as productively, the high probability he and Cadman shared of never being No. 1 in the organization for which they deeply cared. Not being No. 1 had less payoff for Dr. Asche in his personal economy than it did for Dr. Cadman. In fact, the reader has already seen that this sociopsychological condition was becoming increasingly apparent to Dr. Asche during the relatively short period of this study. Asche came to a firmer realization that what he wanted at that present stage of his career was the full challenge and recognition of being No. 1 in a hospital of his own. As for the responsibilities of such a position, he saw himself as carrying out many of them during Dr. Suprin's repeated absences from the hospital, and he felt he might as well get the credit for doing so.

As one staff psychiatrist put it, "Suprin and Asche are too much alike to get along well together." On a different occasion, the same person saw them as two completely dissimilar individuals. Given the complexity of the phenomena being considered, this informant was right both times: (1) Asche and Suprin were alike in their desire for the responsibilities of a No. 1 position. Since there was only one top position within the boundaries of the hospital, that desire became latently competitive. (2) For both men, the preferred mode of interpersonal behavior overlapped, and therefore competed; both were disposed toward a "manly" interpersonal style. However, (3) the differential position of the two men on the power axis of the group and the hospital reduced overt competition between the two to the extent that, in situations where this power was being utilized, they appeared to be very dissimilar individuals.

In such a relationship, each participant was disinclined to proffer much information about the experience of working with the other. Both felt more comfortable thinking and talking about subjects other than how they were getting along with each other. When the observer ventured to persist in this somewhat discomforting line of investigation, the data he received were unidimensional testification that each thought the other was a "great guy." Criticism was a more dangerous business between Suprin and Asche than between Suprin and Cadman, and it was more carefully bolstered with balanced statements and mature insight into the many genuinely fine and productive aspects of the other's character and role in the organization.

Role Performance as a Subordinate

The relationship between Dr. Asche and Dr. Suprin involved various thoughts and feelings by each regarding himself and the other. These had an influence upon, and were influenced by, the role performance of each interactor in the presence of the other. The performances provided the behavioral-observational data by which each interactor judged himself relative to the other on whatever dimensions he experienced as being important.

The following incident demonstrates certain dimensions that were important and recurrent discriminators between Asche and Suprin within the boundaries of their working relationship. Again our analytic technique will be to describe and then interpret an "archetypical" interaction between the two executives. The reader will realize that the following incident was selected as unrandomly as possible. However, it was not unrepresentative of the normal relations between Asche and Suprin. Interactions of this nature demonstrated *and* consolidated the relative positions of the two interactors, both on the power axis and on the instrumental-expressive axis of the executive system.

Putting One's "Weakest" Self Forward in Interaction with a Superordinate

The following interaction had its roots in the problem created by a member of the staff who was indirectly one of Dr. Asche's subordinates. This individual had made what both executives construed as unauthorized expenditures of research funds. His actions stemmed, they believed, from what they felt was the illegitimate expectation that any deficit would automatically be made up by the granting agency, or by transfer of money from a research fund that Drs. Suprin and Asche had established and currently controlled. This researcher had been posing considerable difficulties for Dr. Asche in the recent past. In fact, it was a situation involving this individual's overspending of money that had made Asche the angriest the observer ever saw him during the period of observation.[1] Yet, throughout the following interaction with Suprin, Dr. Asche never lost sight of what he considered to be that individual's best interests; and he never stopped acting on that basis, despite the awkward position it placed him in when he took the matter up with Dr. Suprin. In other words, the "weakness" in the role performance about to be described arose more from the intermeshing of a submissive and an assertive *interpersonal reflex*, rather than from any weakness in the *substance* of the submissive person's stand on the administrative problem in question.

Asche walked over to Suprin's office, and poked his head through the doorway.

Suprin: "Hi, Howie. Come in and sit down."
Asche: "Where have you been?"

[1] Cf. Chapter 6, pp. 216–217.

Suprin: "On American Airlines, mostly. I've been gone all week. I'm here today and tomorrow, and then I'll be gone for the rest of the week. I'm making a lot of speeches on our research."

Suprin liked to keep his people informed of his whereabouts, his itinerary, and the extensiveness of his contacts in the professional-political world outside the hospital. There were both rational and nonrational reasons for this. Suprin wanted his subordinates to be able to plan for his presence and his absence as superintendent. He also enjoyed the extensiveness of his high-level contacts outside the hospital, and he was proud of his position and accomplishments in this realm of psychiatry. He liked to share these sentiments with his subordinates and to receive their reflected appreciation, admiration, and respect for efforts that produced a lot of income for the hospital, and indirectly for them. However, the inside-outside balance of his activities was experienced as problematic, if not by him, then by others in the organization. Although this was raised more often in his absence, now and then it was raised in his presence.

Asche: "The hospital seems to be running O.K.?"
Suprin: "Fine, so far as I can see."
Asche: "That's no fault of mine. I've just been doing my job, and the hospital has been running itself."
Suprin: "Good, that's the way it should be. You've got to keep the damn doctors out of it, and it will run O.K."

We see here that, instead of taking what was intended as a compliment—as direct a compliment as Dr. Suprin usually felt comfortable making—Asche side-stepped the appreciation of reward for work well done by modestly divesting himself of any responsibility for success. The reader will recall that, when "alone" with the observer, Dr. Asche saw himself and his efforts as *very much* related to the smooth functioning of the hospital; particularly during Suprin's absences, Asche felt his administrative responsibilities were tantamount to being No. 1. But, face-to-face with Dr. Suprin, Dr. Asche acted with a modesty that did not adequately represent or communicate the causal relation he experienced between his administrative efforts and the successful operation of the hospital. As the reader will see below, such modesty was apparently lost on Dr. Suprin. (Again, we are referring to the rapid reward-punishment exchanges in person-to-person transactions, not to the more studied appreciation of Dr. Asche that Dr. Suprin professed, and experienced, when making "speeches" on the subject.)

That the hospital ran itself was a joke that Dr. Suprin promulgated among the top echelon administrators who worked closely with him. It was responded to in good humor, since it downgraded the administrative functions that they were all sometimes uneasy about, and upgraded the professional and teaching functions that were the "real" reason they held managerial positions in the hospital. The same joke also conveyed a somewhat demeaning connotation. Whatever a doctor did administratively, good or bad, had little effect. Whatever occurred in the subsystem under him, good or bad, bore little relation to his own actions.

Asche often responded positively to Suprin's maxim that the hospital ran itself. He held the belief that an administrator should elicit all the autonomy and responsibility possible from subordinates and then interfere with them as little as possible. Quite frequently, Asche *initiated* consideration of this point of view, as he did above. When he did so, he usually received both the enhancing and demeaning dimensions of its meaning. "Good," said Suprin. "That is the way it should be." That is, doctors should stick to being doctors, nurses to nursing, ministers to ministering, and patients to being patient. Then the hospital would run itself. But the "damn doctors"—on other occasions, the damn nurses, damn residents, or damn patients—were always messing things up by their actions.

Being a "damn doctor," Asche was thereby shown one facet of Suprin's evaluation and appreciation of his contribution to the organization. Whether this hurt him or not cannot now be determined. If it did, Asche sometimes brought it upon himself. Past experience must have familiarized him with Suprin's customary response to the "old saw" about the hospital running itself. By initiating its consideration, he thereby elicited the reflexive response about "damn doctors" that implicated him as well. It also implicated Suprin, but Suprin always enjoyed implicating himself. He rarely exempted himself from his own critical witticisms. In fact, he was often the butt of his own best "jokes." He did it to others, and he did it to himself. But it was *he* who did it to himself. He did not figure in *other people's* humorous stories that circulated around the hospital. When he did, the stories were usually not humorous.

Asche discussed several points of current administrative interest. Then Suprin initiated the discussion of the problem that they both knew had brought Asche to his office.
Suprin: "Now, what about Williams [the problematic researcher]? What's going on there? . . ."

Without waiting for further clarification from Asche, Suprin immediately proposed that Williams be thrown out. Suprin recognized that this was perhaps his modal response to people causing trouble in "his" organization—"Get the bastard out of here"—and he regularly spoke to others, from residents to senior executives, with candor and some relish about his propensity to eject offending individuals from his hospital. In speaking on this subject, he often contrasted his own propensity with the more protective propensity of Dr. Cadman—"Oh, let him stay another year." Hence the reification of another aspect of the executive role constellation was facilitated.

Suprin: ". . . If you ask me, I'd say we can't afford him. I'd say, give him and his grant back to the god damn Indians. We can get along without that sort of business. Howie, does he really do that good work?"

Asche believed that Williams was one of the "sharpest" researchers that the hospital had ever trained. For a variety of reasons, however, Asche had decided that, "There is no permanent place for Williams in the Institute research organization." According to Asche, *he had already informed the researcher of this decision.* The reader should not forget this as he follows the subsequent transcript of the Asche-Suprin interaction. As far as Asche was concerned, the researcher had to go. In Asche's mind, the problematic question was one of *timing,* not one of eviction. He did not think the researcher was "ready" to go, and he did not want to be "hasty" about the eviction.

Asche was personally convinced that he would know when the time was right to "get rid of" the researcher, and he was confident of his ability to act appropriately when that time arrived. The reader will see, however, how this came across in the face-to-face interaction with Suprin. Suprin thought Asche was being "soft," and he pushed hard on the eviction issue, not on the timing one. That Asche had already *made* the eviction decision, and that he had been "tough" enough to tell the researcher that decision, went completely unrepresented in his observed interaction with his tough-minded superordinate.

Asche: "Well, he, uh. . . ."
Suprin: "Let him go. Did you know that he was trying to get into us for another $1,100? It's gotten out of hand now, if you ask me. Papa's got to get a hold of this: You're too nice, Howie."

As far as Asche was concerned, it was *Suprin* who had slipped up on control procedures, and had allowed the present problem to begin. This will be explained shortly. The point here is that he let this issue go.

Asche: "I'm very upset about this. I've. . . ."
"Yeah, I *know* you are," Suprin interrupted.

Suprin responded forcefully to this verification of what he perceived the problem to be. He went on to restate, reclarify and reinforce his interpretation of the crucial problem.

Suprin: ". . . You're too soft to tell the guy what he's got to hear."

Clearly, Dr. Asche had begun to respond in terms of the "soft" role-expectations that had just been strongly reflected upon him. In lifting up his feeling of being very upset, he validated Suprin's reification of him and lost the initiative he might have held. Dr. Asche continued according to the social definition of himself that he faced. It is important to point out that this was not only an externally imposed definition of his role. He genuinely *cared* for the well-being, the creativity, and the development of the researcher in question. This was not, however, the aspect of himself that he was failing to communicate to Dr. Suprin.

Asche: "I've tried hard to keep him going along, but it's got away from me somewhere."
Suprin: "I know, it's time to say, 'Take off!' "

The more disconsolate Dr. Asche became, the more assertive Dr. Suprin became. The last statement was delivered with such vigor that Dr. Asche aroused himself to set right a misrepresentation of his position that had gone beyond a limit acceptable to himself.

Asche: *"You're* the one that's soft. I told everybody not to give him a penny, but he came to you, and you said it was O.K. for him to spend all that dough."

There was much confusion about what had actually happened in the situation under discussion. Even the amount of

money involved in the illegitimate disbursements was difficult to ascertain. Quotations varied from day to day. The
interpersonal situation was even more indeterminate. From
Asche's point of view, it went something like this. When
Asche was away on vacation, Williams had seen Dr. Suprin
and told him that he needed expense money. He said that his
research grant was a sure thing, that the grant contract permitted reimbursement of whatever funds Suprin would let
him have in advance from Institute monies. Suprin agreed
to lend Williams the expense money he needed. Williams
then proceeded to spend about $3,000, apparently unknown
to Dr. Suprin. Dr. Asche stated that this would have gone on
had he not put a stop to it when he returned from his vacation. "I'm not going to bail him out," he said of the researcher. "He's going to pay back every damn cent, even if
we have to hold him personally liable."

The next day, the sum involved jumped up to $5,800. The
business officer discovered that $2,000 of overhead money was
also involved, plus some other, smaller expenditures that the
researcher had made. It was found that the research contract
in question specified that only $200 would be reimbursed for
expenses prior to the date of commencement of the contract.
"I'm going to get every penny back," Asche told the observer,
"even if I have to dig into Williams' pocket to get it."

The observer remarked that, "$5,800 is a lot of money. Do
you think you could get it from Williams if the [grant]
doesn't come through?"

"Yes, I know," Asche replied. "It's going to be difficult to
fix up. What I can't understand is how Frank [the superin-
tendent] and Francis [the business officer] let it get out of
control to this extent. I think *I* look after their research
money more than *they* do."

This was the background of the meeting, as far as Asche
was concerned. He tried to demonstrate that it was Suprin,
not he, who was soft.

Suprin did not argue the point. He changed it. He turned to an issue that he felt keenly, and that Asche knew he felt keenly.

Suprin: "It's not that, Howard. He told me that part of his grant was to make up for the money we would spend on him. HE LIED TO ME! [The emphasis was Suprin's.] He *lied* to me. That's why I say it's time for him to *take off*. I don't like to be LIED to."

The powerful forces surrounding this breach of under-standing, of working relations, organization structure, con-fidence, trust, and ethics had now been made manifest. Dr. Asche did what he could to fill that breach.

Asche: "Well, he tells me that [the granting agency] will pay us back, and that he has some sort of assurance they will do so, although he doesn't want to push them to get it down on paper, because they might find they can't do it."

After the meeting Dr. Asche told the observer that anyone who wanted to make a career of research at the hospital had to take into account Frank Suprin's opinion, and that the researcher in question certainly had not. "Did you notice what Frank had to say about Williams? He said, 'He lied to me!' That's the way to get yourself fixed around here. You really fix yourself if you do that sort of thing in this hospital." He went on to explain how important "financial respectabil-ity" was to Dr. Suprin in his capacity as fund raiser for the money that supported much of the hospital's extensive re-search program. "Smelly" financial deals that smacked of "double dealing" and manipulation always "panicked" Dr. Suprin, who was concerned that his reputation for scrupulous financial honesty remain unblemished.

Dr. Suprin was somewhat mollified by Asche's last comment.
Suprin: "O.K. You tell Colleen [a secretary], then, that he doesn't get a damn cent from us on anything till we get this

straightened out. Not a damn cent! On anything! I'd rather send him out, and send the grant back to the [grantor] than to go further into hock to him."

It was now obviously a matter of principle for Dr. Suprin. Perhaps Asche felt that, for this reason, Suprin was the one who should deal with the problem-maker. Perhaps he also felt that, since it was Suprin who had slipped up on the controls, it should be Suprin who tightened up on them. In any case, the reader can see how his following response again raised the issue as to who was tough and who was soft.

Asche: "Maybe you should talk with him and tell him that."
Suprin: "I've only one thing to say to him, just one. You want me to say it?"
Asche: "Well. . . ."
Suprin: "You talk it over with Francis [the business officer] and let me know. I've only got one thing to say to him: '*Out.*' Anytime you want me to say it, you just send him in. If you don't want me to say it, you better keep him away from me."

Thus, Dr. Suprin was again provided the opportunity to act assertively. Dr. Asche started to hang back, to the extent that Suprin changed his mind about letting Asche see Colleen. Suprin accompanied Asche to Colleen's desk, and there it was Suprin who "laid down the law" while Asche stood wordlessly by.

The Effect of the Subordinate Role Upon Superordinate Behavior

Suprin was his "old self" again: smiling, leaning back in his chair, one hand behind his neck, the other pointed toward the door of his office. If Asche inferred any insult to his own ability to handle his own subordinates, he did not give any indication thereof. He smiled and responded in relaxed joviality as both men left the office.

Asche and Suprin walked down the corridor to Colleen's desk.
Suprin: "Where's that stuff on Williams?"

Colleen reached into her desk and handed him a file. He picked
it up in one hand and laid the index finger of the second on it.
He tapped the file repeatedly with his finger as he spoke.

"See this?" he asked. Colleen nodded. "Not a penny. Not a
penny. Not one damn cent for this guy, unless Jim or I say so.
Otherwise, nothing, no matter what he says. Understand?" Colleen nodded. "O.K." He handed the file back to her and turned
to Asche. "There, that'll hold him. . . ."

It was clear the "that" which would hold "him" was Colleen.
She would be the one who, face-to-face with the researcher
(who was quite an imposing person), would have to be the
first to deny future requests. Once more Suprin was once removed from actual front-line interaction with the problematic individual. His toughness was symbolically being directed
toward the offender, but was actually being directed toward
those who were called upon to deal with the offender. His
parting interaction with Asche, made in the presence of a
third party, was of this nature. In this way it became potential grist for the mill of reification, staging a further performance of the relationship that existed between himself and
Dr. Asche.

". . . Any time you want me to tell him what I have to say,"
Suprin told Asche, "you just send him in to me. O.K.?"

Asche smiled and nodded, and the two men parted company.

Adopting Asche's *parlance,* the observer asked:

Observer: "Why not let Frank see him?"
Asche: "Frank wants to fire him."
Observer: "Why, do you not want that?"
Asche: "Nope. That would be too quick for [the researcher].
I can't do that to him. I've got a lot of feeling for the man. He's
got to go sometime, but Frank wants to fire him out the door
right away, and that's too quick. I want to talk it over with him
first."

The fact that Suprin had two subordinates—Asche and Cadman—who preferred to "talk it over first" before taking action provided Suprin with a psychosocial situation wherein he could give freer rein to his predisposition to act first and assess consequences later than might otherwise have been the case had his subordinates been equally or more action-oriented than he. Had his subordinates been as quick to act, or to transmit action down the chain-of-command, then events might have created and reflected back to Suprin the necessity of acting less rapidly and with greater perspicacity in his relations with his subordinates. As it was, Asche and Cadman cushioned some of Suprin's impact down the line.

Suprin did not have people fulfilling similar mediating functions between himself and salient representatives of the hospital's *external environment,* and the reader has seen how in such interactions Suprin reduced the assertiveness and increased the deference of his interpersonal behavior. But, being mediated in some of his relations *within* the hospital by Cadman and Asche, Suprin availed himself of the opportunities thus provided for his preferred style of open aggressiveness. Again, this was no secret to him. He was fully aware that he did so, and he enjoyed the situation.[2] It was one of the

---

[2] Suprin enjoyed talking about this aspect of his personality and role-behavior. He also liked to contrast himself and Dr. Cadman in this regard, and did so in a variety of settings within the hospital, thereby staging another facet of the executive role constellation before the audience of subordinates. For instance, during a meeting in his office attended by "the big three" and others, the following occurred.

Suprin: ". . . you've got to take into account differences in style. When Paul and I get mad, we go about it in a different way. It's usually me, but sometimes I hear Paul out there, going at it with Mrs. O'Toole, and I'm sitting in here all peaceful, and I wonder what in the world Paul is so excited about. When Paul gets really mad, then—what would you say, Paul?— In about 30 minutes (Cadman smiled)—he starts taking buckets of aspirins. Me, I feel great when I get mad. I only get to feeling bad, when, for political reasons, I. . . ."

Asche laughed: "You have to hold it in."

Suprin: ". . . I can't get mad."

reasons he enjoyed being "back home" at the hospital after a trip. Suprin was not, however, equally cognizant of the consequences that his role-demands had on those below him in the organization. He was in no position to know directly about such phenomena. Certainly no one came into his office to talk to him on such matters, and he did not go out asking. As a professional, Dr. Suprin entertained several good hypotheses as to the nature of the processes he initiated some of the time among some of his subordinates. But the data that substantiated these hypotheses, that made them more than mere hypotheses for those beneath him, were usually withheld from him.

The reason for this withholding was again twofold. Suprin's interpersonal reflexes discouraged such feedback. Also, interactors who were inclined to attempt the feedback of interpersonal data to Suprin soon learned concretely the validity of Cadman's simile about the fan.

Balancing Interpersonal Specializations in the Executive Role Constellation

Later in the day of the above interaction between Dr. Asche and Dr. Suprin, the two men met by chance in the hospital cafeteria. Without hesitation, Suprin continued the dialogue between them.

Suprin came by the cafeteria, and paused by the table where Asche and the observer were sitting. "You been thinking over what I said?" he asked Asche. "You going to send him to me?"

Asche laughed: "That's because you are so good at getting around the rest of us."

Notice that it was Asche who came the closest to raising the potentially explosive issues of (1) the dependency of Suprin's preferred mode of interpersonal behavior upon the adoption by others of complementary forms of role behavior, and (2) the real or potential incompatibility that Suprin thereby induced—and that others permitted to be induced—in "getting around" the preferred role behavior of these others. Cadman, for whom this induced role-incompatibility was less, remained silent.

Asche: "He's got to go. That's settled. It's a question of when. I want to talk it over with him first. It can't be too fast, on account of his health."

Suprin: "We don't want him doing research here. But of course we'll treat him if he gets sick." He smiled and left the cafeteria.

As far as Suprin was concerned, therefore, the problem and its resolution remained the same. Fiscal responsibility had been weakened, and would be restored and maintained through the firing of the transgressor. Further, Suprin's tacit assumption seemed to be that, of the two executives, he was the better equipped to take the requisite action. Also that Asche was "soft" to the extent that he must be prompted even to send the offender to Suprin, much less to fire him himself. Asche did not succeed in communicating to Suprin anything that modified Suprin's initial stand on the matter.

On the other hand, Asche did not change his response to the pressure Suprin put on him. There were many ways in which Asche experienced the problem that had arisen but after interaction with Suprin, one stance seemed to precipitate out from all the rest. Asche began to argue almost unidimensionally the needs of the individual whom Suprin wanted to fire. We are in no position to assess the merits of either man's stance, nor that of the alleged transgressor (whose case is not at all represented in the above material). Within the focus of this study, however, the above incident illustrated two important aspects of the executive role constellation.

(1) Organizationally, Suprin's primary role-orientation was outward, and Asche's was inward. In evaluating the problem, Suprin's fantasy audience consisted of representatives of agencies outside the hospital, while Asche's came to be the individuals working in his section of the organization.

(2) Interpersonally, in the objective then-and-there reality, the relative positioning of the two executives on the

power and instrumental-expressive axes of their subsystem was unequivocal. Although Asche professed basic agreement with Suprin as to what action was required, Suprin's assertiveness made clear that he did not consider himself in operational agreement with Dr. Asche. His assertiveness, though not his assertions, went uncontested by Asche. The disagreement that Dr. Suprin sensed arose from the discrepancy he perceived between himself and Dr. Asche in instrumental-expressive behavior. His conception of himself as "tough" and Asche as "soft" was differentiated to the extent that, in the above instance, he could not realistically entertain the notion that he and Asche *agreed* on the action required, much less that Asche could *take* the action that Suprin saw himself as proposing and Asche as resisting. Dr. Asche disagreed with this differentiation, but he did not contest it when face-to-face with Suprin. The superior-subordinate relation was thereby established two-dimensionally, according to the role-demands and role-expectations held by Dr. Suprin.

INTERPERSONAL REFLEXES IN MULTIPLE-ROLE SITUATIONS

WE NOW TURN to Dr. Asche's role performance in a wider interactive setting than that provided by his interactions "alone" with Dr. Suprin. We will find both similarities and differences in role performances before smaller and larger audiences. The similarities will be seen to relate to Asche's carry-over of certain self-deprecatory behavior from the more intimate to the more public settings in which he was observed. The differences will be seen to relate to an increased assertiveness and competitiveness that Asche manifested when his field of interaction increased beyond the limits of direct interaction with Dr. Suprin alone.

As in the analysis of Dr. Cadman's interactions, we shall again be looking for a modal type of response toward Dr. Asche by members of his organizational audience. We shall look for indications as to how Dr. Asche's audience conceived of him and his role in the organization, how they perceived and interpreted his role performances. Here we shall not be able to proceed as simply and succinctly as was the case for the modal response to Dr. Cadman and his role performance. There is something paradoxical in the above statement that Asche presented both self-depreciation and assertiveness to his wider audience. How can one be self-deprecatory *and* assertive, at least in a way that is sufficiently simple that one's audience can develop a workable conception of what sort of a person the actor is, and what he represents? That is the paradox that Dr. Asche tended to present to his audiences, and the difficulty they had responding thereto increases our difficulty in describing that response.

Organizational Marginality Induced by Professional Commitment

Important as teaching and research were in the hospital, there were occasions when issues of patient management predominated. When these issues became serious enough to rise up to the top level of the organization, it was Cadman and Suprin who transacted the resolution of the psychiatric and administrative problems involved. Such severe disturbances of the hospital's operations as a training and research center did not occur frequently. That is, they did not occur frequently enough to disrupt to any significant extent the hospital's over-all program of training and research. However, "crises" occurred often enough that the working relation between Cadman and Suprin was interactively closer—and perceived by others as closer—than that between Asche and Suprin. The reader will recall that Cadman thought of himself as No. 2 in relation to Suprin, No. 1. This conception was borne out by the observed facts of interaction and role performance at the executive level. When crises in patient management arose, all three of the executives assumed positions of differential closeness and distance. These relative positions were made manifest by the role performances that they enacted, without discussion, when crises arose.

In these situations, Dr. Asche behaved the role and assumed the position of No. 3 in the triad. This is illustrated in the following incident, which, though far short of a crisis, did involve patient management and the dynamics that have been outlined.

10:06 A.M. Dr. Cadman entered Dr. Suprin's office. Dr. Asche was standing by Suprin's desk, talking with him.

Cadman approached Suprin's desk. Asche and Suprin watched him approach. Asche interrupted his talk with Suprin.

At this point, Cadman reached Suprin's desk. No greetings were exchanged in any direction.

The situation was implicitly friendly. Indeed, the quietly businesslike atmosphere that developed seemed rooted in a common understanding and responsibility of all for getting the work of the hospital done. Asche's relinquishment of the stage to Cadman was performed spontaneously and without ado, as though none of them were actually thinking about what was going on. But the act of his relinquishment, and the factors related to that act, remained as a manifestation and reinforcement of the social system of the executive triad.

Cadman spoke to Suprin about a problem in staffing a course. Then he added, "That old man you mentioned [during their daily interaction around the morning reports]. He's a chronic brain syndrome."

Suprin asked a medical question. Cadman replied, then continued, "They are going to move him out to [another hospital].

"The trouble with [another patient, about whom Suprin had also inquired earlier that morning] is that his therapist went away on vacation."

Suprin: "Is he back now?"

Cadman: "Yes, but they still think that is the root of his prob-

lem. [The chief] assures me he is not drug toxic. I have asked him
to have [the assistant clinical director] check on the case."

Suprin: "Well, you ask [the assistant clinical director] to get
involved in that teaching endeavor [the course problem]."

Cadman: "I'll try." He turned and left the room.

Dr. Asche had taken a seat during the above conversation. As
Dr. Cadman left the room, Asche leaned forward and began his
conversation again with Dr. Suprin.

The reader will see that the closeness-distance issue was
more problematic for Asche and Suprin than it was for Cadman and Suprin. In the former relationship, closeness and
distance varied more widely from situation to situation, and
Dr. Asche's role performances varied correlatively. No stable
resolution of this issue was observed during the field work
period. The variability of Asche's role behavior made him a
more difficult person to "categorize," and thereby a more
difficult person for others to respond to in as simple and
unidimensional a basis as was the case *vis-à-vis* Suprin and
Cadman.

Organizational Marginality Through Role Performance

We shall see how this psychosocial situation was made manifest in still another interactive setting. In the following incident, the reader will note the following factors: (1) Asche's
assertiveness and competitiveness, particularly *vis-à-vis* Cadman, in situations where there were others besides Suprin to
interact with; (2) the comparative eclipse of Asche's assertiveness by that of Suprin; (3) Cadman's characteristic performance of defenselessness, and his use of defenselessness—
his "two cents' worth"—as the best defense; (4) the lack of
any clear response to Asche by group members, again as contrasted to the responses characteristically received by Cadman; and finally (5) Suprin's control and manipulation of
the closeness-distance variable as a reward-punishment device
for structuring the group around him, for guiding its direc-

tion and motivating its members. This last factor will be considered more fully in the next section.

Clinical research conference in Dr. Suprin's office. Those attending: Suprin, Cadman, Asche, Ginsberg, and Pomantzeff. At one point during the conference, the group discussed the pros and cons of using sound tapes to record transactional material for research into the process of psychotherapy.

Suprin: "When you get those things [therapy sessions, group meetings], you just get a room full of tapes. (To Cadman) You already have a room full of tapes. Have you done anything with them?"

Dr. Cadman was the subject of fond notoriety in the hospital for his habit of recording his interactions. He had accumulated a large collection of tapes that anyone could see who went into his office. Dr. Suprin quite often "kidded" him about this. In the above instance, the directly inquisitional approach was a bit more like an attack than a joke. Suprin seemed to have increased the distance between himself and Cadman.

Up to this point, Cadman had not participated in the discussion. He paused briefly to collect himself and respond to Suprin's sortie.

Cadman (pausing) : "Uhhh. Uh, my thought is that when you, uh, do not have tapes, you—ummm—do not have access to the, uh, original data."

Asche: "But what can you do with them? You can't get them typed. Girls that will type from tape are hard to come by. They *kill* a girl. You need some sort of scheme to handle data without putting them on tapes and having them transcribed."

Cadman's response was immediately challenged by Asche, who interacted to consolidate the strength of an opinion he and Asche knew they shared, thereby symbolizing his closeness and Cadman's distance to the No. 1 person in the group.

Suprin smiled. He appeared to be warming up to a good

fight after suffering through what had, to that point, been a rather dull meeting. He shifted in his chair, and glanced quizzically at Cadman, who had lit up another cigarette.

Suprin to Cadman: "That's right. You need an analytic scheme. When you record on tape, you just shift the problem from the meeting to the tape, and when you transcribe the tape, you just shift the problem from the tape to paper. But you haven't solved the problem yet of what you are going to *do* with that data." He smiled.

Cadman sat without replying.

Asche agreed with the content of the opinion Suprin had just expressed. But the forcefulness with which it was delivered was beyond the limit that Asche characteristically found comfortable. Perhaps he had not expected to find himself lined up so strongly "with" Suprin "against" Cadman. In any case, as Cadman's expected response continued not to be forthcoming, Asche quietly disassociated himself from the alignment of opinion.

Asche (pause) : "Well, I don't want to go too deeply into this. I'm cathected against tapes, that's all."

Suprin: "I know. And Cadman is cathected the other way. That's why I brought the issue up."

With this modification of the group's dynamics, Cadman replied.

Cadman: "I think we should tape *one* of the interviews. There are going to be ten of them. That's 10% at least."

Asche: "That makes me 90% happier than I was before."

Cadman to Asche: "I'm holding out to have *my* sessions taped." To Suprin: "I intend to put my patient on the couch, by the way. I'm going to record each session, and then program it."

Suprin (impatiently) : "What do you mean, *program* it?"

Cadman: "I'm going to go through the material and, uh, put symbols on all the important material, and then follow them through the sessions, uh, to see how they develop."

Asche: "That's a very time-consuming thing, tracing through all the interviews in which he mentions his mother, establish the context in which he thinks of her."

Cadman said something in a very soft voice to Suprin, ". . . through all this together," and the two of them laughed together.

Suprin (still smiling) : "What do you do with all those tapes, and all that typing? What do we have to show for it?"

Cadman: "We have some data that is to be surveyed."

Suprin: "Yes, but we spent $6,000 shifting the data from tapes onto paper, and we haven't done anything yet. You've just shifted the problem."

Asche to Cadman: "I want like a bastard to see something come out of it, but I just don't think that you're doing it in the right way."

Cadman smiled at Suprin: "I put in my two cents' worth," he said, "and that's it."

Asche and Pomantzeff turned to a discussion of various analytic schemes designed to handle group meeting material.

Asche (concluding) : "But Bales wouldn't mean a thing to Cadman. On the Cadman and Cape material, they worked on it for three years, and they still didn't bring it home."

Cadman: "That's where Cape and I parted company. He wanted to skim the material and write something up for publication, and I wanted to find out what was going on.

"But I don't want to hold up the meeting. I put in my two cents' worth."

Suprin: "You have taken the problem and moved it from a mass of tapes to a mass of paper. I don't think you are going to find out what's going on that way."

Pomantzeff: "Could you construct a scheme—a sort of checklist—and take notes during an interview? Or would this interfere with therapy?"

Cadman: "It would with the way *I* do therapy. I spend, at the most, 5% of my time in the interview thinking about myself. The rest of the time, I live it with the patient."

Another discussion ensued, this time about secretarial methods of transcribing data as they occurred. Ginsberg spoke enthusiastically to Suprin and Cadman about his fascination with steno-typing, and its possible applicability to the psychotherapy project.

Asche observed pointedly that this would require the retraining of all the therapists.

(Pause) Asche: "Well, that's Round 1 of the battle of the tapes." He smiled at Cadman. "The question really becomes whether it is sensible to do studies of therapists." He reviewed other studies on this topic.

Cadman: "The greatest confusion in therapy is in terms of styles. There is confusion about techniques, when the essence of the transaction is in interaction—process! What goes on!—and on that the literature is almost bare. Styles are almost incidental in terms of what they do that's the same—the *essence*."

Asche, Ginsberg, and Pomantzeff then returned to discussing research studies of psychotherapy. Suprin and Cadman exchanged glances, then smiled broadly at each other. The meeting continued.

Dr. Asche touched on one element in the dynamics of the group in referring to the "battle of the tapes." He had consolidated his position around his professional skills as a researcher, and Dr. Cadman had consolidated his position around his professional skills as a therapist. Dr. Cadman could no more construct "some sort of scheme to handle data" than Dr. Asche could "put my patient on the couch." Dr. Suprin shared in both positions and moved back and forth between the two as he considered appropriate for the task at hand, and also to have a little enjoyment in sparking the proverbial gap between researcher and clinician. His movements back and forth were balanced and controlled, but they seemed to demonstrate a greater closeness of task orientation to the researcher and a greater sense of personal closeness with the clinician. During the "battle," Suprin associated himself with the task recommendations of the researcher, Dr. Asche, and teased the clinician, Dr. Cadman, a little bit about his frustrating and endearing weaknesses in producing research. But when the "battle" was over, he and Dr. Cadman smiled affectionately at each other, removing themselves fleetingly but noticeably into a small private world of their own, leaving Dr. Asche to turn aside to continue his discussion of research with his subordinates.

CHAPTER 13

The Superintendent's Transactions Inside and Outside the Executive Role Constellation

IT IS CONVENTIONALLY EASY, polite, and comfortable to portray a man busily engaged in the work he loves, and for which he is respected. In this way, the individual is presented as he probably best likes to experience himself, living at the center of his personal universe. Especially when one is dealing with productive individuals, such a portrayal can hardly escape being, on balance, favorable to the individual. It is when an individual starts interacting with others that he comes to grief as well as to joy. The observer likewise comes to grief in the interactive setting, through the necessity of having to describe and analyze the interactor's defeats as well as his successes. To quote from Dr. Cadman in his professional rather than in his organizational capacity, "What troubles one human being is other human beings. Did you ever notice that? It's with other human beings that people get into difficulty." It was with something like this in mind that the text was organized to present, first, the positive and productive individual structures on which the executive role constellation was founded, and, following this, the rewards *and* punishments, the understanding *and* misunderstanding, the applause *and* insult that each individual experienced in the interactive setting.

So far the reader has seen many of the rewards and punishments experienced by the subordinate executives in the triad. How was it for the superintendent? In the section on Dr. Cadman's interaction with Dr. Suprin, the reader learned something about Dr. Suprin in interaction, both directly from the observational data and from what Dr. Cadman had to say about his own point of view. Dr. Suprin's propensity to take charge of and control people and events, and his role-demands as a decision maker, became apparent in these interactions. In the section on Asche's interaction with Suprin, we learned more about Dr. Suprin in interaction. In Suprin's interactions with Dr. Asche, his interpersonal manipulation of the closeness-distance, reward-punishment variables became evident. Suprin's interpersonal control was not based solely on the distance and punishment ends of these continua; he made significant use of both closeness and reward symbols in his interactions with Dr. Asche.

DYNAMICS OF SUPERORDINACY

IT IS EASIER to describe the subordinate roles than that of the superordinate. The reasons for this are worth noting because of their relevance for much-needed, though scarce, research on superordinacy. For one thing, the superintendent—like many people in top positions—was not given to the sort of talk that permitted as full an appraisal of his experience as was possible for his subordinates. At the verbal level, everything was "fine" for him. If there was a problem, it was somebody else's, or it existed in some specifiably objective condition in the internal milieu or the external environment of the hospital. Our analysis of his role thus involves greater inference than was required for Dr. Cadman or Dr. Asche.

A more fundamental source of difficulty is that most people have more experience in subordinate roles. Each individual has been more acted upon than acting during many stages of his growth. Each was an infant before becoming a child, a child before becoming an adolescent, and an adolescent before becoming an adult. Some persons never complete this evolution, remaining at a relatively childish or adolescent—thus "subordinate"—level of functioning. In the world of work, the individual must also be a "worker" before he becomes a "boss," and no matter how big a boss he becomes, he usually experiences the presence and the influence of still bigger bosses. Therefore, when faced with a situation in which he must interact with both a subordinate figure and a superordinate figure, he can more readily feel his way into the subordinate role. He has a greater knowledge-of-acquaintance as to what it feels like to be a subordinate than what it feels like to be a superordinate. He has no significant experience as a "big" superordinate until he has advanced to the position of social power where there are "little ones" around whom he can subordinate, and for whom he must carry superordinate responsibilities.

A research implication of the above is that it is harder for the researcher to identify with, and gain empathy for, the superordinate figure in any organizational setting being researched. Also, it is harder for the No. 1 man to communicate his experience, and his appraisal of that experience, since he may not yet be aware of significant dimensions of a relatively new life situation, or may not have been able to formulate any conclusions about the meaning of that situation for him.

Thus, we suggest that an understanding of Dr. Suprin's role must take into account both (1) his superordinacy inside the Institute, and (2) his subordinacy and dependency in relation to key extra-hospital figures who controlled the various resources Suprin needed. We shall consider these aspects in turn, and in relation to each other.

Dr. Suprin as the No. 1 Superordinate in the Organization

As superintendent, Dr. Suprin occupied the No. 1 authority position in the hospital. He fulfilled the guidance and control expectations associated with that position. On the basis of his own role-demands, he made his position of formal *authority* into the No. 1 *power* position in the organization as well. The dynamics of the executive role constellation sustained and enhanced: (1) his desire to realize the full potential authority of his position; (2) his desire to accumulate as full a measure of power as possible; (3) his desire to assert that power and authority; and (4) the interpersonal style by which he made those assertions in the context of administering the hospital. Specialized and complementary roles were ascribed to, and accepted by, members of the executive role constellation. Pressures were then brought to bear upon each actor, both by his audience and by himself, prompting each man to validate the uniqueness of his role through ever-increasing role specialization, and through even more dramatically unidimensional interpersonal role performances. Thus, the psychosocial situation that engaged Dr. Suprin as superintendent in the hospital actively facilitated his personal tendency to maximize his superordinacy to the limit permitted by the others who comprised his interpersonal environment.

Pressures were also brought to bear, both by the actor and by his audience, that hindered any stepping out of role on the part of the actor. This dynamic will be illustrated in the analysis of middle management meetings (see Part V). In the top executive context now being considered, any bid by Dr. Suprin to mitigate the superordinacy of his role behavior was met with resistance on all sides. There was little room in the tightly meshed, highly differentiated role constellation for "out of character" bids by Dr. Suprin or by anyone else. Expectations of "softness"—sympathetically supportive or casually equalitarian—were allocated and appropriated elsewhere in the role constellation but never to Dr. Suprin. Such behavior from Dr. Suprin elicited an undercurrent of embarrassment, and was usually avoided or transformed into a wisecrack.

Dr. Suprin as the Subordinate Articulator of His Organization into a Larger Societal Context

Dr. Suprin's interactions within the hospital were heavily influenced by his considerable involvement with outside persons and organizations. His power and authority inside the organization derived in large part from these external relations. Environmental agencies provided the sanctions on which his superordinacy in the hospital was based. His power to reward and punish the subordinate members of his organization depended on the resources he could mobilize from environmental sources. These he could offer or withhold from his "boys," according to his wishes and best judgments. His success at resource mobilization in turn depended on the effectiveness of his relations with the persons having control over the utilization of these external resources. It was with these people that Dr. Suprin interacted in a subordinate and dependent capacity. His interactions with external power figures were subordinate in the sense that he and the hospital were dependent on these figures for the resources at their command. This subordinacy was also related to interpersonal style, but in a secondary sense. We did not witness enough of these outward-oriented interactions to be able to analyze the dimensions of the difference between Suprin's interactions inside and outside the hospital.

Dr. Cadman phrased this issue in a more personal way.

"The whole thing can be put very simply," he said. "The top man in an organization has to have the capacity to love those he works with in an organization, and get his love elsewhere."

Observer: "Not from the others in the organization?"

Cadman: "No. There has got to be somebody to hate if things go wrong, and he's it. So he has got to get his love from somewhere else."

It would be inaccurate to state that Dr. Suprin received all his affectional rewards outside the hospital, and none inside. However, the above statement is accurate in that it symbolizes the predominance of rewards from outside the hospital in the inside-outside reward balance that Dr. Suprin experienced.[1] We did not observe how "much" reward Dr. Suprin received in his external transactions, or how much this reward exceeded that received inside the hospital. The whole problem of sociopsychological weights and measures is involved in this issue. But we did witness Dr. Suprin's behavior during a number of choice-point incidents, in which he had to decide whether to interact with insiders or outsiders. He consistently decided in favor of the *outsiders,* even when he did not like having to make the decision, or when his dislike for certain outsiders drove him to cursing privately to himself. The reader has seen several of these choices. For example, inside the hospital, "teaching is Dr. Suprin's first love." Yet, the pressure of external events drove Dr. Suprin to the point that, ". . . If things go on like this, I'm going to have to give up this teaching business." The decision-rule in such situations was obvious.

It was from this network of forces that Dr. Suprin's role as the hospital's "front man" emerged. But in this capacity Suprin felt the necessity of having the hospital back him up in his efforts on its behalf. If he went out "beating the bushes for money," then it was up to those in the hospital to maintain the standards of excellence that would facilitate his getting the money. If he was successful in his attempts to get money or to attract manpower, then it was up to the hospital personnel to perform their duties in such a way that future money and manpower would be insured. In this way the hospital was both the *recipient* of Dr. Suprin's successes and the *instrument* he used to achieve them.

[1] The statement is also accurate in pointing to the focal position of the No. 1 man in systems of displaced or projected anger. This will be gone into in Part V.

Anxiety over Controls

Since Dr. Suprin's successes were partly determined by what went on in the hospital, he often experienced considerable anxiety over problematic situations and events that came "accidentally" to his attention. He prided himself about knowing virtually everything he needed to know about what was going on in his hospital. Occasionally, situations of which he had no prior knowledge would be brought to his attention. In several instances these caused him to react so strongly that his response appeared to be inappropriate to the situation. Dr. Suprin manifested a fearfulness that expressed something of an illusion of chaos, as though everything he did not know about was going badly, and only he knew how to put it right. But he was in no position to exert direct control over the, to him, problematic situations. Therefore, he could only *insist* that others handle the situations in the way he wanted them handled.

These insistences were sometimes unrealistically unidimensional. In one instance it might be, "Now look here, the reason you people are in the hospital is to look after the needs of patients. Patients' needs come first around here, not administration. Now I don't want to hear any more of this crap about patients waiting on account of schedules." Or it might be, "I'm telling you that your first responsibility is to teach, and if you don't like to teach, you better get the hell out." Or, another occasion, "See here now. We can't have any more of this monkey business going on around here. We're going to set up a procedure and enforce it, and if people don't like it, they can leave." These outbursts fed into Suprin's customarily assertive and controlling behavior, and other people had difficulty separating the man from the situation. Dr. Suprin's performances triggered off responses in these others that were upsetting to the point where no clarifying attempt at restatement would be made in his presence.

He was thus usually left alone to guess at the consequences of his actions and at the actual status of the situation that was bothering him. This only reinforced his illusions of chaos—"Après moi, le déluge"—and his anxieties over control.

Controlling Others. One can only guess at the strain experienced by both parties when Dr. Suprin interacted with either of his two immediate subordinates in an attempt to achieve control over a situation in which neither was interactively involved. One of Dr. Cadman's attempted resolutions of this issue has already been quoted: "The only way to survive in this profession is to ask people to do only what you would do yourself, because that's the way it usually works out." However, neither he nor Dr. Suprin could realistically afford such a resolution. Both were in charge of getting too much done to be able to circumvent the necessity of working administratively with and through other people.

The reader has already been presented with several of Dr. Suprin's attempts at long-distance control over people and events in his hospital. The stressfulness of such efforts has been indicated in our earlier data on his interactions with Cadman and Asche. The stress for Asche in this respect has perhaps been conveyed more fully than that for Cadman. It should be added, therefore, that Cadman's position of having to mediate between Suprin and his clinical subordinates became so taxing for him that, near the end of the period of observation, Cadman decided that this position and its requisite role were no longer tenable. He altered the residency training program so that his service staff met in his office daily, instead of once a week. Dr. Suprin's presence at these meetings was requested. Thus in the future, when Dr. Suprin was in the hospital, he would be provided with more direct daily access to events in the hospital. Also, his demands and those of the service staff could be negotiated directly, without in-

volving Dr. Cadman so greatly in the process he often referred
to as "collective desperation."

Controlling Oneself. Instances have been presented in
which Dr. Asche or Dr. Cadman felt one way but acted another. Both these men provided information about the process they went through in controlling themselves in accordance
with situational role-expectations. With Dr. Suprin it was
somewhat different. Insofar as interpersonal and administrative processes were concerned, it was his game and he set the
rules. This meant that others had the basic choice of playing
according to Suprin's rules or leaving his team. If they
wished to remain on the team, they were required to adjust
themselves to the interpersonal rules of the administrative
game of running the hospital as Suprin wanted it to be run.

This situation was limited to the internal milieu of the
hospital. Outside the hospital, the game and the rules were
somewhat different for Dr. Suprin, requiring more adjustment and control of himself than was the case when he was
"at home" as superintendent. In the hospital his observed
tendency was to change and control his *situation* rather than
himself. This is not to say that his behavior was characterized
by any more *lack* of self-control than was observed of many
other staff personnel. It means, instead, that the "agonizing
reappraisals" of self, so frequent among Suprin's subordinates, were conspicuous in their absence from Suprin's management of his organizational and interpersonal superordinacy. If such reappraisals and readjustments of self existed,
Suprin kept them private and apparently away from the hospital altogether. One result was that Suprin's role performance
was almost "breezy" as compared with the more "heavy" performance of his immediate subordinates.

Inside the hospital Dr. Suprin appeared to act more the
way he felt and thought than did either Dr. Cadman or
Dr. Asche. Unlike the other two executives, Dr. Suprin pro-

vided no instance in which he chose to act in a manner incongruent with the feelings and judgments he had divulged to the observer either before an incident had begun or after it had terminated. Incongruities of this nature were observed a few times in Suprin's interactions with agents of the hospital's environment, but not with his subordinates. In the internal environment of the organization, Dr. Suprin's behavior was ego-syntonic. He was "open." If he experienced a feeling, a judgment, an opinion, a recommendation, a criticism, he let people have it. This was a characteristic of himself-in-relation-to-certain-others that he recognized, enjoyed, and fostered. In this self-perceptive and self-appreciative process, Suprin reinforced his ego-consonance, in that he had built up a "philosophy" that further prompted his openness and directiveness of expression in his interpersonal interactions in the hospital. The reader has already been introduced to this "philosophy."

The ego-consonance that was potentially available to Dr. Suprin in his position as No. 1, and that was kinetically actualized by his role-conception of that position, was demonstrated in part by the following, already quoted in Chapter 4.

Observer: "How do you feel about your position in this scheme of things? Do you like it?"

Suprin (smiling) : "Well, I guess you can say I fit into it. I'm sort of naturally inclined in that direction. At least you can say I can take it better than the other two [Asche and Cadman] could."

That is, Dr. Suprin experienced himself as more ego-syntonic in his person-position encounter than he felt his two closest administrative colleagues would be in an equivalent position.

The reader will notice the closeness of fit between Dr. Suprin's conception of the proper role of a No. 1 and his own personal tendency toward activity, decisiveness, and direct expressiveness. Also it is interesting to note his correlative incumbency in a series of No. 1 positions, prior to and including his superintendency at the Memorial Psychiatric Institute. It would appear that the No. 1 position in a purposive organization is one that facilitates ego-consonant activities in the person-position encounter to the extent that Suprin demanded it in his organizational behavior. Apparently Dr. Suprin recognized this quite early in his professional and administrative career because, according to his own report, he soon began planning and developing his career on the basis of the decision-rule of gaining the No. 1 position of an organization, and then, by making his "name," moving to increasingly better positions as No. 1 authority figure of increasingly better organizations. Insofar as Dr. Suprin preached the same career decision-rule to his subordinates-in-training, he appeared to be somewhat setting aside the realization that different personalities and different role-demands would require different decision-rules for optimum career development. For other people the person-position encounter as a big or little No. 1 would be different from what it was for Dr. Suprin.

Finally, the reader will notice the extent to which both Suprin's and Cadman's conception of the role of No. 1 emphasized the function of No. 1 as the ultimate organizational cynosure of the frustration and the aggression of the organization's members. Our observations indicate that this was an oversimplification of the reifications that were actually reflected back upon Dr. Suprin. It was also an oversimplification of the performances by which Dr. Suprin often linked up with many of "his" people in the hospital.[2] In both the

2 In this error of oversimplification, Suprin and Cadman were manifesting some of the dynamic consequences upon themselves as individuals of their membership in such a tightly meshed, complementary executive role constellation as the one that existed. In their relative positions in the love-hate axis of interpersonal expressiveness, and their complementary specializations around understanding-and-support vs. direction-and-control, it was almost a foregone conclusion that No. 1 was—"by nature"—a tough, frustrating con-

performance and the reflection aspects of this rotating self-other process, there was no small amount of warmth and affection, success and gratification. Suprin's involvement and participation in a situation often resulted in a larger measure of success and gratification than would otherwise have been the case. Suprin used his skills, his "name," and his position to "look out" for "his boys." Those who were "his boys" recognized and appreciated this; just as those who were not, did not.

Dr. Suprin experienced the giving and receiving of affection as more problematic than equivalent transactions around aggressive feelings. We have already seen examples of Suprin's manipulation of interpersonal closeness to, and distance from, those with whom he was interactively engaged. In comparing him once more with Cadman and Asche, Suprin's characteristic position on this variable was toward the "distant" extreme more than was the case for the other two. This distance was symbolized by the relative infrequency of affectionate expressiveness in Dr. Suprin's interactions. Paradoxically, he sometimes used aggression to symbolize closeness as well as distance. There were occasions when others did not find this form of closeness rewarding, so that the cyclical process of Suprin's distance from others tended to be mutually reinforcing.

Dr. Suprin was more effective at expressing his liking for an individual by "doing something" for him than by telling that individual about his feelings for him. In anger, he would often "tell off" somebody and then do nothing against

---

troller who elicited hostility and aggression, and who had to get his love outside the boundaries of the organization. No. 2 was "by nature" full of love and loved in return. Neither Cadman nor Suprin ever spoke of the affection that Suprin expressed and received—it was Asche who remarked on this— or the aggression that Cadman expressed and received. For Suprin and Cadman the alternative arrangement of a soft No. 1 and a tough No. 2 was not even worth mentioning. Again, it was Dr. Asche, the "in-between" man, who once mused about the dynamics of this alternative structure.

that individual administratively unless there was some history of antagonism involved. But in affection, he would often do something administratively to help an individual without getting into any exchange of feelings on the matter. As superintendent and as a "name" in psychiatry, Dr. Suprin was in an excellent position to express his affections in this way. Once again, the opportunities of position and the dynamics of personality acted in tandem.

CHAPTER 14

The Interpersonal Dynamics Underlying Role Constellations

IN FRANK COPLEY's biography of Frederick W. Taylor—"the father of scientific management"—considerable attention is given to Taylor's growth and development as an administrator.[1] In the course of this analysis, Copley quotes George Bernard Shaw:

> Every man whose business it is to work on other men, whether as artist, politician, advocate, propagandist, organizer, teacher, or what not, must dramatize himself, and play his part.

The three executives of this study, each in his dual capacity as administrator and psychiatrist, were certainly among the ranks of men "whose business it is to work on other men." Setting aside the imperative intent of Shaw's statement for the time being, all three executives were observed regularly, with varying degrees of frequency, to be dramatizing them-

---

[1] This biography portrays graphically but atheoretically the interactions of one man's personality with his social and technological environment. The outcomes of this particular encounter are a matter of record, insofar as the culture of modern industrial management is concerned. The social psychological dimensions of Taylor's life are surprisingly represented. See particularly, Book I, "Ancestry and Boyhood," and the following sections of Book II, Sections IV & V, "His Success as a Subordinate"; Section VI, "His Executive Temperament"; Section VII, "His Fight with His Men"; and Sections VIII & IX, "His Hold Upon His Men." All these are in Vol. I of Frank Barkley Copley's, *Frederick W. Taylor: Father of Scientific Management.* 2 vols., 1923.

selves in their administrative and professional capacities before the audience of their colleagues and subordinates in the
hospital. They were quite obviously happiest and "at their
best" during successful self-dramatizations before responsive
audiences; that is, (1) before audiences who interpreted each
executive's symbolic communications of self and role along
the lines intended in his communication, and (2) who also
responded in ways that demonstrated to the actor a consensus
of understanding, appreciation, and support for the self and
the role he was portraying.

INDIVIDUAL ROLE DYNAMICS IN ORGANIZATIONS

SELF-DRAMATIZATION is only part of the model being presented here. Self-dramatization is embodied in role performance, and role performance influences many people besides
the actor. Many meanings can be, and usually are, ascribed to
a performance intended by a person to be communicatively
symbolic of a particular self he wishes to portray, or of a particular role he wishes to play within the boundaries of a given
social system. Perhaps only in simple systems, as for instance
in a primary group, can one expect to find others responding
to one's performance primarily in the terms intended by the
actor. One reason for this may be that the actor has learned
to behave according to the "persona" and the role-expectations that the others in the tightly knit group ascribed to him.
In larger, less stable, higher dissensus groups, one's portrayal
of self and role has presumably a much smaller probability of
successful communication. What one does in the face of such
a situation is a topic that has hardly been touched by research
except in situations of extreme stress or deprivation.[2] Will
the individual act on the environmental social system to increase his probabilities of successfully disseminating his
propaganda about himself? Or, will he act upon himself, his
self-concept, and his role-demands to bring these more into

[2] See B. Bettelheim, *op. cit.*

line with the discordant "persona" and role-expectations that he perceives being reflected back upon him? What psychological and sociological forces are related to a person's choice among such alternatives?

Insofar as our research is concerned, the boundary of these processes is that of the organizational system. Within the boundaries exists "the universal presence [in small groups] of two axes of differentiation, namely an hierarchical axis of relative power and an instrumental-expressive axis." [3] The boundary denotes the fact that every individual whose linkage with a purposive social system is being analyzed also occupies a position in the power axis of the total group, and a position in its axis of instrumental or expressive role specialization. It denotes that individuals can be ranked according to their differential positions on these axes. "More specifically, the hierarchically uppermost part of the structure, the 'leadership' part, involves *both* predominantly instrumental and predominantly expressive roles; it has a dual character." [4] In other words, the self-other relations among the executive leadership of the hospital, that are our prime concern here, do not take place in an organizational vacuum, as is often inferred from microscopic interpersonal analyses that never reach the larger level of collective generality.

Each individual member of an organization has a personality system. The nature of the personality system, and its development, have been outlined in Chapter 2. We are concerned here primarily with the structure of needs, values, and self-concepts. For purposes of the present discussion, the personality has been schematically reduced to these components. We recognize that many important dimensions of personality have thereby been omitted.

The three interpersonal processes we are concerned with

[3] T. Parsons and R. F. Bales, *Family, Socialization and Interaction Process*, 1955, p. 355.
[4] *Ibid.*

are: (1) the *role performance* (self-dramatization) process; (2) the *reification* process, whereby a modal "persona" and a modal set of role expectations are formulated for a given individual by the members of his social environment; and (3) the *reflection* process, whereby "the chickens come home to roost," so to speak. That is, the individual receives back from the members of his social environment, (3a) confirmation of certain self-concepts and role-demands, (3b) violation or disregard of others, and (3c) indications that he is seen in ways, and is expected to behave in ways, he may not even have thought about prior to a given "notification" by some incident or person in his environment. The individual's ability to perceive the goings-on of this reflection process depends on the functioning of the defenses built into his personality system. His willingness to *act* according to the messages that he does receive is partly a function of his hierarchical position in the organization. Presumably, a superordinate's reflections upon his subordinate prompt the latter toward greater action than do the reflections of the subordinate upon the superordinate.

The individual's conceptions of himself, his thoughts, feelings, and aspirations, usually cluster in more than one configuration. An identity structure is not a totally integrated, monolithic entity. Presumably some relation exists between the several differentiable conceptions of self and role definition, but that in itself is a subject of considerable speculation and investigation. The point here is that an individual is usually trying to portray more than one self, and is usually trying to define more than one role for himself within an organization. For instance, he may wish to appear to be a "good listener," an "incisive thinker," and a "good decision maker." Or he may wish to appear to be a "sweet bastard." Such role definitions are not mutually exclusive, but the relationship between them is problematic for the audience, if not for the actor.

Of the several selves that an actor is communicating, there are some that he is fully aware of and wishes to communicate. Of these, some may exist in firm interrelation with his basic needs. Other self-concepts may be ascribed to him, which he has learned to value—being, for instance, "an all 'round good fellow"—but they may have little or no foundation in the unconscious structure of his personality.

Certain aspects of a person's role definition may be communicated at a preconscious level, without awareness of what one is doing and how one is being received. Depending on the strength of the person's defenses, and on the forcefulness of the reflection process, the individual may slowly become partly aware of certain ways his behavior prompts other people to see him. These are probably conceptions that already existed at a relatively high level in the actor's preconscious, that perhaps occurred to him fleetingly and fragmentarily in the past, but never with the unavoidable clarity forced on him in a given reflective incident. He then may choose to learn something about himself, to play down the stimulus behavior on his part, or to live with the interpersonal consequences thereof.

There may also be certain configurations of feeling, thought, and action of which the individual is completely unaware. These are seen as originating primarily in the unconscious forces of his personality. In his behavior, he is likely to communicate these dispositions in many small ways. He "gets it across with his eyes," or by a gesture or mannerism, the significance of which is not clear either to himself or to many members of his audience. Something in his performance makes his audience uncomfortable, restive, ill-at-ease. This edginess reflects back upon him, perhaps because his audience has been sufficiently distracted by his latent communications that they have not been able to attend to his manifest communications. All he and they know is that something is "wrong." A sense of the uncanny emerges. The manifest agenda lapse. The latent agenda become active but remain covert, repressed by the strength of the actor's and the audience's defenses against the intrusion of powerfully destructive or erotic themes.

Two other sets of variables intervene between performance and reflection. On the side of the individual, there is the mediation between the several segments of his self-concept as he strives for a sense of identity that is consistent within itself and in stable relation with his unconscious needs. On the side of the organization, there is what we have called the reification process. The individual broadcasts the story of himself and his desired roles to any number of others in the organization. What they do with that information, either singly or together, is beyond the actor's control. The developmental ascription of a modal "persona" and a modal set of role-expectations for the actor-referent is determined partly by the projections, the displacements, and the vested interests of these others, as well as by their realistic assessment of the individual. This assessment is influenced by the actor's immediate social context, by the "company he keeps," as much as by anything he might do or not do.

This process has been termed *reification* in that the members of the actor's audience take the unavoidably fragmentary data provided to them by the actor, or obtained through the "grapevine," and build a conception of the way "that man" is, and the way he should behave. These others then typically act as though this conception were the reality. Indeed it is as close to the reality as they will get. Interacting on this basis, they then create a certain "autonomous" reality around that modal "persona" and set of role-expectations ascribed to the actor. The reified "persona" may have great or little validity. It may be accepted or approved in varying degrees by the reified individual. Even in those instances in which the actor rises to do battle with this *conversion of an abstraction or mental construction into a supposed real thing,*[5] he is resisted in his attempts to do so. "My! Isn't he acting strangely today. I wonder what's got into him. That's not like him at all." And to varying degrees, each individual comes to believe that abstraction about himself and attempts to integrate it into his own identity structure.

THE INTERLOCKING OF INDIVIDUAL ROLE DYNAMICS IN CONSTELLATIONS

IN OUR VIEW, the above presents the form of the dynamics every individual initiates and becomes involved in as he goes about the business of establishing himself as a figure in an organization. The substance of these dynamics would, of course, depend on the particular nature of the individual and the organization with which he was interrelating. Individual role dynamics do not necessarily interlock to form role constellations. Such group outcomes are dependent on the persons involved. As we have indicated, persons with unspecialized roles, or with specialized but undifferentiated roles, or with specialized and differentiated roles that lack complementarity, would tend not to form role constellations as we currently understand them.

However, we believe that common observation will reinforce what much organizational research has already indicated; namely, that people tend not to work as solitary individuals in organizational settings. First, people tend to get assigned to formally defined aggregates of individuals that prompt the interlocking of roles. Second, work tends to bring a person into contact with some but not with others in the organization. Such required interaction [6] also prompts the emergence of interlocking roles. Third, on a more personalistic basis, the individual tends to work most closely with those with whom he feels most compatible, with whom he

[5] This is the Merriam-Webster definition of "reification." See Webster's *New Collegiate Dictionary*, 1956, p. 713.

[6] G. C. Homans, *The Human Group*, 1950, Chapters 5 and 6.

can "be himself" with minimal fear of misunderstanding, disdain, and other more organizational repercussions. Sometimes this third tendency works together with the first two, to produce a strong, almost palpable, set of interlocking roles, as in the executive role constellation of the M.P.I. In other situations, these personal relations operate across organizational divisions, resulting in interdepartmental "grapevines" that can never operate with the full force of an organizationally legitimate structure such as the executive role constellation of this study.

The *structure* of the executive role constellation consisted of the specialization, differentiation, and complementarity among the individual roles of the three members. The *dynamics* of the constellation were provided by the performance, reification, reflection, and response processes outlined above. Individual personalities were assigned to organizationally juxtaposed positions. Further, the work of these individuals brought them into close contact, at least insofar as each of the subordinates interacted frequently and sometimes intensely with the superordinate. Each individual performed a specialized role. These roles were initially somewhat differentiated from each other. This differentiation was both symbolically meaningful and organizationally useful; thus it tended to be reinforced and further developed during the existence of the constellation. Relations of trust and respect existed and developed among the executives, based largely on their professionalism. This facilitated the development of complementarity among their organizational roles, whereby cooperation was maximized and competition minimized among them. Over time, the role differentiation induced in the constellation—and we shall see some of this in Part V—tended to move organizationally expected roles further and further toward the limits of personally acceptable role performances. This caused strains within the constellation that were terminated, in part, when outside events brought about the departure from the constellation of one of its members.

Now, having summarized the development, structure, and dynamics of the executive role constellation, we turn, in Part V, to an analysis of the impact of the constellation upon the executives' subordinates. This analysis will demonstrate some of the organizational pressures that proved the major burden of membership in the constellation.

PART V. THE CONSEQUENCES OF THE EXECUTIVE ROLE CONSTELLATION

Subordinates' Response to, and Reinforcement of, the Constellation

THE INITIAL DEVELOPMENT of the executive role constellation has been described in Part III. The dynamics of the executives' role relations, presented in Part IV, contributed both to a maintenance and to a modification of the constellation. They were rooted in the way each executive saw himself as a person and what he was trying to accomplish with his life, both personally and professionally. At the same time, each executive found himself in a network of administrative and interpersonal transactions that had a social reality partly independent of the personal reality that he contributed to it. This social reality was an important part of the total managerial situation facing the executives, individually and collectively. That constellation served both to help and to hinder them in their day-to-day work.

In Part V we shift our focus from (1) the internal structure and dynamics of the constellation, as presented in Parts III and IV, to (2) the impact of the constellation on the organization, and its reciprocal effect on the constellation. The main thrust of our study was toward the internal structure and dynamics of the constellation. Our examination of the mutual impact of the top echelon constellation and the middle echelon professional staff was of secondary importance in this study. Yet it became clear that the functioning of the constellation could not be fully understood without reference to the manner in which it influenced the organizational behavior of subordinates, and to the influence this behavior had when reflected back upon individual members of the constellation.

We turn, therefore, to the relationship of the executive group to subordinates within the medical chain of command in the organization. These subordinates comprised the middle management group in charge of administering the inpatient clinical services. This group consisted of the assistant clinical director, Dr. Ackroyd; the service consultants, Drs. Stanley, Stearns, Steinberg, and Schneider; and the chief residents, Drs. Clark, Chapin, Carver, Cardinale, and Conn. The chief residents were advanced residents, training in psychiatry at the Institute. They were in charge of the day-to-day operation of the services. The service consultants were more experienced psychiatrists on the staff of the Institute who supervised service management on an advisory basis. They reported to the assistant clinical director, who in turn reported to Dr. Cadman.

Chapters 15 and 16 present two critical episodes in the administration of the Institute's clinical inpatient services. Each episode involved a sequence of transactions that implicated all levels of the clinical staff hierarchy, from the clinical director down to the chief residents on each of the Institute's service units. These two chapters demonstrate the subordinates' reifications of executive figures in the interactive context in which those reifications were built up and took effect. In Chapter 17 we formulate the symbolic meanings assigned to the executives by their subordinates and offer a more generalized theoretical view of the processes involved.

Part V will show: (1) the symbolic meanings that subordinates in general tended to attribute to the individual figures within the executive role constellation; (2) the way in which the middle management group in particular responded to the constellation; (3) how the response of this group reinforced the structure of role differentiation among the executives in the role constellation; (4) how executives' attempts at role flexibility, such as they were, were thereby restricted; and (5) how this influenced administrative relations in the services.

CHAPTER 15
Critical Episode I
Subordinates' Wishes for a Militant
Leader Are Frustrated

THE FOLLOWING EPISODE was construed by the staff officers of the inpatient services as an attack against them, as an impugnation of their professional abilities, an invasion of their administrative privacy, a threat to their authority, a disruption of their services, and a breach of their established roles in those services. They believed that this attack against them had little or no basis in clinical fact, arising more from personal motivations and intergroup jealousies than from any rational assessment of conditions on their wards.

Of course, this was not the way the principal instigator of this incident viewed the matter. Dr. Bolen, the director of one of the Institute's outpatient clinics, felt that he was engaged in an honest and straightforward attempt to improve patient care. His primary concern, as he saw it, was to insure that patients who were to become his executive responsibility got the caliber of professional care and treatment that he considered necessary for the proper discharge of his responsibility. All patients of a certain type were the responsibility of his clinic, wherever they were housed in the facilities of the Institute. Certain information had come to Dr. Bolen's attention, both directly and from members of his clinic staff, concerning the care and treatment of "his" patients by residents on the inpatient services. Dr. Bolen concluded that there were deficiencies in the management of that category of patients in the hospital. He acted to achieve the standards of professional treatment he considered necessary, and to maintain such standards through closer supervision by qualified members of his own staff.

This chapter will deal with: (1) the precipitating event; (2) the attempt on the part of Dr. Cadman's subordinates to mobilize a counterattack against Dr. Bolen and his subordinates; (3) the failure of this attempt; and (4) the resultant containment of aggression within Dr. Cadman's group.

THE PRECIPITATING EVENT

THE PRECIPITATING EVENT took place in Dr. Suprin's office, during a meeting of the medical executive committee. Dr. Bolen had planned beforehand to make an announcement about certain arrangements he was formalizing, so that members of his staff might better supervise the care and treatment of certain patients on the house services. He had discussed this with Dr. Suprin before the meeting began, and it was with Suprin's knowledge and approval that he proceeded. Bolen's remarks are quoted at some length, since the *manner* in which he presented them became as important as—if not more than—their *substance* to the resultant dynamics within the house staff group.

The group assembled in Dr. Suprin's office. Dr. Bolen interrupted the initial chatter with, "I have an announcement to make, and it will take about five minutes." He then proceeded to outline certain changes in the staff of his unit. After that, he spoke of the displeasure in his clinic about the care and treatment of certain cases in other parts of the Institute.

". . . and another thing. The clinic is displeased with the way certain cases have been handled on the services. Decisions pertaining to the management of these patients are being made by people with inadequate training, or no training at all, in our field of . . . psychiatry. Therefore, from now on the clinic will be assigning a member of its staff to each service. This clinic representative will be in charge of maintaining the level of care and treatment of the patients on each service, up to the standards of our unit. In addition one senior person in the clinic will always be on call, in case of emergencies. The men are to be in a supervisory and a consultative role on five services, wherever such patients are assigned. They are responsible for everything," Dr. Bolen said with great emphasis, looking around the group quickly. "Rounds, supervision, everything." He paused to get his breath back.

The group sat in silence.

Bolen continued: "That brings up a criticism I have of the residents . . . (Pause) . . . that I might as well make here," he added with a smile. "The second-year residents don't take on two treatment cases in their second year, and most of them don't take on any treatment cases *at all!* I am surprised at the freedom that the residents have in selecting their cases. I had a resident in my office the other day who had the *gall* to say he wouldn't take on a case because it wasn't a good psychiatric case! What's a good psychiatric case? What do the residents mean by the term, 'A good psychiatric case'? How would they know what a good psychiatric case *is*, from their limited experience? But they won't take on anything but good psychiatric cases, and even if you convince them to take one on, they only do so grudgingly."

Bolen: "If you are lucky enough to be able to get them to take on 'poor' cases, then you can be sure you are going to get poor records on the case, or *no records at all*. Poor records are quite the usual thing. I've been shocked by the condition of the records on some of these patients. Either there is nothing at all in the file, or else there are a few sketchy notes. Then when they come in to me for supervision, like as not they will amble in with their hands in their pockets—no notes, nothing—and just start talking to me about the case. Now I don't call *that* supervision. I call it a . . . uh . . . a chat, and I've made it perfectly clear that when they come to me for supervision, they are to come with a complete record. I go through the record, and then we discuss the patient. That is supervision."

The theme that was soon to emerge among the midlevel house staff was that of *injury, justification, and retaliation*.

Certain allegations had been made, and certain situations brought to light, that reflected poorly on Dr. Cadman's effectiveness as an administrator. Dr. Cadman was capable—more capable than many—of living with whatever aspersions were being made against him personally. He was content to hold himself out of the interchanges that were taking place, preferring to strive for a clarification of the organizational situation rather than for personal vindication. His subordinates, however, felt less ready to live under the cloud of negative implications that involved them directly, as the administrators immediately in charge of patient management on the services, and indirectly as Cadman's subordinates. They tended to want both a clarification of the organizational situation *and* a vindication of their professional capacities which had been challenged by Dr. Bolen's "charges." They wanted Dr. Cadman to spearhead their attempts to get both.

To return to the meeting that precipitated Critical Episode I, Dr. Bolen had one further statement to make before his announcement was complete.

Bolen: "I know the residents have a great load to carry. That's one of the troubles of this place. They are let to do what they want, and the first thing you know, they are into everything. Hopelessly overextended. I know they are busy—they are not lazy people—but are they busy doing the right things? Does anyone know that? Does anyone know how they spend their time? Does anyone check?"

Drs. Cadman and Ackroyd replied, almost inaudibly, that the service consultants did something of that sort in the house, but that they did it on their own initiative, and for their own purposes.

"Do you know what the results are?" Bolen asked Cadman.

Cadman shook his head, indicating that he did not know.

"Well, *I* check on how each one of my staff spends every hour of their day," Bolen stated. "I do this several times a year. My staff are accountable to me for every hour of their work day. What they do, they must do with my knowledge and approval. How else am I supposed to know what's going on? I'm responsible for the standard of training given in the unit, and I mean to see that everyone who comes to our unit for training measures up to that standard. How else am I supposed to know that a person isn't branching off into some minor interest of his, and becoming prematurely specialized, and never finding out what his areas of weakness are? I have a responsibility. . . ."

Dr. Bolen leaned back into his chair and glanced around the group with a smile. "I just wanted to tell you," he said.

There was a silence, during which Dr. Bolen extracted his pipe and a tobacco pouch from his pockets, and began methodically to fill the pipe.

Episode I had now been set fully in motion. Even in the exchanges that immediately followed Dr. Bolen's remarks there were indicators as to the course of subsequent events within the house staff group.

. . . Dr. Ackroyd, "Did you say that each man would be assigned to a ward, or to a service?"

Notice that it was again someone other than Dr. Cadman who pressed Dr. Bolen for clarification. This time it was Dr. Ackroyd, Dr. Cadman's immediate subordinate in the house, whose wish to rebut Dr. Bolen was about to go unsupported by his superordinate, both in this meeting and in the future course of events in Episode I.

Bolen: "Did I say ward? I'm sorry, I mean service."
Ackroyd: "Will these people have the status of service consultants?"

This was the first manifestation of the house staff's preoccupation with the status arrangements implied by the setup Dr. Bolen had just announced. This preoccupation was to grow and develop, and become almost endlessly elaborated as the consequences of Bolen's announcement worked their way through the house group. Preoccupations with status were expressed more frequently than were concerns for the caliber of treatment given to the patients in question. This is not to say that such concern for treatment did not exist. Rather, the status preoccuptions that were dwelt on repetitively in Dr. Cadman's presence and elsewhere constituted an indirect request to Dr. Cadman to step in and straighten out these relationships that Bolen's interventions were seen to jeopardize. Dr. Cadman did not do this. Instead, he prompted his subordinates to work through their feelings of jeopardy, in order to establish better working relations with the clinic representatives and to insure the caliber of future care and treatment of all patients.

Dr. Ackroyd's question received scant attention from Dr. Bolen.

> Bolen: "How should *I* know? I'm not in the house. That's your problem. That's for you to work out. All I am concerned about is that the patients get the standard of care that we in the clinic are responsible for. These men [representatives] will be there [on the services] to see that they get it. I expect them to be consulted on all matters pertaining to the care of [these] patients."
>
> Ackroyd nodded. "I see," he replied quietly.
>
> (Silence) Bolen lit his pipe.
>
> After a pause Dr. Suprin shifted in his chair, sat up and said, "Let's move on . . . [to the other topics on the agenda]."

Already in Episode I the defensive position of the house had been established. It had been placed on the defensive partly for whatever objective reasons underlay the dissatisfactions expressed by Dr. Bolen, and partly because of the nature of Dr. Cadman's response to Bolen and the situation. The subordinates were about to make a half-hearted attempt to work their group out of this position and to elicit Dr. Cadman's leadership in doing so. This attempt was to fail. Despite the subordinates' wishes for success, they expected their venture to fail. Their anticipation of Dr. Cadman's refusal to counterattack contributed to their own dispirited and disorganized response to Dr. Bolen's challenge.

THE ATTEMPT BY SUBORDINATES TO MOBILIZE A COUNTERATTACK

IT WAS NOT LONG before the repercussions of this medical executive committee meeting began to be observable throughout the staff hierarchy in the house. The very next day the service consultants and the assistant clinical director met together for one of their regular weekly meetings. The topic of discussion was Dr. Bolen's pronouncement, and the changes his plans would make in the organization and operation of the house. The initial response was basically a rational consideration of the new setup and its implications for the clinical administration of the services. Along with this, there was manifest a certain amount of working through of feelings in order to come to closer grips with the actual changes that were taking place, or were about to take place. There was also a mobilization of efforts to gather factual information into symbolic weapons to be used in counterattacking the "enemy."

The day after the precipitating event, there was no uncertainty among the midlevel house staff as to what would be the topic of conversation. The meeting came right to order.

Ackroyd: "Yesterday's medical executive committee meeting was really something. Bolen really took off at the services for their handling of his patients."

Steinberg, in a loud voice, "What's wrong with our handling of his patients?"

Already the fight modality was beginning to make its presence felt. Dr. Ackroyd demurred, not wanting to get hung up on it right from the start, preferring instead to complete the exposition of the situation before reacting to it.

Ackroyd: "I don't know. I wasn't there for the whole meeting, but whatever it was, it wasn't up to the clinic's standards—whatever they are—and he [Bolen] means to see that there is no more of it. The arrangement he has made is that someone from his staff is to be assigned to each of the services, to supervise the handling of the . . . patients. It's just going to add still another person to the staff of each service. Lord knows we're crowded enough already. The point I want to make clear to you, though, is that *they are not under you.* They are *not* under the service consultants."

Schneider, who had arrived late at the meeting, asked, "You mean they don't come to us if there's trouble?"

Ackroyd: "That's what I'm saying."

Schneider: "You sure?"

Ackroyd: "The impression I got was that these new people would be co-equal with the service consultants, sort of a second consultant in charge of [particular] patients."

Stearns: "That's great! That's all we need. Two consultants on each service, as if I didn't have enough troubles as it is. Now Bolen has to do this!"

Schneider: "You sure you got it straight?"

Ackroyd: "I can only say what I heard! I may be wrong about them being co-equals with you service consultants, but I know for a certainty that they are above the level of chiefs [chief residents], and therefore you can't behave toward them as though they reported to you. There's no misunderstanding about *that,* so far as I can see."

Schneider: "Who do they report to?"

Ackroyd: "I don't know. I didn't dream up this harebrained scheme." He talked quietly [in a simulated aside to himself]. "Buncha prima donnas over there, that's what they are. I've never seen such a collection of prima donnas. Bolen reports to Cadman. [This is the way the relationship was indicated on the table of organization.] It should be Cadman who tells *Bolen* what to do!"

This last statement was an expression of a basic wish that, remaining unfulfilled in the course of subsequent events, added to the general level of frustration and upheaval that ensued. Although the participants in this series of events also expected nothing other than what occurred, the frustration of the unfilled wish expanded the aggressive force that could not be vented against the external "enemy," but had to be contained within the group, with occasional outbursts against each other and Dr. Cadman.

Ackroyd continued: "Never seen such a bunch of prima donnas. Perfectly ridiculous!" He stopped himself [as though remembering where he was and the nature of his formal relations with his audience]. He sat up in his chair and said, "Oh, well, enough of this idle speculation." He returned to Dr. Schneider's question. "To Dr. Bolen, I suppose," he replied.

Schneider: "Oh great." He groaned.

Steinberg: "It *stinks!*"

Stearns: "I can't get over the feeling that it takes away from our jobs to have someone like that assigned to our services with us. It makes our jobs smaller, not to say more complex. It's just another person to bump into in all the administrative decisions. Do we consult with these new persons about Bolen's patients, or does his representative make all the decisions?"

Ackroyd: "I don't know. You'll have to work that out with whoever is assigned to your service."

Stearns: "Another thing I can't understand is how they [1] ever agreed to assign a person to the service who has so little service perspective. The clinic has no concept of the service at all. All they care about is their few patients on the ward. They don't know about the service as a whole, and they don't care. I can't see assigning a person like that to a position of authority over the service. Can you?"

Ackroyd shrugged. "It's hard to understand," he said. "Anyway, I want it to be clear that as far as I know, you do not *outrank* the new clinic representatives. If it comes to a question of disagreement with these people. . . ."

[1] In situations such as this, the organization was made up of *they's*. Everyone outside one's immediate circle of working relations was one of *them*.

Fighting words and fighting concepts began to creep into Dr. Ackroyd's remarks.

". . . I'll support you every time. I want you to know that. We have to stick together and make the best of it with these outsiders. Bolen's charges came out of the blue. . . ."

The sense of injustice that pervaded the whole incident, as the house staff experienced it, began to make its presence felt in the meeting. It led to a statement by Dr. Ackroyd that came as close to implicating Dr. Cadman in the desired counterattack as was observed throughout the rest of the incident.

". . . I've talked with Dr. Cadman," Ackroyd continued, "about getting organized to rebut Bolen's accusations. . . ."

This may be Dr. Ackroyd's wishful interpretation of his reported interaction with Dr. Cadman, or it may be that Dr. Cadman did in fact briefly flirt with the idea of making a fight out of the statements and arrangements Dr. Bolen had made. Whichever was the case, it rapidly dropped out of sight in the current of events that made up this incident.

". . . and I want your help in gathering information to be used in our defense," Ackroyd continued. "We have no problems in this area, so far as I'm concerned.

"Now the second point I want to talk over with you is this. Bolen made a big noise about a second-year resident refusing to take on a patient. I know where he got this, but . . . ," he paused, ". . . I don't think I'll go into it here. It's not relevant. He raised the whole question of residents refusing to treat patients. He said that even when the cases were taken on, the workups weren't adequate. I want you to find out for me if any of our residents have refused cases since July 1st. If so, I want you to give me the full details. Please ask the chiefs and let me know, so that I can submit the case for the defense to Dr. Cadman. Cadman did not speak out at the meeting—all this was news to him— but we got together to discuss what sort of information we would need. We also want to know the total case load in psychotherapy of the second-year residents. I also want to know the diagnoses of these cases, who the supervisor is, and the present status of these cases."

Considering how busy the service consultants, the chief residents, and the residents were in attempting merely to keep up with everyday requirements, this was a tremendously heavy and a tremendously unexpected imposition of paper work upon them. They were unable or unwilling to do this job properly. Considering Cadman's probable use of the information, they felt it was hardly worthwhile gathering it. Also, later events proved the service consultants to be resisting Dr. Ackroyd's apparent bid for leadership in this episode. As a result, another increment of anger was added to the already strained relations between the consultants and the assistant clinical director. But instead of relaying the fact or opinion to Dr. Cadman that these requests for information were unrealistic in their demand for completeness—and out of keeping with culture of freedom that he had helped foster in the house—the midlevel staff group kept it among themselves, feeling badly toward each other without any observed resolution.

". . . I'd like to have all this early next week, if possible," Ackroyd added. (Silence)

"Oh yes," Ackroyd continued, "and there is one final thing. Dr. Cadman has heard that there is a problem with attendance at rounds. We've heard that only a few people have been attending. I want to find out who has been attending, both in the first and second year."

Steinberg: "The trouble is that I hear they are not worth attending."

Ackroyd scowled.

"That doesn't matter," he replied [as though addressing a childish irrelevancy]. "The question *is*, how many are attending? *They are supposed to be attending rounds!* You can tell them that from me, if you like. There's a great deal of excitement . . . these days. . . ."

"Suprin got very excited when he heard. . . . He evidently said that if he catches a resident who won't attend . . . he will throw the bastard out of the hospital."

Schneider grinned. "So it's heave-ho season again, is it?" he remarked.

Stanley: "Now what were those points you wanted information on, again?"

Ackroyd read down his list of points again.

Schneider smiled, and said in a loud voice: "Now hear this. Now hear this. All residents will fall out on the flight deck."

Ackroyd joked that the whole problem of running the residency program was like trying to sail a leaky boat.

"*Sail* it? Hell!" laughed Schneider. "We're not trying to sail it. We're trying to bail it out. Just to keep it afloat. That's what we're doing. Bailing frantically!"

DR. CADMAN DECLINES TO LEAD: THE MOBILIZATION OF AGGRESSION BREAKS DOWN

IT SOON BECAME apparent to the midlevel staff that any form of counterattack against Dr. Bolen and his clinic would expire for want of a leader. Dr. Ackroyd sought to exert some leadership, which was rendered ineffective by the consultants' refusal to back him up. Dr. Cadman made clear his refusal to lead during his next weekly meeting with his subordinates, five days after the interaction between service consultants and the assistant clinical director reported above.

As usual, the house staff—including both the chief residents and the service consultants—met in Dr. Cadman's office. After a preliminary matter, Dr. Cadman looked around the group.

"Is Pete [Ackroyd] coming?" Cadman asked. (Pause) "Is there any urgent business before he comes?" (Silence) "Then there are a couple of things I can mention before we start. First, Pete is in the process of investigating the psychotherapy commitments of the second-year people. He has asked you about this, and I know he would like to get the data as soon as possible.

"Second, I know you all have questions about the relation to the chiefs of the new representatives from the clinic on each service. As I understand it, these new people will have essentially the same function for [specific] patients that the service consultants have for the rest of the patients. The clinic feels that it has suffered many disappointments in that the chiefs have not taken their hints, advice, and suggestions essentially as orders. I haven't heard anything specific on this score, but I feel that it is all probably based on something specific that they are keeping to themselves. I think we should all go over it in our minds carefully and see if any repairs of relationships with the clinic are indicated. And if you find they need work, I hope you will give them work. Because my saddle sores are still open."

Schneider laughed. "You ought to be getting used to that by now, around here."

Cadman chuckled. "Yeah," he replied. "I got them all over my body."

Chapin: "I went over this with [a representative of the clinic], about the clinic representatives giving advice when it is wanted. He objected to the word, 'wanted.' He felt we should be told what to do with all their patients."

Cadman fumbled in his desk and brought out a copy of the rules and regulations governing the residency training program. "I hate to get out the bible, . . ." he said.

"Which version of the bible?" Schneider interrupted.

"The Saint Paul version," Clark replied.

Cadman: "That's about right. I have about as much function around here as a saint, except people around here don't dress me up. They mostly dress me down. I'm as paralyzed around here as the rest of you."

This remark was a considerable understatement of the actual influence that Dr. Cadman could exert upon the organization when he chose to use the power of his position, or his professional-charismatic power as a therapist and teacher of therapists. That he often chose not to use his power to the fullest was very different from not possessing that power, although it was the latter that he usually preferred to communicate to others in moments such as the above. Such communications functioned as positive reinforcement of the reifications of him that were currently holding in check much affect and many wishes that were latently being directed toward or against him. Throughout the course of the meeting that ensued, Dr. Cadman developed an "advertisement for himself" that added further strength to the reification of him as passive and quiescent. That is, he communicated to his staff group his intention to be their *therapist* rather than their *leader* in the current situation that was troubling them all; that he would help them to work through their problems, but that he would not act to eradicate those problems for them.

Not surprisingly, this was not what his subordinates wanted. In this instance, they wanted action, not support. They wanted Cadman to remove the problem and the causes of the problem, and the more violently he did so, the more secretly satisfying it would be for them.

Chapin: "One of our residents took on a . . . case that he really didn't want to."
Cadman: "If they put the word in our left ear, and find it goes out the right, then we're going to have trouble around here."

Cadman was persisting in his efforts to have his subordinates examine their own weaknesses in task relations concerning clinic patients. He was not allowing his subordinates to inventory weaknesses that resided outside his immediate line of authority. This did not go over well with his subordinates. It violated a personal sense of blamelessness that crept unconsciously into many of the subordinates' responses to this meeting and to the more general administrative situation in which they existed. The subordinates seemed to feel that Cadman was transmitting the "heat" to them, rather than insulating them from it and reflecting it back upon its source in Dr. Bolen. This in turn violated their wish to be protected.

Cadman: ". . . There's some confusion about this, so perhaps you should go over it, at least. There is some criticism that in the case of some patients there is *no* record, not even a good physical."

That was too much for Dr. Ackroyd. With great annoyance, he leaned forward in his chair and pointed at Dr. Cadman. *"That's not true!"* he exclaimed. "Every case coming to this hospital gets at least a physical. Except," he added, staring pointedly at Dr. Cadman, "for some of the cases sent in by the senior staff."

Dr. Cadman was quite regularly at a loss on points of specific information. There were many topics around which he had only indirect information, sometimes little more than gossip or hearsay among his fellow executives, or else no information whatsoever. To gather such information would have been a full-time job, and there were other activities that Dr. Cadman preferred instead. However, this made it impossible for him to pursue all but a few inquiries to their full factual conclusion, especially such vague and all-encompassing matters as the current one surrounding certain patients on the wards. This made it necessary to back down on a number of his statements to his subordinates. This was the one situation in which Cadman's subordinates seemed to the observer to go out of their way to make trouble for him. Since he would not lead them in battle against their common "enemy," they were not about to let him carry the "enemy's" attack against them. They used these points of informationlessness to retaliate against their leader-who-would-not-lead.

This was not done with deliberate or intended malice. The house staff were experiencing genuine feelings of being falsely accused, slighted, misunderstood, unappreciated, unable to plead their defense, and convicted without trial by hearsay evidence from prejudiced witnesses. This was experienced as arising from the outsiders' initiative, but was given particular immediacy and sting by the apparent sanction that their loved and admired Dr. Cadman was giving to the outsiders' accusations.

The house staff could have provided Dr. Cadman with the information he needed, but their reification of him as quiescent again influenced their behavior. Why bother going to all the trouble of gathering the information he needed or requested? They believed almost without question that he would never use it, except perhaps against themselves. Certainly it would not be used outwardly, as an instrument of retaliation against the clinic. They "knew" this would be so, no matter how much they wished otherwise, and there was plenty of behavioral evidence from Dr. Cadman that reinforced them in their knowledge. So the service consultants gathered information unsystematically and piecemeal, presented it sloppily and with a disregard that greatly annoyed and hampered the assistant clinical director, whose job it was to organize all the information required.[2] In the absence of

[2] Dr. Ackroyd was meeting with the service consultants in his office 15 days after the precipitating event had occurred. Dr. Ackroyd was examining some papers containing information that he had asked the consultants to gather for him: whether any residents had refused cases. The data indicated that none had refused, but Ackroyd was not satisfied. Scowling, he riffled through the papers.

"What does all this mean? Goodness me, am I supposed to make something out of all this? Bill [Stanley], what do all these little squiggles indicate?"

There was no reply. The service consultants manifested no outward concern over the state of the information they had presented.

"Am I supposed to understand from all this," asked Ackroyd, "that there were *no* refusals of patients by any of the residents? That's very gratifying, I'm sure, but I can't quite believe it."

Stanley: "None on my service."

Ackroyd: *"None?"* . . .

Ackroyd: "But there's nothing *specific* here. It's all general stuff. Can't we get something specific on a few specific cases? That's the sort of stuff we need to fight with. All this is no good to me. Besides, I don't think you really asked them. You don't impress me as knowing what you are talking about. . . .

". . . I say you've got to *pick some cases* and give me all the facts. Not just

a firm informational structure, the emotion-laden processes of accusation and defense, injury and retaliation continued for several weeks. In time they were displaced onto another crisis, which emerged from events that would not have been so problematic had they not tapped into the existing reservoir of inchoate aggression.

To return to the meeting in progress in Dr. Cadman's office, Dr. Ackroyd had protested vehemently that all incoming patients received at least a physical exam, "except for some of the cases sent in by the senior staff." Dr. Cadman responded with a shrug.

Cadman: "I didn't investigate the matter, so I don't know. I'm just passing on the gossip I heard, for what it's worth. I'd like you to discuss the matter among yourselves, and come to some recommendation of what you would like to see done."

Dr. Ackroyd protested. "They are nothing but a bunch of prima donnas over there. They criticize us because we have no progress notes in our records. They want us to have complete admission records and a full set of progress notes in each report. *They* don't have that themselves! We *couldn't.* For one thing, we don't have the typing staff. And neither do they, for that matter. I don't see what they are criticizing *us* for. I think we should stand up for ourselves on this. Will you support me on it?"

Dr. Cadman could neither subscribe to the aggressive mode of defense that had been proposed, nor to the bid that he support such a mode, if not lead it. However, he needed time to make this clear, perhaps because there was some attraction in it for him, and also because he did not relish the necessity of disappointing his subordinates in their aspirations as to what he should do for them. Therefore, his initial reply

---

this general business. Then, maybe we can point out something they did wrong, and argue about *that* for a while. We can't let them keep the offensive, but we can't get it from them either, unless we document our position. We've got to get a few facts, and then maybe we can go to work on them. . . .

"Look," said Ackroyd as the service consultants were leaving his office, "get me some cases, will you? I need *cases.*"

to go along with the intent that Dr. Ackroyd had succeeded in communicating.

Cadman: "I know you all have ideas on this. I think you should go over your ideas and put them on paper. So I can have some ammunition to fight with."

Here we see Dr. Cadman coming close to assuming leadership of the desired counterattack. However, this was rapidly to disappear. First, its impact was vitiated by his immediately apparent lack of grasp of the organizational instrumentalities of intergroup warfare, such as the records committee. Dr. Steinberg brought this particular instrumentality to Dr. Cadman's attention, but the dismaying result was an advertisement of the apparent fact that Cadman had forgotten he was chairman of that committee.

"We've got a records committee that's meeting on just this thing," Dr. Steinberg suggested to Dr. Cadman.

"Yes, that's right," Cadman responded. Then after a momentary hesitation, he added, "Who's on that committee?"

Steinberg stared at Cadman. "You're the chairman," he replied flatly.

"Oh," said Cadman. "Am I?"

At this point the meeting was interrupted briefly by an outside caller. Then Dr. Cadman went out of his way to bring attention back to the point of destructive counterattack *vs.* constructive working through. In doing so he made it increasingly clear that (1) he was putting the "heat" on his own subordinates, not on any outsiders, and that (2) he would aid them supportively in working out their problems with the new policy, but would not join them in aggressively seeking to remove the source of that policy.

Cadman to Ackroyd: "On these clinic representatives, are you clear that they will be equivalent in status to the service consultants?"

Ackroyd: "What I want to know is, will they do what I tell them to? That's what I'm not clear on, from what they have told me so far."

Cadman: "That's what Carver pulled out of it."

Stearns: "I still don't know whether I resent it, this new arrangement. I certainly feel that it takes away from my role as consultant. What I can't understand is why people are placed in the services who are so lacking in the point of view of the total coordination of the wards."

Clark: "That's what I think too. These people from the clinic are very aware of the needs of the clinic but they are not at all aware of the needs of the service."

Carver: "They want us, on my service, to devote a quarter of our time to their patients, but we have only eight of them [out of 60] on our wards. I think that is totally unrealistic."

Ackroyd: "That's why I asked my question."

Schneider: "I think it is unrealistic to have these people acting as consultants to the patients, but not to the services. It creates a vacuum."

Stearns: "I agree."

Ackroyd: "I just know these people are going to go to Bolen, he's going to go to Suprin, and Suprin's going to come to you, and you to us. My god! It's like trying to call Washington through Moscow."

After the barrage of protests elicited by Cadman's question, the cold war analog was interjected by Ackroyd and immediately picked up and amplified by Schneider.

"Say, that's right," exclaimed Schneider. "Did you know that if you want to get a call from East Berlin to West Berlin, that you have to phone through Sweden?"

The feeling tone of the meeting was sufficiently tense that Dr. Cadman's following question was obviously more therapeutic than administrative in purpose. *Here was Dr. Cadman's first clear and public indication as to the role he was going to adopt throughout the remainder of the current situ-*

ation. It was obvious from the responses that Cadman's role-demand was accepted with a pronounced lack of enthusiasm, but in the remainder of the meeting Cadman continued to bolster it. This he was able to do with very little direct opposition, since those in the meeting withheld their real wishes about the role they hoped he would take.

Cadman: "Would you like to meet together on it?"

Ackroyd: "No! Uh, I think the issue of responsibility has to be settled first. I don't see what good a meeting will do until we have this issue settled, *first.*" (I.e., settling it would require some decisions, and some decisiveness from Dr. Cadman, rather than the let's-all-get-together-and-work-it-through approach that Cadman was offering to initiate.)

Dr. Carver presented another instance in which the combined judgment of Carver and Steinberg was disputed by the clinic representative on Carver's service. ". . . Doug [Steinberg] agreed with me that the evaluation was complete, and that we could return the patient to another hospital. No, said the clinic, we need more facts."

Stanley: "Sure, because they assume they have administrative authority equal to the service consultant."

Ackroyd: "Here's the basic difference in philosophy between the house and the clinic, and I think they are asking for a pack of trouble, trying to move in like that."

Cadman: "Should we meet with the clinic staff, ourselves, and Dr. Suprin?"

Here was a suggestion that, in other settings, might have connoted the opening gambit in the counterattack that most of those present wished for. However, the way matters had developed, it was "obvious" that the meeting would not be used for that purpose. Again the suggestion was rejected by the group's spokesman.

Ackroyd: "All that would do would be to produce a feeling of good fellowship between us now. [The current ill feelings should not obscure that fact that, in general, this statement was valid.] A meeting like that might carry us for another two months, but it would only flare up again."

Cadman: "Don't you think two months is worth it?"

Ackroyd: "There's a lot of politics involved. I don't think we'll accomplish anything by just meeting. Something's got to be done beforehand, and I think you're the man to do it."

Ackroyd was beginning to apply pressure to Cadman, to get him to assume the type of leadership that the group felt was necessary, and to dissuade Cadman from acting the therapist in a situation requiring administrative action. But this attempt lacked conviction, and it lacked the manifest support of the rest of the group. The subordinates' conception of Cadman was so strongly oriented away from administrative leadership, activity, and aggressiveness that attempts to demand these of Cadman felt like trying to get water to run uphill. There was probably also the fear that, if these forces were elicited in Cadman, they would be directed against his subordinates themselves, rather than against the clinic. Certainly, Cadman's performance had communicated adequate data on which to base both these premonitions.

Steinberg: "I think also that the clinic tends to overly devalue what experience we have. Some of the service consultants feel confident dealing with their type of patient. There is also a feeling that the chiefs should be just that: *chiefs!*"

Ackroyd: "Period! That's the way we run things, and I think we are being undermined. They're soon going to start dropping things on us. If they are going to be consultants, then we ought to be able to feel free to treat them as such. If they are going to have administrative authority, that's O.K. too. But if they disagree, where do we go? I've got to have that clear. I'm perfectly willing to take the whole responsibility for running the whole show myself. But as I see it now, I think it puts the chiefs in an untenable position. As far as we're concerned, the chiefs work autonomously. Here comes another group of people, and they work a completely different way. What's going to become of us all?"

Cadman: "Would you like to meet with Suprin, you and I?"

This was rather a frightening suggestion, considering that from present indications it would be a contest of feelings and wills between the beset Dr. Ackroyd and the upset Dr. Suprin, with Dr. Cadman sitting quietly aside. People a lot less astute than Dr. Ackroyd realized the impolitic nature of becoming embroiled in a contest of self vs. Suprin. Besides, Cadman was Ackroyd's superordinate; Ackroyd urgently wanted decisiveness, guidance, and protection from Cadman, and was frustrated because these were not forthcoming.

"No," Ackroyd replied. *"You* have authority to tell Bolen what you want him to do. Why don't you do it?" This was said with considerable intensity, and directly to Dr. Cadman.

Cadman looked hurt and discomfited. "Yes, I have," he replied lamely.

Ackroyd shook his head apologetically. "I'm sorry," he said. "That's mean. I'm asking you to do something you can't do."

This was the last attempt to have Dr. Cadman command the counterattack against the insurgents from Dr. Bolen's clinic. From this point on, throughout the several weeks in which the turmoil persisted, Cadman's subordinates attempted to hold their peace. The relations between them and their superordinate, Dr. Cadman, retained an outward equilibrium. However, the feelings of injury and insult, the unfulfilled wishes for militant leadership and the struggle both to express and to resist these forces persisted in the group. This situation was made apparent by remarks made to the observer during this episode that succeeded it, and by the sudden and unrealistic explosion of tempers that precipitated the second episode out of what might otherwise have been a relatively unemotional exchange of information.

However, all this was yet to take place. At the moment, several in the group were annoyed that Dr. Ackroyd had so readily withdrawn his pressure against Dr. Cadman.

"He knows what side his bread is buttered on," observed Dr. Carver sourly, mimicking one of Cadman's favorite folksayings.

"Yeah," said Schneider. "Just another saddle sore," he laughed, reflecting discredit upon Cadman by turning another of Cadman's favorite expressions against him.

Cadman smiled. "It just shows that passivity is expensive," he remarked.

(Laughter . . .)

The meeting ended, and with it ended any real attempt to work through or work out the bind between Dr. Cadman and his subordinates. The subordinates had made a demand for aggressive, outward-oriented leadership, and this was refused by Dr. Cadman. In its place he offered an inward-oriented form of therapeutic support, which in turn was rejected by his subordinates. At this point, both parties to the struggle backed away from further dispute on the matter. The mid-level personnel ceased to press their demands for a type of leadership they now no longer expected from Dr. Cadman; and Cadman refrained from making offers of therapeutic assistance when he saw these were not going to be accepted.

Hostilities Become More Difficult to Manage

Twenty days after the precipitating event, the topics that had been raised in the medical executive committee meeting were *still* under discussion. Dr. Cadman's weekly meeting with the house staff was one locale, but not the only one, in which this dialogue between the several levels and segments of the organization was continued. It was interesting to note that, whereas the house staff continued to experience with some frustration the "heat" they felt Dr. Cadman was apply-

ing to them, they became more protective—even solicitous
—in their attitude toward him. As this protectiveness developed, it became increasingly apparent that each staff member would now and then seek to insulate Dr. Cadman from
the punishment that one of his peers was seeking to administer to their common superordinate. Also, whenever a subordinate's feelings of frustration got out of control, another
of his peers would shut him up or deflect his remarks away
from the intended target, Dr. Cadman. This happened in
many fleeting instances, such as the following.

The meeting in question had begun with some confused
talk about whether or not certain rounds were attended. Cadman had been told that they were not being attended, and
that it was imperative that this situation be remedied. Most
of the house staff disputed the validity of Cadman's remarks.
However, no one had conclusive evidence *either way*. This
put Cadman in the position of pleading with his subordinates
to remedy a problem whose seriousness no one in the group
could determine. Some maintained that the alleged problem
did not exist. One service consultant, however, supported
Cadman in his contention that there *was* a problem.

Stearns: "None of my residents go [to the disputed rounds]."
"I have heard it isn't worth attending," protested Steinberg.
Then, turning to face Cadman and Ackroyd, he reiterated vehemently, "I have heard it isn't worth attending." Both Cadman
and Ackroyd looked away. They did not reply. (Silence) Someone else began to say something, but was interrupted. "I have
heard it isn't worth attending," Steinberg repeated, looking at
Dr. Cadman.

Dr. Ackroyd leaned forward so that he could get a full view of
Steinberg's face. "That is neither here nor there," he stated. "Your
remark is completely irrelevant. That is not what we are here to
discuss." The topic of conversation changed.

This insulating, deflecting, protecting device was soon to
break down, but while it lasted a nurturant relation was sus-

tained between Dr. Cadman and his subordinates that was the *opposite* of the one they desired, and the opposite of the one usually associated with superior-subordinate relations. That is, the midlevel staff group played a nurturant-supportive role *vis-à-vis* Dr. Cadman, and Cadman seemed content to accept this albeit temporary arrangement. He encouraged their sympathy, their understanding, their pity, and their support both directly, by highlighting his helplessness in such problematic situations, and indirectly, through certain attributions about what "the boss" wanted to see done. In the short run Dr. Cadman was successful in his bids for emotional support, but less so with regard to task support. In the short run his subordinates were glad to give him the understanding and comfort he needed, both because of their genuine respect and affection for him, and probably also because it kept them off their uncomfortably nasty feelings about him. However, actual task support was another matter, involving changes in pattern of established routine that the staff were largely unwilling to make.

The group discussed the number of patients in the hospital, the number of staff, the patient-staff ratios of the past and the present, the past and present treatment calibers in the house, the admissions rate, the patient mix, and teaching assignments; all these passed in rapid and unsystematic review.

At several points Dr. Cadman interjected remarks such as, "The boss is all het up about keeping the census down," and "The boss is excited. He says that just when he's going to the trustees for more money, the hospital is taking care of fewer patients."

As the topics continued to pass in rapid succession, Cadman began shaking his head. Finally he turned to Dr. Ackroyd. "Look," he interrupted. "Will you please *document* that *for me*. I am completely at sea. All I can judge is the affect and I don't in the least know where to send it. Let's get some statistics on these matters."

Stearns: "Perhaps the research wing can help."

Cadman grunted. "Let's not get into the problem of the untouchables. They won't do anything for you unless they can get a paper out of it." He smiled and added, "I'm not sour. I'm just curdling." (Laughter)

Cadman turned to Ackroyd. "Pete, I'd like you to form a committee on that, and I'd ask the committee to report in a month, on their own initiative, here."

"Any other burning issues?" Cadman asked. (Silence) "No? O.K. See you all next week."

However, despite the silence, the situation was *not* completely O.K. As demonstrated in the next weeks' meetings, the carefully controlled frustrations of the house staff began slowly to erupt. At first the flarings of temper were fleeting occurrences that nobody paid much attention to, because they were not part of the content of administration as it was then being carried on. Soon these outbursts developed a scope and intensity that consumed, for the time being, the superstructure of polite relations that had so carefully been built up between superior and subordinate.

The initial signs of this process were so isolated, so unrelated, and so picayune as to be almost not worth noting and recording. A case in point would be the following interchange that occurred before a house staff meeting began. It was now 27 days since the beginning of Episode I.

The meeting was scheduled to begin at 11:00 A.M., as usual. At 11:10 there was only one chief resident present. Several minutes later another chief, Dr. Chapin, entered, sat down, and sprawled his legs out in front of him.

At approximately 11:15 Dr. Clark, another chief resident, entered Cadman's office, walking fast. He rounded the corner into the main body of the office before he had had time to put his face in order. His face was set in a dour, glowering, petulant expression, and it took him a few seconds before he could resolve this into a calmer, more sociable expression.

The room was still mostly empty of people, and there were many places to sit. However, Dr. Clark approached a chair, the access to which was blocked by Dr. Chapin's legs. Chapin was listening to Dr. Cadman talk about the complexities of modern drug terminology, and did not move his legs as Dr. Clark approached. Clark paused, then vigorously kicked one of Chapin's feet. Chapin drew in his legs sharply.

"Hey, hey. Take it easy," he said in a low and not unfriendly voice. Clark smiled and sat down.

As unimportant as minute happenings such as this were to the larger picture of administration in the hospital, to the teaching of psychiatry, and to the level of psychiatric services, they nonetheless kept building on one another until they occupied perhaps more of the staff's preoccupation time than did the purposive organizational reasons for their being together as a group. These recurrences built a chain of events that was sufficiently compelling to be noted down, as for instance, the following which occurred immediately after the above.

As the bulk of the house staff assembled in Dr. Cadman's office shortly before 11:30, there were a few bantering exchanges about the number of committees in the hospital, and on the singularly remarkable phenomenon of bureaucratic existence, the committees on committees.

Cadman spoke of being a member of an *ad hoc* committee on committee organization at the medical school. (Laughter) He had been able to play a very useful role, he said. He had gone in with the resolve to do absolutely nothing. Then, when highflown and grandiose ideas were presented for doing things differently, he had always raised the question: how is this better than what we have now?

"It's very interesting," he concluded. "We ended up with the same thing we had when we started."

(Silence)

The group seemed a little disappointed, as though they had expected a humorous anecdote and a few good laughs, but received instead a parable whose moral was a little too pointed for comfort.

Clark broke the silence. "What we need," he observed sourly, "is a committee to study committees." (Laughter) "I suppose that's you," he said, turning to the observer.

"That's me," replied the observer.

The squabbling continued, coming up around almost everything that took place.

Cadman turned to Dr. Steinberg and asked him to read the report of the committee. Steinberg started off reading in an extremely loud voice, almost pugnaciously. The combination of the volume, the tone, and also the content of the report—which was out of keeping with some of the more customary ideas held by Dr. Cadman and others in the hospital—caused someone to say in a distinctly audible aside: "Nothing like hitting them where it hurts." Steinberg continued to read the paper.

Steinberg finished reading. There was a silence. Then Ackroyd sat forward, shook his head, and said, "I'm sorry, but I object strenuously to the emphasis of about the last page and a half of your report. I take extreme exception to your approach to this problem. I disagree most profoundly with the whole system you propose of administrative controls, and ordering the residents to write up their records, and taking *reprisals* against them if they don't. *Do we think the residents are school kids?*"

Ackroyd swiveled around to look Steinberg in the face. Then, looking away, he continued, "Is that the way we are to look at them? I protest!"

Cadman threw a pad of paper that landed on Steinberg's lap, then slipped onto the floor. "Here. Take this down," said Cadman as he threw it.

Steinberg smiled and stooped to pick up the pad. "These gems," he remarked as he took out his pen and prepared to write.

Ackroyd continued: "Heaven knows the residents are acting like school kids now, but must we perpetuate what I am sure we all hope will be a temporary situation by building it right into our program formally, as you suggest? I mean this is a teaching hospital. . . ."

This criticism continued at some length, with Dr. Cadman lending his support. It continued to the extent that it began to feel as though the two superordinates in the group were ganging up against the subordinates by taking it out against one of them, who had only done what he had been asked to do, namely write down and deliver some of his opinions and those of other members on the committee whose report he was reading. Despite the length, passion, and articulateness of the criticism, other subordinates in the group were left obviously unmoved and nonplussed.

". . . Now this is the way it should be in a teaching program," continued Ackroyd, summarizing a point. "Not like a bunch of school kids," he went on, "that have to be *told* to do their work. Our residents may be acting like that now, but if they are, I would say it is because we have failed in our relationship with them. We can't just tell them to do another thing. We're probably telling them to do too much as it is. There has to be an element of leadership. . . ."

Cadman nodded. ". . . positive leadership . . . ," he interjected indistinctly.

Ackroyd continued uninterrupted: ". . . This is a teaching hospital. Our residents are professional men, not school kids. I think we should be concerned with what they are not doing, and work with them on it, rather than acting like a bunch of policemen, and start threatening them. . . ."

Cadman: ". . . leadership. . . ."

Ackroyd: ". . . If we have to make rules to do it, then I would say we have failed in our responsibilities to the residents and to the program. In my opinion, every time we make a rule, it is because somebody has failed."

Cadman nodded.

(Pause) Carver: "Yes, but if we are to get any enthusiasm for this in the residents, we've got to catch fire ourselves."

The group was, in fact, beginning to catch fire. Dr. Ackroyd returned to the attack.

Ackroyd: "There's another thing, Doug, and I'm sorry to say this, because I am probably taking you way out of context, *but* I couldn't disagree with you more over your opening statement about. . . ."

Dr. Steinberg was silent, but not cowed. Later in the meeting he returned to the attack. He made a statement casting doubt on the professional wisdom of maintaining the full and complete records on patients that the administration was currently emphasizing, given the existing charter under which the hopital was operating. There was a flurry of response to this point.

Stearns leaned forward, responding to Steinberg's point. "Yes. When Dr. Sherman was here, he used to say to us to be very careful what we put down in the patients' records, and to put down as little as possible. . . ."

Carver laughed. "Well, that's a switch."

Conn: "Is that right?"

Schneider chuckled. "Times have changed. Times have changed."

Cadman was leaning back in his chair, running his fingers through his hair. To the observer, he looked quite distraught. After several of the group had joked together about this new consideration regarding patients' records, Cadman sat up straight and addressed Ackroyd.

"Let me get real practical for a minute," he said. "From now on, I want you to see to it, Pete, that the following stuff is in every patient's record." He read a list of required information, and the time period during which that information had to be supplied to the record. Before the group could respond to this new demand, Cadman went quickly on to another subject.

Cadman: "And now what's this I hear about discharge rounds being held informally here and there all over the hospital?"

There was an observable mobilization of energy centered on this new field of conflict. The subordinates pressed their counterattack against Dr. Cadman. They used his informationlessness—and he made it easy for them to use it—to gain and keep an advantage. In this exchange, they achieved short-term victory. Dr. Cadman gave up the fight temporarily and turned to Dr. Ackroyd to be rescued by being supplied with a more adequate arsenal of written-down information with which to rout his intransigent subordinates.

Stearns: "No!"

Chapin: "No. That's not so."

Stearns: "We hold them regularly once a week."

Cadman shifted around in his chair. "Well, all I know is. . . ."

"That's not *so*," Chapin interrupted loudly. "Every Friday we get together with the residents. . . ."

"And Dr. Hoople is there," Stearns interjected.

Chapin: ". . . and we bring in the patient and ask him what he got out of the hospital."

Chapin: ". . . And usually get spat in the face for our efforts, I might add."

Cadman became immobile. "ALL I KNOW IS," he shouted, getting red in the face. The room became silent. "All I know is," he repeated, "is what the head of the discharge service told me. He told me that discharges were being handled very informally, with little get-togethers and informal meetings in this office or that."

"*Oh,* no!" Chapin objected, vigorously shaking his head. "We have *regular* meetings." Cadman began to twist in his chair again.

"Yes we do," nodded Stearns.

Cadman held up his hand. "All . . . I . . . know . . . is . . . what . . . he . . . *told* . . . me!" he repeated with elaborate emphasis.

Steinberg: "Well, that only reflects the state of ignorance of the gentleman in question."

Cadman ran his fingers through his hair again, several times. "Will someone please tell me, then, how discharge rounds are run?"

"That's hard to say," replied someone in the group.

"Every service has its own way," Carver replied.

Cadman swiveled around to face Ackroyd. "Will someone please tell me?" (Silence) "Pete, will you write it up for me. And put it down too, that from now on discharge notes are to be included in the records." Ackroyd nodded.

However, this tactical victory on the part of the subordinate members of the house staff soon turned into a strategic defeat for the whole group. From the longer-term organizational point of view, the battlefield was Dr. Cadman's to control, and control it he did, by bringing more powerful armament into play in the weeks to follow. The meeting that took place one week later was begun by Dr. Cadman in a way that indicated he was about to direct increased firepower against his insubordinate subordinates. The group responded to this with revolutionary fervor. This was of course just the outlet for their aggressions that they had been searching for, and what had been passive insubordination quickly became outright, though short-lived, rebellion. Episode II was the result.

CHAPTER 16

Critical Episode II
Dr. Cadman "Gets Tough": Subordinates'
Resistance to Unexpected Assertiveness

THE SECOND EPISODE reflected more of the impact of the total executive role constellation upon subordinates than did Episode I. Episode I demonstrated a few of the consequences of one executive role specialization. Episode II demonstrates a few of the dynamics of response to the *juxtaposition* of two specialized, differentiated, and complementary executive role performances. Episode II could be captioned from the subordinates' point of view: "Cadman's getting tough. It must be Dr. Suprin who's behind all this."

Episode II was precipitated by two substantive matters of administration: (1) the introduction of a change in schedule for the house and the residency training program, and (2) an effort to control the so-called "wild family therapy" that was allegedly taking place. Both these substantive concerns were integrated within the single dynamic of Cadman's attempts for assertive control over his subordinates, their resistance to his "unCadmanian" efforts, their displacement of executive initiative away from Cadman, and their shifting of that initiative to Suprin, through the allegation that it was "really Suprin who is behind all this."

Both substantive issues might, in other circumstances, have led to relatively affect-free exchanges of information, but in this episode, almost before anyone realized it, the clinical staff group was involved in heated charges and countercharges.

The subordinates were demonstrating to Cadman that they would make it as difficult as they could, within the wide limits of organizational tolerance that existed in the M.P.I., for him to take the initiative and refuse the initiative whenever he wanted to. They were protesting against what they considered unfair and illegitimate behavior on his part: he would not become the aggressive initiator with regard to objects outside their group when they wanted him to, as in Episode I, yet he became the aggressive initiator inside the group when he chose to, as in Episode II.

The subordinates' behavior also demonstrated that, given the clearly visible specialization, differentiation, and complementarity of roles between their two superordinates, Drs. Suprin and Cadman, it was impossible for the subordinates not to construe the "untypical" initiative and control expressed by Cadman as "really" originating elsewhere in the executive group, namely from Suprin. This *irresistible transferring of initiative* from its obvious source to its reified source influenced subordinates' thinking and behavior through the whole episode.

THE PRECIPITATION OF EPISODE II IN THE HOUSE STAFF SYSTEM

IT IS NOT DIFFICULT to illustrate the transferring of executive initiative that took place among subordinates during Episode II. It occurred *immediately* upon the precipitation of Episode II into the house staff system, well before the events in question had reached crisis proportions. In fact, this transferring of initiative from Cadman to Suprin, with the corollary tendency not to take Dr. Cadman seriously in his initiative, was one of the principal factors contributing to the rapid escalation of a routine inquiry into an episode of considerable consequence within the house.

The preliminary signals of what was to become Episode II occurred during the time that Episode I was being worked through the management ranks of the house. As such, the item pertaining to the future Episode II received scant attention from the staff, but the attention it did receive was interesting. The event was as follows:

The service consultants were meeting with the assistant clinical director. Several items of immediate administrative concern were discussed.

Ackroyd: "O.K., then, I'd like to bring up something else that will really make your week bad. I've got a memo from Dr. Cadman concerning family therapy."

Schneider (in a loud voice): "Oh, I know where *that* comes from!"

Even before the matter of *"wild"* family therapy had been broached, the initiative was being attributed to that reified source of all initiative, "Ferocious Frank" Suprin. The words had no sooner left the mouth of Dr. Ackroyd than the decision was made that the unseen mover of the piece was "really" Dr. Suprin. Despite the fact that Dr. Ackroyd sat there with what he said was Dr. Cadman's memo in his hand, at least one of the midlevel staff members had his interpretation of the precipitating structure of the event "all wrapped up." This stereotyped conception of the executive constellation at work was soon to be widely expressed within the midlevel group, but for the time being the senior person in the group tried to control Dr. Schneider's rapid jumping to conclusions.

"No you don't," replied Ackroyd in a matter-of-fact voice.

"Oh yes I do!" Schneider persisted.

Ackroyd: "Well, why don't you tell us about it later." At this point Ackroyd read the memo from Dr. Cadman. The memo asked him to investigate "how widespread" was the practice of family therapy within the house.

Schneider: "I know where this came from. Dr. Suprin! One of the residents Suprin is supervising is taking on a family case and now he [Suprin] wants to know what's going on. But what's Cadman doing, writing a memo like that?"

Here we see the first of many puzzled queries, all directed at that one refractory piece of data that stubbornly refused to fit into the reifications of the middle management personnel concerning relations among the top executives: and that one piece of data was the undeniable fact that it was *Dr. Cadman* who was doing the actual initiation of the incident. From this puzzlement emerged the hypothesis that Cadman was the "mouthpiece" for Suprin. Although this hypothesis helped the midlevel personnel to maintain their reifications of the top executive figures, and their conception of the executive constellation, it also caused a lot of trouble in the chain of events that was about to get under way. It caused trouble for Dr. Cadman, in that his subordinates could not believe that it was really "the old Cadman that we used to know" who was talking, and therefore they did a very poor job of attending to what it was that he was trying to communicate to them. It caused trouble for the subordinates in that Cadman simply did not act like a "mouthpiece." Pressure him as much as they would, they simply could not get him to let down and admit to them what they "knew": that he was not representing his own concerns in the matter of family therapy but rather those of Dr. Suprin. This struggle rapidly developed its own face-to-face validity, deriving much of its impetus from the energies stored up during the previously unresolved struggle over leadership and followership.

". . . I thought I had succeeded in getting him [Cadman] interested in family therapy," Dr. Schneider continued.

Ackroyd: "Poor old Cadman. All he wants to do is run a residency program that will give the residents some freedom, and he gets constantly subjected to demands for more control, and people criticize him for things he doesn't know anything about because he doesn't have everything under his thumb."

Steinberg: "We all agree with you on that."

Stearns: "We all agree with you." There were nods and sounds of general agreement throughout the group. Stearns continued, "We've got none like that on my ward, none of that sort of therapy."

Despite the feelings that were latently directed against Cadman for his performance during the Episode I, or perhaps *because* of these feelings, the "party-line" evaluation of him was still the sympathetic, understanding, pitying, "Poor old Cadman." This occurred even though the midlevel personnel were back-stage in the company of their peers: and positive reinforcement was immediately reflected back, "We all agree with you on that," and again, "We all agree with you." All the nastiness in the situation was localized at a point in the organization above Dr. Cadman—"he gets constantly subjected to demands for more control"—and the particular object of this statement was, of course, Dr. Suprin.

. . . Ackroyd turned to Schneider. "And where did you say it comes from, again?"

Schneider: "I say from Dr. Suprin. I say, when he heard about family therapy, he wanted to know what was going on. That's not the sort of thing a guy like him would go for."

Ackroyd: "If he made this request of Cadman, I would say it was because he wishes Cadman would control things more. He wants Cadman to get in there and do more directing, and this is one way of making him do it, I suppose."

Schneider: "That's *nothing!* I was speaking to [a social worker] just a little while back, and she was saying, 'Wait till Suprin gets back in February.[1] He's really going to blow up, because patients on the wards are really not moving like they used to. Some have been on the ward over a year. He's going to jump on Cadman and everybody else around here to increase turnover.' Which is something I've been saying all along."

Steinberg "I don't agree. I think they have been moving, but we've got sicker patients now than we used to, and they take

[1] It should be noted that Dr. Suprin was physically not present in the hospital while many of these events took place.

longer. People like Billy [a patient] are puttering along at their own speed."

Ackroyd laughed and slapped his forehead. "Oh God! When they go through the wards, put *him under* the bed, will you? Don't show him to Suprin, whatever you do. I think he spends more time in bed than any other living American."

Steinberg: "So?"

Ackroyd: "So plenty. Unless you're out for trouble, and you'll *get it,* believe you me. You know how Suprin feels about patients staying in bed. Look at Ward B, if you want an answer."

Steinberg: "So we get sicker patients than we used to."

Ackroyd: "I don't care whether we have or not, frankly, so long as they're not in bed when Suprin comes through."

Schneider laughed. "All you have to do is electrify the beds."

Steinberg: "Well, I say we've got a responsibility to treat patients and these include the sicker ones. This is supposed to be a teaching hospital and we're learning what it is to treat the sicker patients. What's wrong with that?"

Ackroyd "No. No. I agree, Doug. That's just the position I've taken several times in Suprin's office when he's been in a mood to throw a few people out. I point out we're here to treat people like that, that the job is more the improving of the liaison and organization of services, and the inspiration through supervision that should take place. I point out that we can always sweep clean, but that we do have an obligation to treat, and to learn."

At this point, in this particular meeting, Dr. Ackroyd turned to a discussion of other matters, and the matter of family therapy was not referred to again. The subordinates were not about to initiate anything on a matter such as that. Therefore, the initiative came by default to be Cadman's. It was only when Dr. Cadman acted—adding the insulting adjective "wild" [2] to the injury of further questioning the professional competence of the staff members to conduct and

---

[2] Probably a historically and professionally significant adjective, since it was used in the title of Freud's paper, "Observations on 'Wild' Psychoanalysis (1910)."

to supervise family therapy—that the relations between Cadman and his subordinates suddenly broke into a knock-down, drag-out battle about something of which none were certain by the time the fighting had terminated.

THE OPENING PHASE OF EPISODE II: DR. CADMAN INCREASES THE PRESSURE

THE MEETING that signaled the start of Episode II began with a warning of what was to happen. One month had elapsed since the precipitating event of Episode I. It was ten minutes after the scheduled beginning of a house staff meeting in Cadman's office, and still only one service consultant and one chief resident were present. Lateness to this regularly scheduled meeting had always occurred to a certain extent. In the last several weeks this lateness had reached unavoidably conspicuous proportions, involving most of the staff group, and cutting off from one-third to one-half of scheduled and available meeting time.

11:10 A.M. Only Stearns and Chapin present. Dr. Cadman continued his dictation to Mrs. O'Toole. He was reading from a text, and she was attempting to transcribe it into shorthand. Cadman was reading with considerable rapidity.

"Wait a minute. Wait a minute, will you?" Mrs. O'Toole complained in a low voice, as she continued to write.

"What's that?" Cadman asked brusquely, interrupting his dictation.

"Wait a minute, will you?" Mrs. O'Toole repeated. "What do you think I am?"

"Whassa matter?" Cadman queried. "Can't you keep up?" he asked pointedly, with a smile.

The mood was one of fight. Dr. Cadman appeared untypically zealous in realizing that mood, in starting a fight, and then relishing its interpersonal consequences. In the following few minutes, he went out of his way to say something antagonistic to his subordinates as they belatedly entered his office. In each case, this had its desired effect. Especially in view of the staff's covertly sensitized condition, it was not long before their response to this aggravating and unstereotypical aggression was made manifest.

Dr. Cardinale entered at 11:15 A.M. He sat down without a word and did not speak once throughout the rest of the meeting.

11:18 A.M. Drs. Clark and Stanley entered and sat down on Dr. Cadman's couch. Clark still wore the dour, glum expression of the preceding week. Stanley also looked glum.

Cadman glanced up at the clock on the wall. He mumbled indistinctly, ". . . burden on me, being this late." [Perhaps the full statement was: you place a burden on me, being this late.]

Clark stared at Cadman. "What's that?" he asked.

Cadman: "Do you have a burden on your soul?" Clark frowned at him, apparently uncomprehending. Cadman proceeded to explain. "The face of the clock tells me that you have a heavy burden on your souls." He smiled at Clark, but Clark only stared back, expressionless. Stanley sat without motion, looking at the point where the two walls intersected with the ceiling above Dr. Cadman.

Cadman's smile died gradually. "I hope I didn't traumatize you," he observed, looking straight at Clark, quietly but with sarcasm.

Still Clark looked Cadman straight back, while Stanley shifted his gaze to the windows.

The expression made current by the Cuban crisis—"They were staring eyeball to eyeball, and somebody just blinked"— comes to mind in reporting this incident. There was to be no blinking of the obviously aggressive nature of the transactions between superordinate and subordinate. But just in case there were, Dr. Cadman underlined his meaning with a smile.

Cadman smiled again. "Now that you have got all the notes caught up," he said to Clark, "there's nothing more for us to fight about."

His message had been received, however, and was soon to be transmitted back with considerable amplification.

"We can always find something to fight about," Clark replied.

It is important to note that it was Dr. Cadman who took the initiative in this incident. His subordinates were still holding back—holding back their presence at meetings in his office, for instance, by their increasing lateness. They were still disengaging themselves from the negative relations existing between themselves and the person for whom they possessed such positive thoughts and feelings; and still refusing to address the issue that separated them from the kindly figure with whom they wished to be so close. By initiating, Dr. Cadman both opened up and added to the dynamics underlying the events about to happen. It was "obvious" that this new behavior from Cadman—certainly not the Cadman of old—was "really" initiated by the source of all initiative, Dr. Suprin. It was "obvious" that in feeling angry, this anger must not have come from the source of all love, Dr. Cadman, but from the source of all anger, Dr. Suprin. Therefore, the anger was to be directed to the "real" source, not to the immediately apparent one.

However, these displacements and projections were some time in making themselves apparent. As before, we shall trace the build-up of these pressures and the defensive manifestation of these reifications by following the historical and dynamic development of the incident.

To return to the meeting in progress, the exchange between Drs. Cadman and Clark was followed by almost a minute of silence. Then, after some intervening discussion, Dr. Cadman initiated a new topic.

Cadman: "I have another project I would like you to work with me on. I would like it so that we would meet in this meeting more briefly, but more often, perhaps once a day. I find the need to meet with you more often. It is embarrassing to me that I should feel out of touch with the organization, and find myself being held responsible for things that are going on that I have never heard of." He laughed. No one else did. "There have been a lot of changes in the organization over the last few years," Cadman continued, "and I think the time has come for us to clarify what some of these are. Do I make myself clear?"

Herewith, Dr. Cadman presented the first of the two major themes around which he based his initiations upon his subordinates. The proposed change in timetable was based on a genuinely felt need on Cadman's part to restructure his day, and that of the subordinates and the superordinates around him, so as to eliminate a situation he found to be no longer tolerable. As presented in Chapter 5, this situation required Dr. Cadman to check every morning with Dr. Suprin. During this early morning interaction, the two executives would review together the progress of certain patients on the wards. Quite often, Dr. Suprin would ask questions of Dr. Cadman that required Cadman to return to his office and spend significant time and effort contacting his house staff subordinates in order to obtain the necessary answers. These he would then relay to Dr. Suprin, who thereupon made further inquiries that demanded further investigation on the part of Dr. Cadman. Dr. Cadman was tired of navigating between these requests for information and the source of their answers. His suggested revision of the timetable was based on a desire to place his superordinate and his subordinates in closer contact, so that questions and answers could be obtained more expeditiously, and with less inconvenience to himself.

Another factor involved was the subordinates' disengagement from their superordinate, as indicated in Episode I. They had been disappointed by Cadman's decision not to lead. This had left them with strong feelings that they were still attempting to withhold. The result for Cadman was that he felt even more out of touch with the organization beneath him. It was perhaps the last straw that broke the camel's back

—an expression Cadman was fond of using in diagnosing the precipitating events in patients' psychoses. Feeling embarrassed, Cadman decided to act, and the proposed change in timetable was the result.

Yet his subordinates seemed to experience real difficulty in perceiving this initiation as "really" coming from Dr. Cadman, based on his feelings and his objectives in the matter. They could more easily interpret this sort of thing as coming to them from Dr. Suprin through Dr. Cadman. Any administrative initiative and any organizational changes seemed more naturally to originate from Dr. Suprin, based on his attributed and real feelings for neat organization and tight controls, and his objectives of hierarchialization and rationalization of the management structure. As such, Cadman's suggestions tended to evoke the customary response of the staff against any perceived attempt to infringe their cherished and somewhat illusory freedom of decentralization, and to incur their resistance to such obviously "creeping bureaucracy."

The rapidity with which the house staff began to think of Dr. Suprin is manifest in their replies to Dr. Cadman.

Chapin: "I think I speak for all the chiefs when I say that the chiefs have felt the need for more direct contact with the teaching that could be made available to us. This has come up in the meetings we have had. There is some feeling of trepidation and embarrassment about approaching—uh—Dr. Suprin, especially. (Pause) I guess since I've been here, I've had about two hours—perhaps four or five—with Dr. Suprin. I think the others have had the same experience as mine. I know with George it has been the same. Sure, the door is open, but many invisible chains bar the way. I think if we could meet sometimes with Dr. Suprin, it would make for the running of a better hospital. I don't know how much time it would take. Probably not much. What do you think, George?"

Carver: "I agree. I think it would be very useful for us as chiefs to meet with Dr. Suprin."

Chapin: "This is our idea that comes out of our own needs. I think the way we think of it is not so much to get decisions out of these meetings—I don't think any of us wants that—but just to discuss whatever it is we want to talk about. I know that something like that appeals to me."

In other words, the house staff had the wishful but unrealistic fantasy of sitting next to the source of power in the organization while at the same time retaining their freedom to decide and their independence from the decisiveness residing in both the superintendency and the superintendent. Also, that they might be able to "just discuss" with a man whose dislike of just discussing was proverbial and real. After a pause Dr. Cadman proceeded with what he appeared to have in mind. Perhaps he was not excited about hearing how much the chiefs wanted to listen to Dr. Suprin. Perhaps he wanted them to listen to him for a change. Perhaps he realized what was involved in this seemingly unwitting change from his proposed meeting to one with Suprin, but was not ready to confront this.

Cadman: "I have been thinking of a better way of organizing the day. What would you think if it were to start at eight?"

Carver, Clark, and Stearns objected, each pointing out that the nursing service needed more time than one hour after going on duty at 7 A.M. to get organized for morning report.

Cadman continued to press his points. He most definitely took the initiative. He put forth his ideas, did not allow himself to be sidetracked, and held people to a discussion of the issues he raised. He appeared to be fed up with being "out of touch" and was definitely attempting to rectify matters. He presented a proposed timetable he had worked out. The protests were not long in coming.

. . . Dr. Ackroyd: "I don't think this is too relevant, but I can't help mentioning all the military analogies that are being thrown around here. You know, teaching formations and all that stuff."

Cadman (matter-of-factly) : "That's right."

Ackroyd (laughing) : "Wow! This *is* getting like the army. I'm going to start doing my physical exercises tomorrow."

". . . annex of Fort Dix," added Dr. Schneider from the back of the room.

Carver: "This is another similarity between all this and the military. As is also the case in the military, there seems to be some doubt about the purpose of all this."

Cadman looked at him levelly. "The purpose of all this is (1) *time*—you know what I mean?—and (2) purposeful organization. You know what I mean? *Clean.*"

Dr. Stearns made a plea for loosening up the strict time allotments in the proposed table. "It takes time to let the residents talk, and others talk. Human intercourse takes time."

Other objections were registered. There followed a discussion of the variety of services offered on the wards, which became an argument among midlevel personnel as to the caliber of one of the nonmedical services. Carver then observed that he preferred to deal with his residents one by one, in his office.

Cadman: "That's time!"

Carver: "Pardon me?"

Cadman (emphatically) : "That takes time. *Time. Time. Time.* That's the problem, administratively.". . .

Chapin: "As I see it, it does a lot to overcome what I might call 'Old Chiefs' Disease.' (Laughter) It helps get things more organized."

Carver: "I don't know that things are that *dis*organized as it is." To Cadman, "Do you?"

Cadman: "Listen. I had two chiefs here recently that caused me to spend about fifty years of my time with the nursing staff, just to hold off homicide."

(Laughter) 12:00 noon. The meeting ended.

It should be pointed out that while changes had been occurring in interpersonal relations between superordinate and subordinates in the house management group, no changes took place in the round of daily events that comprised the workday for these people. Such changes in the objective schedule of activities were being discussed, but even if adopted, were not to be placed into effect until the beginning of the next academic year. Patients were still being admitted, diagnosed, treated, transferred, and discharged as before. Ward conferences and treatment meetings were being held as before. Didactic seminars and group meetings were taking place according to the existing schedule. None of the routine activities of the Institute appeared to manifest the underlying development of the subjective processes we are highlighting.[3] This may explain why the covert processes of Episode I and Episode II were so slow in working themselves through. It was now over a month since Episode I had begun, and it was to be almost another two months before Episode II evolved through to any sort of resolution. It was as though the covert processes went into some sort of suspended animation between meetings of the house management group, terminating at a given point at the end of one week's meeting, and resuming at the same point one week later. In this sense, the group manifested the ability that some individuals have of going to bed and picking up a dream where they left it the night before.

THE MAIN EVENT

THE STAGE had now been set for phase two of the second incident: the protest over "wild family therapy." This occurred

---

3 Perhaps an observer on the wards might have been able to detect the working through of management issues in the behavior of service staffs and patients. However, the observer in this study was not on the wards, and therefore—much like the executives he was observing—had no direct access to this range of data, crucial though they were to comprehend the results of the executives' administrative efforts.

at a meeting of the staff group in Dr. Cadman's office two and a half months after the precipitating event of Episode I. Again, the issue of lateness to the meeting arose. As usual, the meeting was scheduled for 11:00 A.M. At 11:05 the observer was the only person in the office besides Dr. Cadman. At 11:10 Dr. Stearns arrived. By 11:20 several were still absent, but Cadman began the meeting anyway.

Dr. Steinberg came in. The real business of the episode was now about to begin.

Dr. Cadman held up a paper he had on his desk, which he had received from Dr. Steinberg. "I got this, by the way," said Cadman. "I think it is fine, except that it doesn't answer the question I asked you."

Steinberg: "About family therapy?"

Cadman smiled. "Yes, but it doesn't answer my question. Otherwise it is fine, and I appreciate getting it." Steinberg shrugged and remained silent. Cadman went on with the conversation he had been having with Dr. Stearns. . . .

At 11:20 A.M. Dr. Cadman asked, "Is Al here?"

Steinberg replied that the service consultant in question was away sick, and explained the nature of the disorder.

Cadman: "That's too bad, because I have something very crucial to discuss today, and it involves the family therapy workshop. I have what you gave me on it, Doug, and it's O.K. except that it doesn't answer my question. The thing that's worrying me, I don't find here. And what is worrying me is that there have been three instances now where residents, on their own initiative, have gotten the whole family together without checking it out with anybody first, and the whole upshot of it has been that they have upset the hell out of everybody concerned."

Carver leaned forward in his chair and, looking at the floor, began to shake his head.

Cadman continued: "I just can't tolerate this sort of thing going on around here. It's not good for the patients. It's not good for the family. It's not good for anybody."

The protest was not long in coming.

Carver: "Wellll. . . ."

Cadman: "Wait a minute! I'm not finished yet. Wait till I'm finished, and then you can tear into it all you like. I'm responsible for what goes on with the patients around here, and I say that this sort of thing has got to stop, and the only way that I can see is for it to stop entirely, and then if anyone wants to do something like this, they can take it up with Pete [Ackroyd]. It will be up to Pete to decide if they can go ahead, and if he decides they can deviate from this policy, then it will be only in set instances. This is the only way I know that we can control it, and also know what's going on around here in this hospital."

As the reader is about to see, this meeting really exploded. Cadman and Carver came close to calling each other names. They were soon yelling at each other, and Cadman actually did get to swearing. During this meeting the group fought Cadman's initiations and his assertions of authority every inch of the way. There is no attempt to indicate by this that there was no reasonable basis for their various and collective stands, but their resistance to even the most reasonable of Cadman's statements multiplied the unreasonableness on both sides of the dispute.

Steinberg: "What is it that you are objecting to?"
Cadman: "What I am objecting to is all the wild psychotherapy, uh, all the wild family therapy that's going on these days. The residents all seem to be . . . uh . . . to think . . . to want to get the whole family together these days. It's not that I object so much to their getting the family together, if it's all right with their chief and the social worker, or even the therapy. But it shouldn't be *wild therapy!* That's what I object to. I object to *wild* family therapy. . . ."

It is obvious that this was a legitimate and praiseworthy professional objective, one which in other situations the subordinates—who as trained professionals cared equally for the proper treatment of their patients—might well have replied quietly, succinctly, and unemotionally: "We object to wild family therapy, too. What can we do together to make sure that none of it occurs?" However, there were other issues to be addressed, which made this ideally rational and appropriate answer the *least* represented of all responses to Cadman's initiation.

". . . This is the odoriferous part of it all," Cadman continued. "This wildness of the therapy that seems to be going on now. Where the residents get the families together as a group, and get them all stirred up, so that they beat the hell out of each other, and nobody knows what the hell to do about it, not even the residents. *That's* what I object to."

Steinberg was searching for a specific source of irritation. "I think you are referring to [a resident's] work with a family, but I don't think you would call that wild family therapy. The family has come to have a whole new concept of what it is that is making that boy sick, which they never would have got except in family therapy. I don't see how you can say. . . ."

Cadman smiled as he interrupted. "That is not what I am objecting to then, is it? I'll take your word for it. I have to. I have nothing else to go on, do I?"

Steinberg: "But I think it *is* what you are referring to, even if you don't admit it. And I wish you wouldn't take my word for it, but would read some of [the resident's] notes. Let me bring. . . ."

Cadman: "What I am objecting to is wild family therapy, that's all. It's really very simple."

Steinberg: "But it isn't that simple. If you would just let me bring in some of the notes, you would see that. . . ."

Cadman: "Why is he catatonic?"

Steinberg: "What?"

Cadman: *"I said,* why is the boy catatonic?"

Steinberg: "Why don't you ask him?" (This was an angry remark.)

Cadman: "You see! You won't answer my question. You give me a lot of answers to a lot of questions I never asked, but you can't answer the one I do."

Steinberg: "But it's not that simple."

Cadman smiled. "I know," he replied softly, implying that the difficulty in replying to his request resided in the staff, not in the patient.

Clark: "I mean, I don't think you have the whole story." He then gave an example of a family group that was working very successfully on his service, with the full cooperation of the nurses and social workers.

The reader will recognize that this was irrelevant to the problem as Cadman had defined it. Cadman had stated and reiterated that his concern was with *wild* family therapy, not with controlled and productive family therapy. However, the sense of injury among his subordinates was too great for them to make such distinctions, to do much business with his delineation of the matter.

Clark continued: "I think this kind of thing can be of great benefit. I would hate to have to tell my residents that they are not to see any more families, just because a few of the groups were handled poorly."

Cadman: "That's exactly what I'm saying."

Clark laughed. "I know it is."

However, the unleashed emotional forces within the group had gained too much momentum to be stopped by this small voice of reason. The argument continued to grow in volume and intensity.

Steinberg: "I think you should know what you are forbidding before you go ahead and forbid it. I'm not certain what it is."

Cadman: "I've told you. I want to bring this family group business back into line. It has gotten out of hand somehow. *The residents are not here to train themselves as social workers.* That's what I am saying. They have other things to learn first, and they should let the social workers do what they are trained to do. What I am saying is, that if a resident wants to get a family together, he should check with Pete first, and Pete should O.K. it if he thinks it is all right. Otherwise, there should be none, or we won't be able to control what's going on around here. The way it is now, it's gotten out of hand.". . .

Cadman: "Let me say again that I am not against all family groups, but that I am against family therapy, especially wild family therapy."

Carver: "Welll . . ."

Clark: "I'd like to express further regrets about this. . . ."

Clark had, several minutes before, signified his understanding of what it was that Cadman was talking about. His continued "regrets" pertained not so much to the matter of understanding as to *the wish not to understand,* because, once understood, what Cadman was saying was professionally so incontrovertible that *there would have been left nothing to fight about.* A number of the staff still felt the necessity to fight, to let go with their accumulated bad feelings toward their benevolent mentor who would lead only in the sense of initiating against them, rather than against their common "enemies." This process had begun and could not be stopped until a great deal of these energies had been dissipated. This was what continued to move the meeting, and it was related only tangentially to matters of understanding or not understanding what Cadman had said. No matter what he might have said in his current initiating, authoritative mode—except perhaps that they were all wonderful people, doing excellent work, who had nothing to worry about from anybody else in the organization, because he would protect them from all intruders—a number of his subordinates would object to it even before he was finished saying it.

. . . Carver turned to Cadman and said: "On several of the points you raised, I would take exception."

Cadman looked Carver full in the face. "Look. There is a perfect example of what I am talking about right on your service."

Carver: "Oh? Who?"

It is hard to describe the tone of voice used here, but it was such that the observer felt that what Carver really wanted to say was, "Says who?"

Cadman: "John."

Carver: "Who?"

Cadman: "The Smith boy." (Disguised names, of course.)

Carver: *"Welll nowww . . ."*

Steinberg: "I disagree." He was about to continue, when Cadman interrupted in a most unusual manner.

"I DON'T CARE WHETHER YOU DO," Cadman shouted. Then he continued in a more collected tone of voice. "Since I have to take responsibility for cases like this, that's the way I see it."

If Dr. Suprin had made a statement like this, the chances are that it would have been recognized for its worth. However, with Dr. Cadman it was ignored, behaviorally at least. Subordinates continued right on with their dispute.

Steinberg: "If you'll let me present the data. Let me bring in the notes and read them over, and you'll find out that there has been nothing wild about it."

Carver to Cadman: "From what you have said, I gather that you think the family groups have grown out of hand, that they have grown like Topsy, and to single them out in any way for this sort of criticism I think only means that they are being scapegoated for other things."

Here we see the preliminary attempt to ferret out what was "really" going on in Cadman's mind, to find out what was "really" bothering him, other than wild family therapy, and to determine who was "really" behind all this untypical behavior on the part of their superordinate.

Steinberg: "Would you like to see the notes?"

Cadman: "But I know the case. I heard it reviewed at staff [conference]. That's why I have so many questions."

Carver (disgustedly in a low voice) : "Thirty minutes worth."

Cadman turned to him. "I have another example, if you want to hear about that, too." He paused, thought for a minute, then continued, "I can't remember his name."

Carver: "To hear you talk, one would think that we never

reviewed any of these cases ourselves at all, but we do. We go over just such considerations as the ones you have been raising in our discussion and seminars and things like that. And very thoroughly, I might add."

"THAT'S JUST WHAT I CAN'T SEEM TO GET A RE-PORT ON," shouted Cadman suddenly, the color welling up in his neck and cheeks.

Carver was taken aback. "On what?" he asked quietly.

"On the *wild* ones," Cadman replied.

Carver: "I'm not too sure what you mean by 'wild ones,' but I think it is a very serious accusation."

There was a silence in the room for an instant as Cadman looked at Carver with something resembling a smile.

It seemed to the observer that Carver had gone too far in his last statement, that Cadman knew it, that Carver knew it, and that the group was waiting Cadman's response.

"It's not an accusation," Cadman said quietly.

Carver: "What is it, then?"

Cadman: "It's an observation. Just an observation."

Carver smiled and shook his head. "All right. I'll admit that certain paranoid tendencies may have gotten the better of me."

Cadman: "Look, all I am saying is that there should be no wild family therapy. Period. I'm not saying that the residents should never meet with the family, or even conduct some therapy with them. But under adequate supervision, and not in their first year."

"Oh *well!*" exclaimed Carver in a loud voice. "This is very different from the way you started out."

Cadman: "What is?"

Carver: "What you've just said."

Cadman: "Is it?"

Carver: "Yes it is. It is not the way you started out at all."

Cadman (quietly): "It was the only thing I ever had in mind." . . .

At this point, Dr. Stearns broke in with an expression of frustrated cohesiveness.

Stearns: "I don't know what has been going on here, but it seems that everybody is talking about something different. We are really not disagreeing. I don't think we know what the others are saying."

Ackroyd and the others regarded Dr. Stearns in silence for a brief period. No one responded to these remarks.

The observer's impression was that Stearns' remarks were out of tenor with the rest of the meeting. Nobody else wanted to stop fighting just yet. People were not in the mood to make peace.

. . . Steinberg: "Nonsense."

Cadman: "Oh, yes!"

Steinberg: "Nonsense."

Cadman: "Oh yes! You'll see. . . . I want to see case work-ups done in three days."

Carver: *"Three days!* Impossible."

Cadman: "How long do you think they should take, then?"

Carver: "I think they should take two weeks at the shortest."

Cadman's voice rose almost to a shout, and his face became redder than it already was. "TWO WEEKS! Oh, shit! If you'll pardon the language. Let's cut the crap, Carver. What do you think this is, a country club? We are supposed to be doing work around here, you know. You've got to learn to slice the baloney sometime. I've already compromised for a week, but that is as far as I go. From now on, I expect those anamneses to be in within a week."

This struggle between the clinical director and his subordinates continued to the point of physical exhaustion. Finally, Dr. Cadman appeared to give up the fight. He concluded in a quiet voice:

"Occupational therapy is for occupational therapists. And family therapy may be therapeutic, but our residents have got to get their *own* therapy on their *own* time. They should get their dramatics on their own time as well, and with a good coach, too, so that they don't waste their talents. I know what you are thinking, but I have no quarrel with individual initiative. I have no quarrel with [a resident conducting family therapy]. But it is a risky business. So much of this family business seems to be activity for activity's sake, and I don't like it. There is too much of this sort of thing—activity for activity's sake. Relief of anxiety, that's what it is. Relief of anxiety. There has been an increasing amount of anxiety in the hospital over the last three years, and it has got to stop. We've got to stop it."

There was a note of victory in the bantering among the staff that followed. The meeting relaxed and became more casual.

Chapin smiled. "Who has it?" he asked. Several people laughed.
Clark: "Where does it come from?" More laughter.
Steinberg: "You know, this meeting has reminded me of an old African proverb I heard once: when the elephants fight, the grass gets trampled." General laughter.

The observer took this to mean that when the staff fight, the patients suffer. But later it turned out that several of the chiefs—particularly Dr. Carver—felt that the chiefs were the functional equivalent of the grass in this proverb. Probably everyone else in the meeting was also feeling more than slightly trampled on by this time, regardless of what might eventually happen to the patients.

Cadman (smiling): "Well, Doug, you know what I always say to you: that the one thing I can't delegate is my scapegoat function. As far as that goes, I am going to be taking it up with my in'ards tonight. And," he laughed, "tomorrow morning around 2 A.M."

It was obvious that Dr. Cadman was one of those feeling trampled upon, and he was herewith appealing to the elephants to cease and desist. But not all were inclined to do so. The emotionality of the group dictated against that possibility. There was still a residual desire to fight rather than to understand. This was demonstrated in a flare-up about nursing that occurred at the end of the meeting. It was in the quieter days and weeks to come that Cadman's subordinates worked to understand what was going on at "the top," and what was going on in their relations to "the top." In this process, both the functionality and the dysfunctionality of the subordinates' responses to the executive role constellation were illustrated.

WORKING THROUGH THE CONSEQUENCES OF DR. CADMAN'S ASSERTIVENESS: SUBORDINATES' REAFFIRMATION OF THE EXECUTIVE ROLE CONSTELLATION

CADMAN'S ASSERTIVENESS set in motion a series of responses that took some time to work through. This required some energy on the part of all members of the house staff group, more for some and less for others. This process was most clear-cut among the chief residents. The data obtained from the chiefs reflected their working through of the disturbance to their reifications of the executives, based wholely on the perceived differentiation within the executive role constellation.

We shall use the data obtained from the chiefs here to demonstrate the working through of Cadman's unaccustomed assertiveness in matters of administration, and to communicate the manner in which the pre-existing system of reifications was reinstated in the minds of subordinates with little modification. This re-established the certainty and the warmth of consensus among equally beset peers as to what was "really going on" in the upper segments of the organization where so many important things were happening that influenced subordinates' lives, about which they had little knowledge and over which they had no control.

Two days after the above meeting of the house staff in

454 *Consequences of the Executive Role Constellation*

Dr. Cadman's office, the chiefs met together as they regularly did on Fridays for lunch. They met in Dr. Carver's office.

The chiefs expressed surprise and wonderment over what had transpired in that meeting in Cadman's office, and what the undercurrents and hidden causes might have been. They felt that they had not really known what was going on, and still did not know. They asked each other if they felt as excited as each had felt then. The consensus was that a considerable amount of cooling off had taken place, although concern over the changing atmosphere in the hospital still remained. Carver turned to the observer and said that he still thought Steinberg's aphorism about the elephants fighting and the grass getting trampled was the best possible summary of what it was that had gone on in the meeting. His comments indicated that he thought of the chiefs as being the "grass" and, by implication, that the top executive group were the "elephants" who were fighting.

"I was sure surprised to see how much Cadman's behavior has changed," observed Cardinale. The others nodded. "You know I attended his post-graduate lecture the other day, and he got onto the business of work-ups, just like at the meeting."

Carver nodded.

Cardinale: "He repeated again what he said to us about his thinking that work-ups should be done in three days, and he made a big point of it. He got quite excited when he said he had to compromise and settle for *seven days at the most!* But *no more!* He said: 'You've got to get the work done, got to move it along. The cases can't just stall around. They have to be worked up quickly and completed just as soon as possible.' He was most outspoken about this, and he was assertive and aggressive. Quite demanding, in fact. So unlike Cadman. I could hardly believe what I was hearing."

The others shook their heads.

"It's funny," said Carver. "There is something going on around here."

"Yes. I wonder what he is up to?" asked Clark.

Carver: "It sounds like the executive committee is in a real turmoil about something." (Silence) "The place is sure changing," Carver mused quietly.

The chiefs compared their impressions about the increasing directiveness from the top of the staff hierarchy and the diminishing freedom at the level of service administration.

. . . Clark: "No. After next year, it will be just flunkies." He paused, and then asked in a wondering tone of voice, "What does Cadman think he's *doing?*"

Carver laughed and shook his head. "I sure as hell don't know," he replied.

Cardinale: "And such unaccustomed behavior, too."

Clark: "I'll say."

Observer: "You had no idea what was going to take place in that Wednesday meeting?"

Clark: "No indeed."

Carver: "None whatsoever. You could have bowled me over with a feather when he came out with that business about wild family therapy."

"You hadn't heard about it either?" the observer asked Cardinale.

"No," Cardinale replied. "Not me."

Carver: "I felt that what he was throwing at us was so unjustified that I was enraged. I knew it wasn't getting us anywhere, but I couldn't give up trying to set him straight as to just what *was* going on. He made me mad the way he acted as though he knew all about what was going on, when there wasn't a word of truth in it, so far as I was concerned. That business about the boy being catatonic because of family therapy, that's just nonsense. Pure nonsense."

Clark: "I felt that way, too. But I gave up on it after I saw how set he was. It sure wasn't Cadman as I've come to think of him."

Carver: "There wasn't a thing you could say to make him change his opinion. He had his mind all made up on the matter before the meeting began. That's the sort of thing you'd expect from Suprin, but not from Cadman! *Well!* This place is getting to be like the army: kiss up and kick down."

This statement was too extreme for Clark's more moderate views. He stated what he considered to be a correction of Carver's oversimplified conception of the different authority relations emanating downward from Suprin and Cadman. However, within a matter of seconds thereafter, Clark slipped back unnoticed into the same pattern of reified thought as that more explicitly and more forcefully manifested by Carver.

"I don't know about that, George," Clark objected. "It's not as simple as you think. Even I was surprised when I went to see Suprin about something one day, and talked a bit about his philosophy on how to get things done in organizations. He was telling me you have to take things slowly, you have to let people express their opinions, you can't expect to change things too fast because people will feel disturbed and build up resistance to change. All that sort of thing. I was surprised. He seemed to be very sensitive to that sort of thing, at least from the way he talked. And Cadman told me once that you can't get a thing done in a group. Groups are no good. You have to do things individually. So you never can tell. I though he was sold on group work."

The rest of the group were still musing over the disruption of their notions about the central executive triad. Either way they were not listening to Dr. Clark, or they could make nothing of what he had said.

Carver shook his head. "I don't get it," he said. "I don't get it." Cardinale: "Whatever it is, I would expect it from Suprin, but not from Cadman. That sort of thing is so unusual coming from Cadman, it makes it hard to take."

Dr. Clark's preoccupations fell back into line with those of the group. In the following statement, he set aside the carefully balanced observations he had just reported to the group, and returned to the less complicated symbolizations of the top executives induced by the differentiation of roles in the executive constellation. These reifications were not only less complicated; they also were more meaningful in a primitive sense, more emotionally significant and wishfully satisfying than the colder, more abstract, almost exhaustingly untenable insights into the true multidimensionality of each top executive in his relations with other executives and with subordinates. Clark's statement below illustrates that these reifications of superordinate figures were not subject to full and complete control on the part of those who possessed them, but kept reappearing and reactivating certain chains of consequences, sometimes despite the conscious realization and the better judgment of the persons involved.

Clark: "You know what I think? I think Suprin is really starting to take over the place. He's been here for two or three years now, and he's starting to make his move to take over the place —for real, this time. When he came in, he must have sized up the place and decided what he wanted done with it in the first six months he was here, and he's been lying low for a while, waiting for when he thought was the right time, and this is it. I don't know how this is going to affect his work. . . ."

. . . Carver: "I don't know, but one thing is sure, and that is that the executive is in a real turmoil these days. Did you hear what Suprin said . . . ?"

Clark: "No. What?"

Carver: "He said . . . Can you imagine? . . ."

Clark: "No! Really?"

Carver: "So it shows what a state of mind Suprin must be in these days." . . .

"You know, Bob," said Carver, "if it is true what you say about these changes coming from Suprin, how come they always come to us as Cadman's proposals? That's the thing I don't get."

Clark: "I don't know. I can't get it either."

Here we have the most concise delineation of the dilemma that underlay the entire second episode. The observable fact of Cadman's initiative ran contrary to the reified fact that Suprin possessed all the initiative in the top management situation. This produced a cognitive stalemate. Historically speaking, it was at this point that the observer began to get a specific interpretive notion as to some of the dynamics of what he had been observing over the preceding months. The chiefs, and others on the house staff, simply could not give true credence to the possibility that action might be originating from Dr. Cadman, not always from Dr. Suprin; that Cadman might be acting to reduce genuine problems that were frustrating to him, rather than transmitting Suprin's actions through make-believe problems spuriously chosen for that purpose, having nothing to do with Cadman in any direct personal sense. For the house staff, Dr. Cadman was primarily a man to *help others* with problems. For confirmation of this belief, we have only to look at Cadman's behavior toward his subordinates during the first episode, when he sought to help them with their problems of wanting him to lead them in a counterattack against insurgents from Dr. Bolen's clinic. Now, however, Cadman was attempting to take active leadership, to act in an aggressive problem-solving way. He was addressing his *own* problems, and was requiring and requesting *others to help him*. His subordinates' deeply held beliefs about him could not keep up with such stimulus variability. They regressed back to the oversimplified reification of him, induced partly by the primitive, familistic role complementarity that existed for all to observe within the executive role constellation, and partly by the wishes which these subordinates themselves infused into the system of relations between them and the top executives. As a corollary of this, their reification of Dr. Suprin provided the most efficient conceptual mechanism for them to understand what it was that affected them so deeply. Dr. Suprin must have been behind it all.

Nonetheless, the brute, stubborn reality that it was Cadman who was acting up, while Suprin was often absent from the hospital, kept nagging away at their interpretive scheme of things, as the above statements indicate. There was to be no resolution of this impasse.

Carver: "One thing is sure. Cadman is not good at it. He got us all angry at the meeting. I thought the way you're supposed to handle it is to mention a topic and let your subordinates give their thoughts and opinions on the matter, and then take these and come to some agreement on the matter. But on Wednesday he just blasted right from the start. He certainly wasn't the Cadman that we all know and love."

The behavior in that Wednesday meeting demonstrated the *active* resistance of subordinates to Cadman's stepping out of role. The above indicates the more *passive* and more pervasive form that the same resistance took. Since their reifications of the management system were being violated, the subordinates' tendencies were to limit—or at least to hedge—their further contributions to it. Under such conditions, further contributions made somewhat of a risky interpersonal investment. They felt safer, and more certain of the payoff at lower levels in the organization, in their dealings with residents, nonmedical service staff, and patients. It was to this level that the subordinates tended to withdraw psychically —to get on with the job at the service level—until the executive situation had "settled down" and "got back to normal." Required interactions with executive figures remained the same, but the amount of cathexis that made meaningful transactions out of these routine interactions was significantly reduced. The subordinates tended to lie back and expect to be stroked by the principles of good human relations— "I thought the way you're supposed to handle it is to mention a topic and let your subordinates give their thoughts and opinions on the matter, and then take these and come to some agreement on the matter." But Cadman was too busy prodding to be bothered stroking, and this brought to mind a different chain of thoughts than the one usually associated with him.

Clark: "That reminds me of some stories that I heard once about Cadman. . . . I couldn't believe them at the time, but now maybe they make a bit of sense to me. It seems that [in his previous job] the people on the wards were frightened for their lives of him. Some said he was the most frightening person they ever met in their lives. Can you imagine that? A real Napoleon! They tell stories like his finding an attendant asleep on the job, and firing him on the spot." (Silence.)

The others apparently did not know what to make of this. They had difficulty responding.

Clark: "Well, anyway, it's an interesting story."

Cardinale: "Maybe we're beginning to see the other side of Cadman."

Carver: "Well, I objected to what he had to say, but what got me most annoyed was his manner."

One week later there was further evidence that the executive role constellation was still figured importantly among the chiefs' more salient preoccupations. One of the chiefs complained to his peers about Cadman's response to certain information that the chief had provided him. He stated his wish that he had never brought the matter up the chain of command in the first place. He had done so only on the instigation of his service consultant. His peers disagreed with him about the appropriateness of his sentiments on the matter.

Clark: "I would say that Dr. Cadman had a right to know about [things like that]. I wouldn't worry about it if I were you. Dr. Cadman has great love for his residents, from what I observe. When one of his residents is in some difficulty, Cadman will give him fatherly advice and help him out considerably. It's just as Suprin said during the medical meeting on Wednesday."

Carver made an inquiring gesture, and Chapin replied: "He said that Cadman had a soft spot in his heart for all the residents. He said it in such a way that it was clear he thought that Cadman's soft spot was upwardly displaced to between the ears. He implied that Cadman was being unrealistic. . . . I was offended by the whole thing. It was obvious that he was getting into dangerous territory. There was a gale of inappropriate laughter at what he had to say. I didn't laugh. I wouldn't gratify him to that extent, when he talks like that. I think it's very cruel and cutting. He destatused Cadman right there in front of all the residents. We still have hatchetmen around here, only they used to cut off heads. Now they cut off dicks."

Clark: "I disagree with Suprin. I don't think Suprin is more realistic than Cadman. I know that's the way he likes to think of himself. I think *Cadman* is more realistic. It's a different sort of reality."

Chapin: "There's an internal reality and an external reality, and I guess Cadman's is more of the first."

Clark: "I think Suprin is more practical."

Chapin: "I wouldn't say that. It depends on what you mean by practical. I would say that *Cadman* is more practical. For one thing, he doesn't always go around shooting his mouth off."

Clark: "More pragmatic, then. Oh, I don't know. He's certainly a lot more external than Dr. Cadman.

Chapin: "Suprin is active. Cadman is passive."

Carver shook his head. "Something must be going on up there in the way of agonizing reappraisals. What do you make of all the stuff that's coming down from the top these days?". . .

At this point the established reifications of the figures within the executive role constellation were reaffirmed with their accustomed clarity, simplicity, and forcefulness. It became apparent that whatever disruption to the system had occurred during the two episodes we have reported, the equilibrium was being re-established for the time being around the compelling symbolic significance of role complementarity in the executive constellation.

CHAPTER 17

A Symbolic Interpretation of the Two Critical Episodes

IN STUDYING subordinates' responses to the executive role constellation, a distinction needs to be made between what the constellation was "really like," and what the people around it—especially those who had little or no access to it—thought and felt about its members, and about the relations between its members.

THE MEANING OF THE EXECUTIVE ROLE CONSTELLATION TO SUBORDINATES

THE IMPACT of the executive role constellation upon subordinates was complex. First, the subordinates responded to the executives *as individuals*. Each of the executives had a personality and a specialized role performance in interpersonal and administrative settings, as has been described. Subordinates' relations with executives were influenced by the symbolic value of each executive's role performance in the minds of subordinates. This symbolic value arose partly from the nature of each executive's own role performance. However, it also arose in part from the properties of the *constellation* in which the individual executive roles were imbedded. The constellation's properties of role differentiation and role complementarity were a major source of impact upon subordinates.

The symbolic meaningfulness to subordinates of each executive was related in part, but only in part, to what that executive *was* and what he *did.* This meaningfulness was also delineated by what he *was not,* and what he did *not do.* Whatever a given executive was not, or did not do, there was an organizationally juxtaposed executive who was a graphic exemplar of that lacking quality or activity. It has already been demonstrated that subordinates had great difficulty responding to one senior figure without responding explicitly or implicitly to one or more of the other senior figures at the same time. In this sense, all evaluations of the top men by their subordinates were comparative. These tended to be paired comparisons. A wide variety of pairs was chosen for a wide variety of evaluative purposes. As Chapters 15 and 16 indicate, the comparisons between Drs. Cadman and Suprin were particularly rich in implications.

Subordinates' responses to the executive role constellation were also a function of *their own personalities.* The "eye of the beholder" was particularly active in assigning meanings to behaviors and relationships as symbolically rich as those we have described among the superordinate triad of the Institute. Subordinates had various motives in comparing their superordinates: to figure out the "politics" going on between the executives; to keep superordinates separated and as powerless as possible; and more positively, to learn from these superiors, to take from their example as much as could be useful for one's personal and professional development. Certainly the amount of time spent speculating about the executives—indulging free association in one's thoughts, feelings, and wishes about them, often in the company of peers or subordinates—was out of proportion to the actual amount of time spent in concrete interaction with the objects of speculation. These processes of fantasy and subsequent reification figured importantly in the covert dynamics of administration in the services.

In working through these processes of fantasy and reification, the subordinates established certain attitudes and evaluations that served to orient their concrete interaction with executives. These orientations were sometimes appropriate to the form and content of an interaction with an executive, but they sometimes had nothing to do with the way the executive was acting or what he was trying to accomplish in a given situation. In other words, the attitudinal sets of the subordinates, based on their own needs, were both accurate and inaccurate. Their accuracy tended to increase, however, as they elicited verifying behavior from the executives. The executives, despite intentions to change, were often induced by these set responses from their subordinates to act in ways different from their intentions.

The executives were complex men, forming a complex social entity. They resisted categorization in any static typology of roles. The character of these men and their interrelations was not the caricature that was so easily invoked to encapsulate them conceptually and orectically, both by those at some distance from them, and occasionally by the executives themselves. When a role scheme has primitive, archetypically familistic properties, it is difficult and time consuming to prevent one's view of it from being overly colored by unconscious wishes and fantasies. There were other, more pressing tasks that required the attention of the hospital staff. The archetypes filtered into the administrative dynamics of the hospital through the interstices of the staff's professional work, and were explicitly reinforced by the persons figured in these symbolic processes.

In the symbolic representation of the executive role constellation, the images of the executives tended to become differentiated and polarized around such issues as activity *vs.* passivity, egoism *vs.* altruism, will *vs.* emotion, strength *vs.* weakness, and independence *vs.* dependence. Three mythical figures were built up in the minds of many persons within the organization. Two of these figures represented opposing antithetical polarities on all of these issues. One figure, which we may indicate as Suprin[m], was characterized by the extremes of activity, egoism, will, strength, and independence. The second figure, Cadman[m], was characterized by passivity, altruism, emotion, weakness, and dependence. The first took the organizational form of a lurking, omnipresent, and malevolent figure of superhuman power, who was behind everything bad that happened in the organization. The second took the form of a benign, lovable, approachable figure from whom one received the good things of organizational membership, and from whom one received less than one wished of those rare and precious gifts that made life in the Institute a sometimes enchanting experience. The third figure, Asche[m], represented the more difficult, varying, and nebulous intermediary resolutions of these issues, resolutions that incorporated elements of both extremes to produce a result different from both. This triad of figures comprised the symbolic representation of the executive role constellation in the minds of subordinates.

It is a truism that none of the three mythical figures actually existed in the persons who comprised the top executive group, and that everyone in the staff hierarchy recognized this. Nonetheless, the imagery persisted and expressed itself in a variety of ways. One mode of expression was the Christmas party skits—the parodies of hospital life that were staged every year by hospital personnel. The imagery was also expressed in the administrative behavior of the medical staff group, as demonstrated in the two critical incidents reported in Chapters 15 and 16.

Balance and proportion tended to drop out of the reification of the role constellation as one moved down the chain of command. At several levels removed from the executives, a rudimentary representation existed that was often correct in as far as it went, but became incorrect in its incompleteness. Subordinates tended not to take their understanding of this particular matter further. It probably would have seemed inappropriate for them to try to do so. Such an attempt would have appeared as a desire to "touch the peaks," and as indicating insufficient motivation to "get on with the job" at their own levels in the organization. Understanding their bosses was not what subordinates were there to do. They were too busy doing what they were supposed to be doing—working with patients, learning about patients, and helping others learn about patients—to do much exploratory investigation up the chain of command. Most of them would not have cared to do so, even if the opportunity did arise in the course of everyday affairs. Their conception of the executive structure was settled in their minds to their satisfaction. They "knew the way things were" at the top, and this stable set of apperceptions helped to hold their organizational world steady for them—or at least to limit the amplitude of its fluctuations—so they could get on with the business of becoming psychiatrists. This was the way most of the staff, from superintendent to first-year resident, wanted it.

The symbolic representation of individual executives picked up salient aspects of each person's role specialization: the warmth and supportiveness of the clinical director, the friendliness and equalitarianism of the assistant superintendent, and the interpersonal, self-distancing fierceness of the superintendent. The symbolic representation of the relations among these individuals was also quite clear. It was basically and brutally hierarchical, with the direct physical immediacy of the juvenile gang and the barnyard pecking order. There was no room in this representation for the equalitarian relations of mutual help and consideration that existed in the actual system of relations comprising the executive role constellations. It was these more humane qualities, plus the very real complexities in reconciling them with the hierarchical and antagonistic relations that *also* existed, that tended to drop out of subordinates' representations of the constellation.

What did subordinates' fantasies about the top executives

have to do with the serious business of running a hospital and a residency training program? The connections between symbolic representations and administrative behavior, between reifications and reality, were largely covert. They operated in ways that were often subtle and indirect, yet accessible to careful observation. The subordinates' reifications of the top executives, and the resultant symbolic representation of the executive role constellation, had their own intrapsychic and peer group realities. These in turn had an influence upon the administrative and hierarchical realities, as the two critical episodes have shown.

The three top executives all had nicknames among their subordinates. The nicknames had quite wide currency in the organization. Like all nicknames, they captured a dominant but unofficial facet of each executive's organizational "persona," and made that facet of central importance in the interpersonal underworld of the organization. Frank Suprin was "Ferocious Frank." Paul Cadman was "Paul the Doll." Howard G. Asche was "Hi Guys." Ferocious Frank, Paul the Doll and Hi Guys all figured to a significant degree—along with their real-life counterparts—in the dynamics of administration in the Institute.

The major executive figure in the episodes described above was Cadman^m and the real-life counterpart, Dr. Cadman. In the first episode—an "attack" upon the house—a situation arose in which Dr. Cadman's subordinates wished him to mobilize a counter-offensive, and lead them forth into battle against the "aggressors." This Cadman would not do. After what may have been an initial flirtation with the possibility, he declined the implicitly proferred position of generalship. The position, however, was not proffered with any strength or determination. His subordinates' conception of him as a lovable pacifist was strong enough to hold their militant wishes in check. Perhaps these wishes were controlled too much, because, throughout the whole episode, Cadman was nudged only once by the most senior of his subordinates. The wish for a strong, aggressive leader was conveyed most elliptically and retracted almost immediately, without any real test of Cadman's pacifism, or potential for aggressive action. In other words, the mythical conception of Cadman as passive and peace-loving was strong enough to hold subordinates' aggressive wishes in check, but they were left with a palpable amount of aroused anger and indignation. They were unable (1) to retaliate against the "aggressors" outside their group, since Cadman's lack of leadership in this action made it illegitimate, or (2) to direct their anger against such a kindly, peaceful figure as Dr. Cadman, who had done nothing to warrant such aggression, particularly from the members of his own team. Their final adaptation was (3) to turn the hostility within the group itself, each member directing it against his peers (and probably his subordinates, although we have no data on this).

The intragroup hostility reverberated from one week to the next, unattached to anything except interpersonal antagonisms, until another crisis came along, upon which the pent-up energies in the group were inappropriately transferred. In this way, the succession of crises that punctuated the administration of the hospital throughout a year ran into one another, gradually gathered steam, and eventually dissipated through the slower summer months, when a new generation of residents and chiefs began their duties in the hospital.

The second episode was bipartite. It involved a proposed change in the daily schedule of events on the wards and in the residency training program. This proposal was put to the staff group by Dr. Cadman. Juxtaposed with this unexpected bit of bureaucratic initiative was Cadman's attempt to gain information about, and control over, a certain class of events taking place on the wards. Both the proposed change and the attempt to control were motivated by genuine convictions on Cadman's part. However, his subordinates could not conceive of him as acting administratively on his own initiative for his own interest. This possibility seemed never to occur to some, and others refused to believe that such initiative originated with Cadman. Instead, they speculated that the initiative must have been Suprin's, and this speculation in turn gave free-associative reign to further speculations about the nature of the personal motivations underlying his devious attempts to change the service organization and the residency training program. Everyone "knew" this was Cadman's program; therefore, "Frank must be trying to take away Paul's baby"—and the symbolic representation of Ferocious Frank began to ramify freely. Frank was the cold, impersonal, impervious, devious, frighteningly effective, behind-the-scenes manipulator. One of the criteria of his effectiveness was the very impossibility of finding any trace of him in Cadman's words and action, but "of course" he must be behind it all. After all, everyone "knew" that Ferocious Frank was the source of all administrative initiative. Administration didn't interest Cadman. He said so himself. (Which was true: he had said it to the observer more than once, but he had also added that, despite what he knew about himself, he still hankered a bit for administrative power and organizational leadership.) It was "obvious" to the subordinates in this incident that Cadman was being used by Suprin, that Cadman was a gullible or defenseless pawn. In their view, Suprin was hoodwinking the organization into accepting, as a gift from Paul the Doll, a policy that was really an expression of Ferocious Frank's desire to introduce more of the stultifying, centralized hierarchy of which he was so fond. Suprin's real program, as everyone "knew," was to locate all power and initiative at the top, so that the rest of the organization would be forced to respond with womanly subservience to directives from on high.

In fact, so preoccupied were the midlevel staff in these compelling ruminations, and so sure were they that Cadman was a mere "mouthpiece" of higher authority, that they would not take what Cadman had to say to them at face value. This in turn led to some rather inept interpersonal assertions of administrative authority by Dr. Cadman. These were vigorously resisted in their atypicality. The symbolic representation of Cadman among his subordinates was so strongly built up around the properties of love and supportiveness that his unaccustomed assertiveness was not to be received without a fight. To make matters worse, he had the "gall" to direct it downward at his own subordinates—at his very flesh and blood, so to speak—and not outward toward their common "enemies," as his subordinates had wished him to do in the first episode.

THE IMPACT OF SUBORDINATES ON EXECUTIVES: CONSTRAINTS AGAINST CHANGE IN THE ROLE CONSTELLATION

THE EXECUTIVES were sometimes at a loss to understand what was happening as they gave way to subordinates' unnoticed enticements to fulfill the subordinates' hypotheses about them. Having gone into a meeting with the resolve to handle a certain matter in a certain way, the executives might suddenly find themselves the focus of a lot of unanticipated turmoil. Even in retrospect, they often found it hard to understand how the turmoil was related to what they had said or done. When this process was in operation, the executives found themselves behaving in just the way they had resolved *not* to behave, and this compounded their inner confusions. When this experience of being caught off base occurred, the executives resolved never to behave *that* way again, but instead to stay on the base of their practiced and proven role specializations.

In this way the subordinates' responses to the executive role constellation, and to the figures in it, tended to reinforce the existing differentiation of their superordinates' roles. The subordinates had a considerable investment in the *status quo* within the constellation. The characterizations of super-ordinate figures that subordinates held in common produced certain intrapsychic and peer group economies that none of the subordinates were ready to abandon. To put it crudely, subordinates tended deep down in their own minds to have the "good guys" separated from the "bad guys." This provided the private luxury of not having to go through the energy-consuming diagnosis of the social contexts surrounding the specific problem situations. Subordinates usually felt certain, beyond all observable indications, as to which superordinates were behind what events and happenings: "Don't ask me how I know; I just *know*, that's all." Similarly, subordinates often tended to possess consensus on these orectically derived conclusions. The sharing of these conclusions, and the pooling of the inner dynamics that produced them, was observed to be a very rewarding experience for middle management participants. It increased group cohesion in an otherwise divisive, internally competitive organization, and it provided the only sure basis for the sharing of primary group experiences when the psychiatric staff of the hospital got together.

The middle managers tended to act more conservatively than did the executives. The executives acted in ways that both maintained *and* modified the structure of role relations existing between them. However, the subordinates acted almost exclusively to *maintain* the patterning of their superordinates' roles. The executives were, each in his own way, as much interested in improving the constellation and the hospital as they were in maintaining the existing balance of rewards and costs accruing to their chosen interpersonal roles. For the subordinates, however, *any* change in the alignment of forces within the constellation—regardless of the substance of the change—was experienced as a loss of the clear, satisfying, emotionally and motivationally economic conceptions they held about the executives.

In other words, subordinates resisted any change in the existing relations among their superordinates' roles, particularly in the differentiation that existed among them. This was not merely a passive attempt to hold onto what they were "used to"; both the constellation and the midlevel personnel were too much in transition for anything customary to have become established. Their resistance to the superordinates' stepping-out-of-role stemmed directly from the satisfactions of indulging in uncomplicated emotions and oversimplified beliefs about the superordinates.

This response greatly restricted whatever role flexibility the executives sought to exert. Usually the executives were content to play their typical roles in the routine transactions of administering the Institute. The roles were highly effective over a wide range of contingencies. They were the product of much role-task work, and they enabled the executives to express important parts of themselves in ways that were satisfying, or that they at least could live with. However, there were situations in which the executives realized that a change of behavior was needed; they tried to modify their behavior according to the requisites of an external administrative reality. It was in such situations that trouble arose. The executives' attempts to move out of typical roles were often somewhat inept, and matters were made worse by their subordinates' tendencies to fight the "hypocrisy" that they felt was being foisted off on them from above. "What the hell does he think he's trying to pull," was one expression of the opposition that subordinates brought to bear in the face of executives' attempts at role flexibility, when they feared that the symbolically meaningful executive role constellation might be breaking down.

PART VI.   CONCLUSIONS

In PART VI we summarize the findings and interpretations of this study. We consider briefly some implications of the method we used in gathering, analyzing, and presenting the data reported here. Finally, we state our current understanding of the function of personality and role relations in the conduct of administration. Certain implications are presented as to the social psychological forces contributing to effectiveness and ineffectiveness in top management groups.

CHAPTER 18
Review and Discussion

THE FINDINGS and interpretations of this study have now been fully reported. The analysis contributed to the understanding of the data of this particular study, and more generally to the possible development of a role theory of organizational behavior. Before stating some of the implications of the present work, we shall summarize the material on which they are based.

SUMMARY

THE STRUCTURE of the book reflected our method of analysis as well as the results of that analysis. Part I outlined some of the personal issues facing executives as members of organizations. Most research into executive behavior focuses on what the executive accomplishes for the benefit of his organization. Our study focused on the more personal, less organizational matter of what the executive does for and to himself, for and to others, as he directs the operations of the organization. The link between administration and the performance of the organization is important, but it fell beyond the empirical limits of this initial study.

Chapter 1 established the organizational context in which our three executive subjects worked. Assessed in terms of growth, innovation, and wider societal impact, the organization was highly successful. The dynamic *proactive* properties of the organization were importantly related to the behavior of our subjects. The implications of the setting for our own research behavior was also outlined.

Chapter 2 presented the general theoretical framework in which the observation of the executives, the analysis of the executive role constellation, and the interpretation of its consequences was conducted. We viewed executive behavior as the observable manifestation of the developing individual's response to the ongoing organization. The here-and-now behavior of an executive in an organization was seen as an expression of his personality, his past experiences, and his aspirations as to the sort of person he wished to become. His behavior was considered to be, at least in part, a manifestation of the *developmental issues* inherent in the particular stage of the life cycle in which the executive found himself. The primary function of the mature executive was not the internalizing of existing organizational values, but the institutionalizing of values new to the organization, drawn from the executive's personal value system.

Our theoretical emphasis on the emission of values, rather than their internalization, on proactive rather than reactive behavior, was reflected in our use of the concept of the *interpersonal reflex*. Our observations indicated the importance of the individual's active setting up of situations satisfying to him for both personal and organizational reasons. The proactiveness of the interpersonal process seemed to take primacy over the more frequently conceptualized process wherein the individual merely responds to the forces and problems in the interpersonal situation around him.

The proactive elements of behavior assumed a patterned consistency over time when the executives engaged in *self-dramatization*. Through self-dramatization, the executives attempted to establish certain concepts of themselves in the organizational system around them. As executives our subjects had the power and the opportunity to use the organization as a stage on which self-dramatization could be performed. The organization could, therefore, provide a setting in which an executive's development as an individual was greatly facilitated, depending on the dramaturgic effectiveness of his *performance,* the *reification* of that performance by the members of the executive's organizational audience, and the way that reification was *reflected back* upon the executive.

Chapter 3 presented the specific theoretical approach used to analyze the executives' behavior and their relations with others. The pattern of their behavior, their self-dramatizations, comprised their *organizational roles.* Consistent with our observation of proactivity in interpersonal situations, personality forces were seen as exerting a crucial influence upon role performance. The emotional and motivational forces of the personality were expressed in the executive's *personal role-demands.*

The executives' roles in the organization tended to become specialized around the performance of certain tasks and the expression of certain emotions. Role specialization was seen to have important roots in the executive's personality and important consequences for his behavior in the organization. Several specialized roles were differentiated from one another in the top executive group, yet maintained a tightly integrated complementarity. They formed what we have called an *executive role constellation.*

Part II laid the basic descriptive groundwork for our analysis of the executive role constellation. Chapters 4, 5, and 6 described the individual roles of the superintendent, the clinical director, and the assistant superintendent as each went about his work in the hospital. In each case, our main interest was in the man's behavior, in the manner of his interactions with others, and in the consequences of those interactions. The main interest of each man, of course, was in the substance of his work, in what he wanted done in the organization, and in the best way to get that work done. We attempted, therefore, to organize our description of each executive's behavior using his orientation to work as the major point of departure. Chapter 7 presented the concept of *role-task* in executive work, a concept that highlighted the often problematic intermeshing of the individual and the organizational system surrounding him.

Part III, Chapters 8 and 9, dealt with the emergence of the executive role constellation as a multiperson system. We delineated the psychological, interpersonal, and historical process whereby the constellation came into being. The constellation was regarded as an outcome of the role-task work of its members. Following the *management* succession that brought the present superintendent into the hospital, every executive was faced with a changed organizational situation and with the necessity of working through certain changes in career aspiration. Each executive was involved in diagnosing the new management system, what his social position in it would be, and the functions he would assume or be assigned. Also, he was involved in establishing in his own mind the needs and aspirations he could leave unfulfilled and those he would hold on to; the personal role-demands he would maintain and those he would let go; the role-conceptions he would put aside and those he would defend to the point of leaving the organization. The gradual reconciling and integrating of those two sets of forces—personal and organizational—comprised the role-task work posed by the succession of superintendents for the remaining executives. The product of this process was the executive role constellation.

Chapter 8 analyzed the initial phases of the management succession out of which arose the executive role constellation. Chapter 9 analyzed the final stages of the succession, in which the interlocking set of role definitions emerged.

Part IV analyzed the dynamics of the executive role constellation as it functioned during the field work. Starting with situations in which the executives were essentially alone, and moving through situations of increasing interactive complexity and inclusiveness, we analyzed each executive's contribution to the role constellation. This analysis occupied Chapters 10 through 13. Again, the proactive nature of the executive's participation in the role constellation was highlighted. Chapter 14 presented the *performance-reification-reflection* model that emerged from, and contributed to, this analysis of organizational behavior.

Part V analyzed some of the reciprocal effects between the executive role constellation and the middle management members of the organization. Subordinates' thinking about and behavior toward the executives were influenced by the symbolism inherent in each executive's role specializations, and by the symbolization of the role differentiation and complementarity within the constellation. Subordinates' behavior tended to reinforce the specialized and differentiated *status quo* in the constellation. At the same time, it tested to the fullest the durability of the integrated complementarity that also existed among the executives. Subordinates' response to the constellation made role flexibility within the constellation a difficult and at times thankless process for the executives. Chapters 15 and 16 presented two critical episodes involving some dynamics of the subordinates' response to part of the constellation. Chapter 17 summarized the symbolization that underlay relations between the executives and their subordinates.

Conclusions Regarding Research Methodology

The methods and procedures used in this study were presented in Chapter 1. Considering the current emphasis in the field of behavioral science methodology, one could read far and wide in the literature without finding much explication of the procedures we used in developing this particular study.[1] We consider this to be an unfortunate factor related to the

---

[1] One exception is B. H. Junker, *Field Work: An Introduction to the Social Sciences,* 1960.

infrequent publication of good clinical studies of behavior in ongoing organizational settings. In this field, as in others, it would appear that the researchers are not clinicians, and the clinicians do not publish much research. One of the drawbacks of clinical research is the cumbersome method of gathering, analyzing, and reporting data; something with which the reader of this book is now familiar. Statistical and survey methods of research greatly expedite these tasks. Yet, we believe clinical research can perform a function in contributing to knowledge that is closed to nonclinical research. That function is in the gathering and analyzing of data in unresearched areas, in opening up heretofore uninterpreted relationships, in developing new concepts that can then be subsequently tested by more rigorous methods. Without the preliminary clinical development of concepts, deductive methods of research must proceed with relatively uninformed hunches masquerading as hypotheses. Without the subsequent testing of hypotheses, clinical research can move little beyond the art of storytelling.

The procedure we used in this research produced findings, stimulated hypotheses, and contributed to the integration and building of theory. All of this would have been closed to us if we had held inflexibly to an initial desire to order our data through the administration of tests and questionnaires. Tests were explicitly excluded. "What do you want to know that for?" replied one executive upon request that he might complete certain items. "Haven't I been telling you about that for two weeks? If you don't know all about it now, a test certainly won't help." That, plus the hurried tempo of the executives' days, excluded any testing from our research operations. Questionnaires were likewise excluded from our repertoire. To construct questionnaires, we had to know the salient dimensions of the situation we were studying. It took about a year of field work to find them out, and by that time we were already obtaining so much data that questionnaires would have been of no incremental value; also, the reader can readily see that constructing questionnaires on the topic we were researching would have been indelicate, to say the least. Even if our respondents had been able to answer such questions as we might have asked, they would have tended not to, and their trust in our discretion would have been greatly reduced. We chose to use what methods we could to continue investigating a topic of interest, rather than to abandon the project because the "objective" methods of research were closed to us. Having proceeded as we did, we now have the option of continuing with a more deductive, hypothesis-testing development of our interpretations of executive behavior and role relations in other research settings.

We conclude that the observational and conversational method of clinical inquiry, in other settings as well, may be particularly fruitful for the development of concepts and hypotheses in fields where theory is quite embryonic. In such research, the use of multiple researchers in joint, collaborative research is of crucial importance in correcting individual predilections and biases, both observational and theoretical. Such collaborative efforts also help in achieving validation among researchers of inferential descriptions of complex interpersonal processes. The more controlled measurement of specific variables is an important step that can best be undertaken *after* some groundwork has been laid by methods of the type used here.

TYPES OF EXECUTIVE ROLE

IN OUR ANALYSIS particularly in Part II, we sought to describe the nature of specialized work performances and differentiated interpersonal styles of administration among executives in organizations. Ours has been a study of only three executives in one organization. Our theory indicates that we may have been extremely fortunate in the three executives we studied. From each we observed a specialized role that was differentiated from the other two. The superordinate role was specialized around the instrumental function of relating the organization to its environment, and around the expressive functions of assertiveness and control. The No. 2 role, working in closest interrelation with the superordinate, specialized around the instrumental task of operating the clinical services inside the organization, and around the expressive function of love and supportiveness. The third role, functioning at a relatively greater distance from the other two, specialized in innovative activities that resisted tight integration into the central flow of administrative routine. On the expressive dimension, this third executive was specialized around the interpersonal style of friendliness and equalitarianism.

The functional similarity of this executive role constellation and the familistic triad of father, mother, and uncle was not only unmistakable. It was important to the functioning of superordinate-subordinate relations in the organization's hierarchy, and to the manner in which the top executive group articulated the organization with its environment. We entertain the idea that our analysis of the executive role constellation has delineated three common or modal types of executive role in organizations.

The role types we refer to are the paternal-assertive, the maternal-nurturant, and the fraternal-permissive. These three role types are archetypical in their significance. There may be other types: for instance, the rational-bureaucratic, in which symbolically significant elements of an organizational role are suppressed. Also, there may be many permutations and combinations of these types in the concrete behavior of individuals. However, we posit the predominance of the three types delineated in our study, and do so by reason of the theory of individual development and socialization presented in Chapter 2.

Every member of every organization has had his preliminary organizational experiences in the structure of his family, or family surrogate. It was there that he learned his first
lessons about dependency, authority, and power. He learned
about the differentiated structure of superordinate roles that
exist between his parents. He learned about peer relations
from his siblings, from his friends outside the family, and
from adults outside the family who could afford to be casual,
relaxed, and equalitarian with him because they didn't assume responsibility for him. These lessons are carried through
life, being more or less enriched, debunked, and modified, but
persisting in their essentials.

When the individual becomes, as a young adult, a member of a purposive organization, he is entering a social system
in which issues of dependency, authority, and power are
probably clearer, stronger, and more persistent than anywhere except in his family. His experience as a new member of the purposive organization has many of the qualities
of his adolescent struggles with the authority structure in
his family. Probably, his experience with the latter influences
his response to his new membership. If and when the individual proceeds to advance up the hierarchy of power and
authority in the organization, he must put away some of
his practiced behavior as a subordinate and adopt new elements of a superordinate role. At about this time in life, he
is probably having to come to grips with his superordinacy
as a father in his own family. His children demand a superordinate figure with whom to identify. Both at work and at
home, similar limited role opportunities are available to him.

Drawing on his earlier experiences with authority, and his
relations to the several authority figures in his life, he can
build his role as a superordinate around the assertive and
controlling behavior of paternal authority, the loving and
supportive behavior of an essentially maternal authority,
or the less authoritative and more equalitarian behavior of

a relatively detached adult or his older brothers. The more the individual advances to positions of higher executive authority, the more his behavior becomes that of a superordinate, the more he draws on his own relations with authority, and the more completely he performs the authoritative role with which he is identified.

Of course there are as many variations in the pattern of family authority as there are families, and there are as many idiosyncratic lessons learned from them as there are individuals to learn. The existence of variability, however, does not contradict the coexistence of central tendency, and it is the modal types of executive role that have interested us here. Having developed some germinal ideas about executive role types through the method of intensive case study, we must next proceed to test out these ideas through more extensive and comparative methods of research.

EXECUTIVE GROUPS: CONSTELLATIONS AND AGGREGATES

WE THINK of the roles described in this book as exemplifying three of the major types of executive role. However, the structure of relations that existed among these roles was but one of many possible structures. There are probably as many executive role structures as there are executive groups in operation. At the same time, we offer the hypothesis that there are but a limited number of basic, modal types of role structure in such groups.

The role structures of executive groups may vary on a continuum of complexity and interrelatedness, from the highly specialized, differentiated, and complementary systems we have called *constellations,* to loosely structured *aggregates* of unspecialized, undifferentiated roles. At the complex and interrelated end of the continuum, constellations possess not only specialization, differentiation, and complementarity of role relations. They also possess important unifying properties of symbolism, through which the emotions and strivings in the group are expressed, and by which the identity of the group is established. These identities, and the symbolism from which they emerge, vary in pattern. The following are among the major types.

Types of Constellation

A constellation can be made up of a varying number of people performing certain roles that are interrelated in a number of different ways. The constellation we reported on in this study had three people in it, related covertly to each other and to their subordinates in an archetypically familistic triad of father-mother-uncle. There are other types as well.

The Patriarch and the Horde. Presumably, each symbolically significant role structure can be begun with a single superordinate individual and a group of equally subordinated people under him. Such an arrangement would be the organizational expression of Freud's concept of the dominant father and the primal horde. The dominating superordinate rides roughshod over his subordinates, appropriating all the sources of gratification for himself, denying those under him everything but a sense of protection by a feudal lord against aggression from outsiders.

The history of business provides many examples of such powerful figures and of what they can produce while still vigorous and able to command what they will. The same history also demonstrates the demise of the autocrat and the system he has built up around him. Problems of succession tend to be extremely difficult and disruptive. As the autocrat grows old and loses his powers, he either clings too long to his position of superordinacy, or else he is unseated by the revolt of his subordinates. These younger individuals throw their now dethroned superordinate out of the organization and set up a management system approximating a "band of brothers." Equality is rigidly adhered to, for fear that one of the group may get a superordinate edge over the others. The result is a partial antithesis of the previous management system. Equality replaces superordinacy and subordinacy. However, rigidity characterizes both systems. A rigid similarity of equal status roles has replaced a rigid system of specialization and hierarchialization. An aggregate replaces a constellation, and one set of functional strengths and weaknesses replaces another. We shall have more to say about aggregates after we have delineated the major types of constellation and the nature of the continuum between constellation and aggregate.

The Diad. Pairings are probably also quite frequent in ongoing executive teams. The roles linked together could be any combination of the aggressive-controlling, supportive-loving, and friendly-equalitarian role specializations described in this study. The roles could be related to each other on one level of power, as in the father-mother or sibling relationship, or they could encompass two levels of power and two generations, as in the parent-child relationship. The pairing may provide the basis of a very effective means of coping with the inside-outside problems of the organization. One of the pairs looks after the boundary processes of the organization, while the other looks after its internal dynamics. Pairings of top executives may prove to be the most stable of all role constellations, and at the same time the most difficult to dislodge or to succeed.

The Triad. Triadic constellations, such as the one we have reported on, are perhaps the most intrinsically unstable of all. Triads always have that "third party" who is somewhat "in between" and two others. This may be a rotating "third party" or, as in this case, that position may be held consistently by one member. As the expression goes, "three is a crowd." A constant pressure exists for the third person to remove himself from the constellation; but if he does, the constellation may not be able to cope with the trauma of his departure. Its subtly reciprocating role system may be irreparably ruptured, or it may realign itself around an emerging and more stable diad.

Larger executive groups in larger organizations probably possess more extensive, more complex, but less articulated role systems than the one presented in this book. In such groups, the notion of role constellation may well be inapplicable, but our working hypothesis for the present is that careful analysis of a larger executive group will reveal sub-units that function as role constellations, producing many of the personal and organizational consequences we have outlined above.

The Continuum from Constellation to Aggregate

We have started with a sharp distinction between the integrated role relations, the symbolic character, and the group identity of the constellation and the loose, flat, meaningless nonentity of the aggregate. These are to be conceived, however, as opposite poles of a continuum having many intermediate positions. As the properties of the constellation are gradually taken away, the properties of the aggregate are more closely approximated. We shall follow this subtractive process, moving from constellation to aggregate. We concentrate on role relations. The basic identity of constellar groups was presented in the above typology, and aggregates are seen as lacking identity.

The interpersonal structure among a group of executives may involve specialized and differentiated roles that are unrelated by any complementarity. This would indicate that the executives had formed no coalition among themselves to cope with either their environment or their subordinates. Worse, the lack of complementarity could indicate that the executive role specialists were using their specializations *against* each other, each trying to dislodge the others, to become undisputed *numero uno*. Such an interpersonal structure, with specialization and differentiation but no complementarity, would not qualify as a role constellation as we are currently thinking of it.

Similarly, an interpersonal structure that contained role specialization, but all in the same direction—that is, no differentiation—would not be a constellation of roles. For example, it might contain only "tough guys," with no one to support, encourage, sympathize, and otherwise hold the organization together around the accomplishment of its tasks. This would be an executive group in which everyone talked but no one listened, in which everyone controlled but no one motivated. Alternatively the system might consist of a number of lovable "softies" who just adored talking with people, but who could not get the work out, who could not enforce standards, ensure deadlines, or otherwise discipline those who were taking advantage of their kindness. Again, a specialized but undifferentiated management system might provide a friendly, casual, and equalitarian atmosphere in which the group of "buddies" provided many of the rewards that, because of the lack of wiser, more knowledgeable, and experienced superordinates with whom one could identify, were unattainable from one's work.

All specialized but undifferentiated systems leave important organizational functions unfulfilled. The consequent level of organizational performance would be quite low. Implicit here is a refutation of quite widespread thinking about *the* executive role. This stereotype of the executive role is all assertiveness and decisiveness. A management group built around *the* executive role would be one instance of a specialized but undifferentiated system. In seeking to duplicate existing assertive and decisive roles, its members would be leaving important functions and duties unfulfilled, such as the more supportive and equalitarian requirements of administration. In emulating one role type, the executives of such a group would thereby insure their failure as members and the failure of their group.

The Aggregate

Finally, in antithesis to executive role constellations, there probably exist executive groups that are what we have termed aggregates. In groups, the members are unable or unwilling to develop specialized roles, or are prevented from doing so by social pressures. Without specialization there can be no differentiation, and therefore no possibility of complementarity. Without complementarity, the possibility of internal competition would exist, but this would be much more muted and lower-keyed than in specialized and differentiated situations. In the aggregate system, insufficient aggression could be mobilized or directed toward objects to make constructive whatever competition existed. Members of an aggregate would only be a little bit nasty and a little bit nice, a little close and a little distant. They would be somewhat skilled in the administrative sense, but not too much so. They would be competent at their work, but not outstanding. They would be interested in a little bit of everything, but in no one thing in particular. Such aggregates would be without structure. They would have no organized means of coping with external and internal problems. They would be incapable of responding to pressures from the organization's environment, and even more incapable of mobilizing themselves to put pressure on that environment. We consider such aggregates to have short lives as executive groups. They are perhaps a transitional stage, as, for instance, the band of brothers that exists immediately after the patriarch has been removed, and before another powerful individual or other constellation has emerged.

The Symbolization of Roles and Role Structures

A THIRD MAJOR IDEA in our analysis is that of the symbolization, in superordinate-subordinate relations, of executive roles and role structures. Observing the executives in daily action, we learned rapidly and forcefully that there was a manner in which they viewed themselves, and were viewed by others, which supplemented their conception of themselves in the formal executive structure of the organization. These self-concepts were extremely personal, tapping deeply into needs and feelings that had no initial referent in the organization, and which the executives often wished to keep out of the organization. But this wish for bureaucratic impersonality was just as unsatisfied as their other wishes. Rational though their behavior was, it nevertheless tended to manifest and support the most personal elements of their self-concepts. The response of subordinates also demonstrated an over-all tendency to respond to the executives according to their archetypical self-concepts.

There was nothing fuzzy, indirect, or inscrutably mysterious about the process of performing and responding to a self-concept. Performance of and response to a self-concept were the most salient, experientially compelling characteristics of the executive role constellation. They were more obvious, and more obviously in operation, than were the divisions of duty and privilege that made up the official content of the executives' roles in the organization. Finally, the symbolic properties of the executives' roles were much more detectable in their effect upon the organization than was the substance of their professional beliefs, and the differences among their beliefs.

Some would say that the symbolic properties of the executives' organizational roles were "latent," but such terminology would distort the fact that these properties were as obvious as the men themselves. Some would say that the symbolization of the constellation was "covert," but this would deny the quite conscious imagery of the executives by their subordinates in the organization. One had only to observe and listen, to detect the supposedly latent and the so-called covert nature of the territory. The latency and the covertness resulted mostly from personal defenses against experiences in relation to one or another of the executive role types, and from bureaucratic pressures that limit or deflect the intrusion of powerful emotional and conative materials into the rational operation of the organization.

Let us consider first the symbolic aspects of constellations involving a highly *assertive-controlling superordinate*. A person's experiences as an assertive and controlling superordinate, or as a subordinate with such a superordinate, have both attractive and repulsive components. He may well be attracted by the neatness and clarity of administration, and by the efficiency and directness by which work is dispatched. He may also be repelled by the predominantly aggressive manner, and by the imperious behavior that exudes self-esteem at the expense of others' feelings about their own worth. At a deeper level, he experiences other less conscious attractions and repulsions. He feels irresistibly pulled toward such dominance and assertiveness. He wishes to "touch the peaks," to "sit next to" a source of power to whom he can relinquish the responsibility for directing and controlling his life. Then, it is hoped, freedom from personal conflicts and anxieties will be found in perfect subservience to an omniscient superordinate. He also feels repelled by such abject subordinacy, by the slavishness demanded and evoked by such a superordinate. He fears the possibility of never developing his own power in life, or of having that power taken away by the superordinate figure.

The longing for a father figure and the concomitant anxiety about the harm that figure may impose are inextricably intertwined. Surrounding this issue are the most intense fantasies deriving from childhood. The individual's oedipal struggles contribute to the orectic immediacy of his organizational situation. Also, the mere fact that such intimations of *childhood* are elicited in an adult organization member by his assertive and controlling boss is usually sufficient to call personal defenses into operation. Nothing is particularly interesting about the superordinate, it is professed. He is the superordinate, and that is all. There is nothing to report about one's relations with the boss. It is all routine; very ordinary. "Just get out the work, and he will leave you alone."

But extended observation reveals the inaccuracy of this statement. It reveals the futility of the wish, by both subordinate and superordinate, to leave and be left alone. Both are psychologically and organizationally locked into the struggle between the superordinate who asserts himself to manifest his power and the subordinate who fights back or acquiesces in order not to lose the power he already possesses. Both are parties to the archetypical contest between the superordinate who controls his subordinates to keep safe his own ascendancy and the subordinate who rebels or conforms. The rebel assertively casts aside all superordinate control. Symbolically, he is seeking to cast aside the superordinate, in order to occupy that position himself. The conformist meekly incorporates the superordinate's controls into his own system of intrapsychic controls. This incorporation is outwardly passive but inwardly much more active. The conformist welcomes a new source of external control to help bolster an ego already straining to hold aggression in check.

Our second modal type is the constellation built around the *maternal-nurturant superordinate*. Being a loving and supportive superordinate, and working for one, has its mixture of attractive and repulsive components as well. It is pleasant to be the head of, or a member in, a cohesive work group. The group atmosphere is warm. Interpersonal relations are close, affectionate, all-embracing. Members look to each other, but especially to the superordinate for love, support, and sustenance. The superordinate loves to give that sustenance and to receive the affection that is its reciprocal. He loves the consideration and deference that this affection brings with it. It is a subordinacy he receives without direct demand. It reinforces his superordinacy without unseemly displays of power, without discomforting outbursts of aggression.

There are two limiting factors, however, from which the repulsive features of loving and supportive superordinacy flow. First, there are a number of subordinates in whom this constellation engages an almost infinite need to be loved and supported. But there is only one superordinate, and his supplies of love and supportiveness are necessarily limited. The cozy group has no institutionalized means of managing the competition that thereby results. Second, the superordinate can lovingly and supportively lead his subordinates only in the direction, and at the pace, they want. If he wishes them to move toward *his* goals, at *his* pace, then he becomes involved in a form of assertiveness and control antithetical to his preferred style. Again, the group possesses no institutionalized means of handling the resulting clash of wills.

Aggression arises among subordinates out of their competition for the superordinate's love. Aggression arises between superordinate and subordinate as to who controls the direction of the group. This aggression is resisted—it has no place in this type of group—until it is impossible to restrain. Then it bursts chaotically into the open. There is no organized form for handling aggression in the group, and members of any standing in such cohesive groups have lost what ability they possessed to entertain, express, and control their hostilities. If the group survives an eruption of this sort, it reverts to its previous utopian method of operating, unless the superordinate's style has been modified in the process.

Many of these personal experiences and group processes

lie closer to the unconscious than to the conscious. Individuals may be aware of their enjoyment of warmth and cohesiveness in a group, but the symbolic presence of the love relations that they initially experienced in the bosom of their families is often defended against. Subordinates report a liking for their superordinate, but not a love for him. They experience their membership in the group as pleasurable, but the erotic components are denied. Similarly hostility in the group is suppressed, and hostility toward the superordinate is repressed. This hostility tends to get turned inward, causing members of the cozy group to have problems with their feelings of depression. However, in extended observation of such groups the unconscious aspects are often manifested, as aggression bursts forth in episodes critical to the life of the group and to the development of each of its members. Two such episodes were presented in Chapters 16 and 17.

Our third type is the friendly-equalitarian superordinate. He is perhaps the least richly symbolized and symbolizable of superordinates. This is true despite a widespread tenet of our culture that holds friendliness and equalitarianism to be the ideal form of superordinacy. The paucity of this ideal is revealed by analyzing the cultural belief itself, and the psychological realities of authority that it professes to represent but in fact distorts. Culturally, the friendly and equalitarian ideal of superordinacy has the implicit objective of success or popularity. One uses friendly equalitarianism to achieve a superordinate position in which one can infuse increasingly salient elements of assertiveness and control, or of love and supportiveness. Developmentally, this is similar to adopting the role of the responsible sibling on the way toward becoming a responsible fatherly or motherly authority.

The developmental parallel points to some of the psychological limitations of the friendly and equalitarian role. The child's first experiences are with parents; only later does he enter transactions with siblings and peers. His basic identifications are with his parents, not with siblings and peers. Identification with the latter helps him to get where he is going, but his destination is different from his means of getting there. Once his behavior in the organization has come to express his basic identification with authority, the behavior he used to get there tends to drop away. Only if he is blocked from expressing these more basic identifications—for instance, if the assertive-controlling or loving-supportive roles in the organization have already been appropriated by others —does he perseverate around friendliness and equalitarianism. This blockage may also have psychological origins, for instance, in unresolved ambivalences toward parental authority. The executive can step back from the intensive working through of these ambivalences by adopting the more casual mode of friendliness and equalitarianism.

The attractiveness of this mode lies in the relaxed, freewheeling camaraderie of being "buddies." Its repulsiveness to many people lies in the aura of homosexuality that tends to surround such relationships. Elements of homosexuality are present in constellations involving assertive-controlling and maternal-supportive executive role types. The adoption of, or attraction to, the fraternal-permissive role is in part an attempt to resolve the homosexual issue by removing oneself from the dominance and submission relating to the other types. This resolution may be sufficient for the individual, but it is purchased at the cost of marked barrenness of social relations and personal development in the fraternal-permissive system. Of course, the parental symbolism of assertiveness and control, or of love and supportiveness, has only limited application in a purposive organization. A home should not be run like a business, nor a business like a home. However, these two modes of superordinacy are symbolically a part of the development of one's posterity in the organizational setting. They provide a symbolic basis for building a progeny, a group of younger people coming up in the organization, who will struggle to carry forward that which the aging superordinate has worked so hard to achieve. The parental styles of superordinacy foster the identifications of subordinates with superordinates. Without such identifications, there can be no posterity. Peer-like friendliness and equalitarianism do not foster the development of subordinate identifications with superordinates. Growing old in an organization, the friendly and equalitarian executive finds fewer persons with whom to be friendly. He finds fewer persons who are willing to interact with him, an individual so much their senior, on an equalitarian basis. The posterity of others seems assured. His own seems problematic. Others face their imminent retirement with integrity, knowing their work has produced productive results and organizational continuity. He looks forward to retirement with a sense of despair. He has worked hard, but there are no young men coming up in the lines he has established. His work may have produced results, but it lacks continuity in the organization and does not carry through to the succeeding generation of executives.

Our statements about the symbolization that gets built up around executive role types have tended to dwell on the more problematic aspects of each. In summarizing these symbolizations we shall pay specific attention to the positive aspects of each role type, as well as to its critical weaknesses.

The controlling and assertive superordinate establishes a clean-cut management system around him. He provides an effective organization of work. He also provides a legitimate target for aggression in the group. Aggression can be released, thereby allowing subordinates to get to work again. However, the hazard of this mode of superordinacy is that it may be so intimidating, may provoke so much anxiety in subordinates that they flee from the group, fearing for their manhood. Or else they stay quietly, either too scared to gripe and too angry to work, or patiently waiting for an opportunity to displace the leader.

The loving and supportive superordinate provides rare and valuable experiences to his subordinates. He sets a tone of warmth and closeness that makes subordinates' entry in his group as smooth and attractive as possible. His love for them gives them the confidence to establish their competences in the organization. His supportiveness provides the superordinate sanction to express these competences in action. Once the basis for work has been established, the actual working relations run into difficulty. Aggression is poorly managed. Except for occasional outbursts, subordinates tend to withhold their aggressive feelings from their kindly superordinate. They bicker among themselves, but mostly they turn their anger inward. Depression thereby becomes a problem. This depression cuts into the competence and productivity that was initially established in such a promising fashion under the loving and supportive superordinate.

The friendly and equalitarian superordinate establishes casual, peer-like relations around him. The free flow of ideas between superordinate and subordinate is facilitated. The atmosphere he generates is ideally suited for easy participation in group process. Members of "the gang" can discuss any "offbeat" ideas they have in mind, with a minimum concern over the hierarchies of status, power, and authority. Unorthodox ideas are encouraged, not penalized. Members may tend to become somewhat uneasy at times over the closeness between themselves, particularly with regard to the lack of social distance between their superordinate and themselves. They may tend to "back off," thereby leaving the superordinate to cope with a lack of follow-through in his programs of action.

When the structure of an executive group is highly differentiated and integrated, as in a constellation, the symbolizations around each role type tend to reinforce one another. Each pattern of symbolization becomes clearer and stronger through its juxtaposition with different patterns. Superordinates benefit in this situation by being able to build up the desired type of relations with subordinates with a minimum of effort, building those relations partly on the basis of their fellow executives' efforts. The hazard of such a situation lies in one's becoming stereotyped, or "slotted" in an inflexible pattern of symbolization or reification, that is almost as much of a distortion of the executive's personality and of the organization as it is a representation of them. The executive then has to fight constantly to undo certain impressions before he can proceed to impart others.

When the role structure is undifferentiated and loosely held together, as in an aggregate, the symbolization of role is held to a minimum. The symbolization of individual roles tend to be that of the friendly and equalitarian type. This loose structure avoids some of the pitfalls of symbolic stereotypy that reside in the constellation. However, it misses the very real advantages to be derived from the richness of symbolism surrounding the constellation. It misses the powerfully motivating forces that get aroused in the constellation. It does not possess the means of harnessing motivation into the structure of the organization. It lacks the driving force that the executive role constellation can impart to the organization, and it has none of the emotional richness of the constellation. The organizational milieu of the aggregate is dull and boring compared to the milieu of the constellation. Rationality in both systems may exist at the same level. In an aggregate structure, the rationality may be acted upon competently. In a constellar structure, the rationality may be destroyed by the emotions and strivings active in the system, but those same forces properly oriented can impart a momentum to rationality that carries it far beyond the level of mere competence, to a level of excellence unattainable in the routine of the aggregate. Strategically, the constellation is a higher risk, higher payoff form of executive organization than the aggregate.

These reflections on the differences between competence and excellence in organizations conclude this study of an executive system. In presenting theories about executive systems generally we have stated neither the first nor the last word on this subject. Only further analyses of the kind of data presented in this book, carried out in many types of organizations, will provide the needed empirical foundation for understanding how executives live and work in organizations.

BIBLIOGRAPHY

Abraham, K. *Selected Papers on Psychoanalysis*. London: Hogarth Press, 1927.

Bales, R. F. "The Equilibrium Problem in Small Groups." In P. Hare, E. F. Borgatta, and R. F. Bales (eds.), *Small Groups*. New York: Alfred A. Knopf, 1955.

Bettelheim, B. *The Informed Heart: Autonomy in a Mass Age*. Glencoe, Illinois: The Free Press, 1960.

Blau, P. M. *The Dynamics of Bureaucracy*. Chicago: University of Chicago Press, 1955.

Blau, P. M. and W. R. Scott. *Formal Organizations: A Comparative Approach*. San Francisco: Chandler, 1962.

Bruner, J. S. and R. Tagiuri. "The Perception of People." In G. Lindzey. *Handbook of Social Psychology*. Cambridge, Mass.: Addison-Wesley, 1954, *II,* Chapter 17.

Caudill, W. *The Psychiatric Hospital as a Small Society*. Cambridge, Mass.: Harvard University Press, 1958.

Copley, F. B. *Frederick W. Taylor: Father of Scientific Management*. New York: Harper & Bros., 1923, 2 vols.

Dill, W. R., T. L. Hilton, and W. R. Reitman. "How Aspiring Managers Promote Their Own Careers." *California Management Review,* 1960, *2,* 9–15.

Erikson, E. H. "Identity and the Life Cycle." In *Psychological Issues*. New York: International Universities Press, Inc., 1959, *1.*

Erikson, E. H. "The Problem of Ego Identity." In *Psychological Issues*. New York: International Universities Press, Inc., 1959, *1.*

Erikson, E. H. *Young Man Luther: A Study in Psychoanalysis and History*. New York: The Norton Library, 1962.

Freud, S. "Character and Anal Erotism." *Standard Edition of the Complete Psychological Works of Sigmund Freud*. London: Hogarth Press, 1959, *9.*

Freud, S. "Libidinal Types." *Standard Edition of the Complete Psychological Works of Sigmund Freud*. London: Hogarth Press, 1959, *21.*

Freud, S. "Some Character Types Met With in Psychoanalytic Work." *Standard Edition of the Complete Psychological Works of Sigmund Freud*. London: Hogarth Press, 1959, *14.*

Freud, S. "Three Essays on Sexuality." *Standard Edition of the Complete Psychological Works of Sigmund Freud*. London: Hogarth Press, 1959, *7.*

Goffman, E. *Asylums*. New York: Anchor Books, 1961.

Goffman, E. *The Presentation of Self in Everyday Life*. Garden City, New York: Doubleday Anchor, 1959.

Gouldner, A. W. *Patterns of Industrial Bureaucracy.* Glencoe, Illinois: The Free Press, 1954.

Guest, R. H. *Organizational Change: The Effect of Successful Leadership.* Homewood, Illinois: Dorsey Press and Richard D. Irwin, 1962.

Harvard Business School. "Changes in the Business Environment." EA–R 353, 1963.

Henry, W. E. "The Psychodynamics of the Executive Role." In W. L. Warner and N. H. Martin (eds.). *Industrial Man.* New York: Harper & Bros., 1959, 24–33.

Homans, G. C. *The Human Group.* New York: Harcourt, Brace and Company, 1950.

Homans, G. C. *Social Behavior: Its Elementary Forms.* New York: Harcourt, Brace and World, 1961.

James, W. *The Varieties of Religious Experience.* New York: Collier Books, 1961.

Junker, B. H. *Field Work: An Introduction to the Social Sciences.* Chicago: University of Chicago Press, 1960.

Leary, T. *Interpersonal Diagnosis of Personality.* New York: The Ronald Press, 1957.

Levinson, D. J. "Role, Personality, and Social Structure in the Organizational Setting." *Journal of Abnormal and Social Psychology,* 1959, *58,* 170–179.

Levinson, D. J. and E. B. Gallagher. *Patienthood in the Mental Hospital.* Boston: Houghton Mifflin, 1964.

Mills, C. W. *The Power Elite.* New York: Oxford University Press, Galaxy Books, 1959.

Moment, D. and A. Zaleznik. *Role Development and Interpersonal Competence.* Boston: Harvard Business School, Division of Research, 1963.

Parsons, T. "Suggestions for a Sociological Approach to the Theory of Organizations—I." *Administrative Science Quarterly,* 1956, *1,* 63–85.

Parsons, T. "Suggestions for a Sociological Approach to the Theory of Organizations—II." *Administrative Science Quarterly,* 1956, *1,* 225–239.

Parsons, T. "The Mental Hospital as a Type of Organization." In M. Greenblatt, D. J. Levinson, and R. H. Williams (eds.). *The Patient and the Mental Hospital.* Glencoe, Illinois: The Free Press, 1957, 108–129.

Parsons, T. "Social Structure and the Development of Personality." *Psychiatry,* 1958, *21,* 321–340.

Parsons, T. and R. F. Bales. *Family, Socialization and Interaction Process.* Glencoe, Illinois: The Free Press, 1955.

Pine, F. and D. J. Levinson. "A Sociopsychological Conception of Patienthood." *International Journal of Social Psychiatry,* 1961, 7, 106–122.

Reich, W. *Character Analysis.* New York: Noonday Press of Farrar, Strauss and Cudahy, 1949.

Slater, P. E. "Role Differentiation in Small Groups." In P. Hare, E. F. Borgatta, and R. F. Bales (eds.). *Small Groups.* New York: Alfred A. Knopf, 1955.

Smelser, N. J. and W. T. Smelser. *Personality and Social Systems.* New York: John Wiley & Sons, 1963.

Stanton, A. H. and M. S. Schwartz. *The Mental Hospital.* New York: Basic Books, 1954.

Strauss, A. *Mirrors and Masks.* Glencoe, Illinois: The Free Press, 1959.

Sullivan, H. S. *The Interpersonal Theory of Psychiatry.* New York: W. W. Norton & Co., 1953.

White, R. W. *Lives in Progress: A Study of the Natural Growth of Personality.* New York: A Holt-Dryden Book, Henry Holt and Company, 1952.

Zaleznik, A. and D. Moment. *The Dynamics of Interpersonal Behavior.* New York: John Wiley & Sons, 1964.

Zaleznik, A. "Interpersonal Relations." In James March (ed.), *Handbook of Organizations.* Chicago: Rand McNally and Company, 1965

Zaleznik, A., G. W. Dalton, and L. B. Barnes. *Career Orientation and Conflict.* Boston: Harvard Business School, Division of Research, work in process (1965).

Zaleznik, A. *Worker Satisfaction and Development.* Boston: Harvard Business School, Division of Research, 1956.

Index

Abraham, 52

adjustment and personality, 54–56

administrative rounds, 99

aggregate, 487, 498

aloneness, concept of, 294

alone-time, executive behavior in, 292–293; of assistant superintendant, 294–306; of clinical director, 306–315; of superintendent, 315–318; *see also* entries for the three executives by title

assistant superintendent, accentuation of positive, 208–215; attitude toward work, 182–197; avoidance of being critical, 191–193; comparison of his ways of getting things done with other executives, 225–226; concern with long-term research and needed grants, 188; concern with research workers and output, 189–191; duties of, 11; enthusiasm of, 196–198; perception of role in developing psychiatry and response to this, 198–204; reaction to research worker's overspending contrasted with superintendent's, 353–358; reaction to this by superordinate, 358–363; relationship to clinical director, 271–278; response to administrative work compared to research, 204–208; role as subordinate, 353–363; role change in plans for future, 226–229; role costs to, 215–225; role per-

formance, illustrations of, 366–371; role relation with superintendent compared with that of clinical director, 347–349, 364–366; view of research and its effect on stature, 193–196; view of self in functioning of hospital, 351–352

assistant superintendent's alone-time, lack of, 296–298; performance in 298–299; personal response to, 294–295; role performance in, 300–303; response to others' reification, 303–306; structural aloneness due to research involvement, 295–296

axes of differentiation, 387; ranking of individuals on, 387

Bales, coalition of top ranking role specialists and control over total group function, 75; cyclical patterns of group processes, 66–67; relation to role specialists, 69–70; rewards and costs of role specialization, 76

binary fission, 41, 43–44

central executive triad, 11; role specialization in, 70

clinical director, administrative discretion of, 164–165; administrative duties of, 154–156; attachment to hospital, 173–75; availability to residents, 133–134; basis for adaptation to new